Student Solutions Manual for Turner/McKea[gue]
Intermediate Algebra

Prepared by

Ross Rueger

Department of Mathematics
College of the Sequoias
Visalia, California

*Student Solutions Manual for Turner/McKeague
Intermediate Algebra*

Ross Rueger

Publisher: XYZ Textbooks

Sales: Amy Jacobs, Richard Jones, Bruce Spears,
Rachael Hillman

Cover Design: Rachel Hintz

ISBN-13: 978-1-630980-62-7 / ISBN-10: 1-63098-062-5

For product information and technology assistance, contact us at
XYZ Textbooks, 1-877-745-3499

For permission to use material from this text or product,
e-mail: **info@mathtv.com**

XYZ Textbooks
1339 Marsh Street
San Luis Obispo, CA 93401
USA

Printed in the United States of America

For your course and learning solutions, visit **www.xyztextbooks.com**

Student Solutions Manual to Accompany

Intermediate Algebra
By
Mark D. Turner
Charles P. McKeague

Prepared by
Ross Rueger
Department of Mathematics
College of the Sequoias
Visalia, California

XYZ Textbooks

Contents

Preface

This *Student Solutions Manual* contains complete solutions to all odd-numbered exercises, and complete solutions to all chapter tests, of *Intermediate Algebra* by Charles P. McKeague and Mark D. Turner. I have attempted to format solutions for readability and accuracy, and apologize to you for any errors that you may encounter. If you have any comments, suggestions, error corrections, or alternative solutions please feel free to send me an email (address below).

Please use this manual with some degree of caution. Be sure that you have attempted a solution, and re-attempted it, before you look it up in this manual. Mathematics can only be learned by *doing*, and not by observing! As you use this manual, do not just read the solution but work it along with the manual, using my solution to check your work. If you use this manual in that fashion then it should be helpful to you in your studying.

I would like to thank Amy Jacobs and Mark Turner at XYZ Textbooks for their help with this project and for getting back to me with corrections so quickly. Producing a manual such as this is a team effort, and this is an excellent team to work with.

I wish to express my appreciation to Pat McKeague for asking me to be involved with this textbook. His books continue to refine the subject of intermediate algebra, and you will find the text very easy to read and understand. I especially appreciate his efforts through XYZ Textbooks to make textbooks affordable for students to purchase.

Good luck!

Ross Rueger
College of the Sequoias
rossrueger@gmail.com

January, 2016

Chapter 1
Real Numbers and Algebraic Expressions

1.1 The Real Numbers

1. Labeling the point:

3. Labeling the point:

5. Labeling the point:

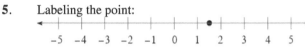

7. Labeling the point:

9. Converting the fraction: $\dfrac{3}{4} \cdot \dfrac{6}{6} = \dfrac{18}{24}$

11. Converting the fraction: $\dfrac{1}{2} \cdot \dfrac{12}{12} = \dfrac{12}{24}$

13. Converting the fraction: $\dfrac{5}{8} \cdot \dfrac{3}{3} = \dfrac{15}{24}$

15. Converting the fraction: $\dfrac{3}{5} \cdot \dfrac{12}{12} = \dfrac{36}{60}$

17. Converting the fraction: $\dfrac{11}{30} \cdot \dfrac{2}{2} = \dfrac{22}{60}$

19. Converting the fraction: $-\dfrac{5}{6} \cdot \dfrac{10}{10} = -\dfrac{50}{60}$

21. The opposite is -10, the reciprocal is $\dfrac{1}{10}$, and the absolute value is 10.

23. The opposite is $-\dfrac{3}{4}$, the reciprocal is $\dfrac{4}{3}$, and the absolute value is $\dfrac{3}{4}$.

25. The opposite is $-\dfrac{11}{2}$, the reciprocal is $\dfrac{2}{11}$, and the absolute value is $\dfrac{11}{2}$.

27. The opposite is 3, the reciprocal is $-\dfrac{1}{3}$, and the absolute value is 3.

29. The opposite is $\dfrac{2}{5}$, the reciprocal is $-\dfrac{5}{2}$, and the absolute value is $\dfrac{2}{5}$.

31. The opposite is $-x$, the reciprocal is $\dfrac{1}{x}$, and the absolute value is $|x|$.

33. Simplifying the expression: $|-2| = 2$

35. Simplifying the expression: $\left|-\dfrac{3}{4}\right| = \dfrac{3}{4}$

37. Simplifying the expression: $|\pi| = \pi$

39. Simplifying the expression: $-|4| = -4$

41. Simplifying the expression: $-|-2| = -2$

43. Simplifying the expression: $-\left|-\dfrac{3}{4}\right| = -\dfrac{3}{4}$

45. The correct statement is: $-5 < -3$

47. The correct statement is: $-3 > -7$

49. The correct statement is: $|-4| > -|-4|$

51. The correct statement is: $7 > -|-7|$

53. The correct statement is: $-\dfrac{3}{4} < -\dfrac{1}{4}$

55. The correct statement is: $-\dfrac{3}{2} < -\dfrac{3}{4}$

57. Factoring: $266 = 14 \cdot 19 = 2 \cdot 7 \cdot 19$

59. Factoring: $111 = 3 \cdot 37$

61. Factoring: $369 = 9 \cdot 41 = 3^2 \cdot 41$

63. Reducing the fraction: $\dfrac{165}{385} = \dfrac{3 \cdot 55}{7 \cdot 55} = \dfrac{3}{7}$

65. Reducing the fraction: $\dfrac{385}{735} = \dfrac{35 \cdot 11}{35 \cdot 21} = \dfrac{11}{21}$

67. Reducing the fraction: $\dfrac{111}{185} = \dfrac{37 \cdot 3}{37 \cdot 5} = \dfrac{3}{5}$

69. Reducing the fraction: $\dfrac{75}{135} = \dfrac{15 \cdot 5}{15 \cdot 9} = \dfrac{5}{9}$

71. Reducing the fraction: $\dfrac{6}{8} = \dfrac{2 \cdot 3}{2 \cdot 4} = \dfrac{3}{4}$

73. Reducing the fraction: $\dfrac{200}{5} = \dfrac{40 \cdot 5}{1 \cdot 5} = 40$

75. The perimeter is: $P = 4(1 \text{ in.}) = 4 \text{ in.}$

The area is: $A = (1 \text{ in.})^2 = 4 \text{ in.}^2$

77. The perimeter is: $P = 2(1.5 \text{ in.}) + 2(0.75 \text{ in.}) = 3 + 1.5 = 4.5 \text{ in.}$

The area is: $A = (1.5 \text{ in.})(0.75 \text{ in.}) = 1.125 \text{ in.}^2$

79. The perimeter is: $P = 4 \text{ cm} + 3.5 \text{ cm} + 2.75 \text{ cm} = 10.25 \text{ cm}$

The area is: $A = \dfrac{1}{2}(4 \text{ cm})(2.5 \text{ cm}) = 5 \text{ cm}^2$

81. The wind chill is $-15°\text{F}$.

83. **a.** The number of entertainment applications is: $5(52) = 260$ apps

b. The number of book applications is: $2.5(52) = 130$ apps. The statement is false.

c. The number of game applications is: $16(52) = 832$ apps. The statement is true.

85. The area is: $A = (8.5 \text{ in.})(11 \text{ in.}) = 93.5 \text{ in.}^2$

The perimeter is: $P = 2(8.5 \text{ in.}) + 2(11 \text{ in.}) = 17 + 22 = 39 \text{ in.}$

87. Finding the calories burned: $2(544) + 299 = 1{,}088 + 299 = 1{,}387$ calories

89. Finding the difference in calories burned: $3(653) - 3(435) = 1{,}959 - 1{,}305 = 654$ more calories

91. Two numbers are 20 and -20.

93. No, the absolute value of a number cannot be negative.

95. The exit is $141 + 16 = 157$.

97. You are either 20 miles north ($141 + 20 = 161$) or 20 miles south ($141 - 20 = 121$). So you are either at exit 121 or exit 161.

99. Answers will vary.

101. Converting the fraction: $\dfrac{3}{4} \cdot \dfrac{9}{9} = \dfrac{27}{36}$. The correct answer is a.

103. Simplifying the expression: $|-8| = 8$. The correct answer is a.

105. The reciprocal of $-\dfrac{2}{3}$ is $-\dfrac{3}{2}$. The correct answer is b.

1.2 Properties of Real Numbers

1. Commutative property of addition
3. Commutative property of multiplication
5. Additive inverse property
7. Commutative property of addition
9. Associative and commutative properties of multiplication
11. Commutative and associative properties of addition
13. Distributive property
15. Multiplicative inverse property

17. Using the associative property: $4+(2+x) = (4+2)+x = 6+x$

19. Using the associative property: $(a+3)+5 = a+(3+5) = a+8$

21. Using the associative property: $5(3y) = (5 \cdot 3)y = 15y$

23. Using the associative property: $\frac{1}{3}(3x) = \left(\frac{1}{3} \cdot 3\right)x = x$

25. Using the associative property: $4\left(\frac{1}{4}a\right) = \left(4 \cdot \frac{1}{4}\right)a = a$

27. Using the associative property: $\frac{2}{3}\left(\frac{3}{2}x\right) = \left(\frac{2}{3} \cdot \frac{3}{2}\right)x = x$

29. Applying the distributive property: $3(x+6) = 3 \cdot x + 3 \cdot 6 = 3x+18$

31. Applying the distributive property: $2(6x+4) = 2 \cdot 6x + 2 \cdot 4 = 12x+8$

33. Applying the distributive property: $5(3a+2b) = 5 \cdot 3a + 5 \cdot 2b = 15a+10b$

35. Applying the distributive property: $\frac{1}{3}(4x+6) = \frac{1}{3} \cdot 4x + \frac{1}{3} \cdot 6 = \frac{4}{3}x+2$

37. Applying the distributive property: $\frac{1}{5}(10+5y) = \frac{1}{5} \cdot 10 + \frac{1}{5} \cdot 5y = 2+y$

39. Applying the distributive property: $(5t+1)8 = 5t \cdot 8 + 1 \cdot 8 = 40t+8$

41. Applying the distributive property: $3(3x+y-2z) = 3 \cdot 3x + 3 \cdot y - 3 \cdot 2z = 9x+3y-6z$

43. Applying the distributive property: $10(0.3x+0.7y) = 10 \cdot 0.3x + 10 \cdot 0.7y = 3x+7y$

45. Applying the distributive property: $100(0.06x+0.07y) = 100 \cdot 0.06x + 100 \cdot 0.07y = 6x+7y$

47. Applying the distributive property: $3\left(x+\frac{1}{3}\right) = 3 \cdot x + 3 \cdot \frac{1}{3} = 3x+1$

49. Applying the distributive property: $2\left(x-\frac{1}{2}\right) = 2 \cdot x - 2 \cdot \frac{1}{2} = 2x-1$

51. Applying the distributive property: $x\left(1+\frac{2}{x}\right) = x \cdot 1 + x \cdot \frac{2}{x} = x+2$

53. Applying the distributive property: $a\left(1-\frac{3}{a}\right) = a \cdot 1 - a \cdot \frac{3}{a} = a-3$

55. Applying the distributive property: $8\left(\frac{1}{8}x+3\right) = 8 \cdot \frac{1}{8}x + 8 \cdot 3 = x+24$

57. Applying the distributive property: $6\left(\frac{1}{2}x-\frac{1}{3}y\right) = 6 \cdot \frac{1}{2}x - 6 \cdot \frac{1}{3}y = 3x-2y$

59. Applying the distributive property: $12\left(\frac{1}{4}x+\frac{2}{3}y\right) = 12 \cdot \frac{1}{4}x + 12 \cdot \frac{2}{3}y = 3x+8y$

61. Applying the distributive property: $20\left(\frac{2}{5}x+\frac{1}{4}y\right) = 20 \cdot \frac{2}{5}x + 20 \cdot \frac{1}{4}y = 8x+5y$

63. Applying the distributive property: $3(5x+2)+4 = 15x+6+4 = 15x+10$

65. Applying the distributive property: $4(2y+6)+8 = 8y+24+8 = 8y+32$

67. Applying the distributive property: $5(1+3t)+4 = 5+15t+4 = 15t+9$

69. Applying the distributive property: $3+(2+7x)4 = 3+8+28x = 28x+11$

71. Adding the fractions: $\dfrac{2}{5}+\dfrac{1}{15} = \dfrac{2}{5}\cdot\dfrac{3}{3}+\dfrac{1}{15} = \dfrac{6}{15}+\dfrac{1}{15} = \dfrac{7}{15}$

73. Adding the fractions: $\dfrac{17}{30}+\dfrac{11}{42} = \dfrac{17}{30}\cdot\dfrac{7}{7}+\dfrac{11}{42}\cdot\dfrac{5}{5} = \dfrac{119}{210}+\dfrac{55}{210} = \dfrac{174}{210} = \dfrac{29}{35}$

75. Adding the fractions: $\dfrac{9}{48}+\dfrac{3}{54} = \dfrac{9}{48}\cdot\dfrac{9}{9}+\dfrac{3}{54}\cdot\dfrac{8}{8} = \dfrac{81}{432}+\dfrac{24}{432} = \dfrac{105}{432} = \dfrac{35}{144}$

77. Adding the fractions: $\dfrac{25}{84}+\dfrac{41}{90} = \dfrac{25}{84}\cdot\dfrac{15}{15}+\dfrac{41}{90}\cdot\dfrac{14}{14} = \dfrac{375}{1260}+\dfrac{574}{1260} = \dfrac{949}{1260}$

79. Simplifying: $210\left(\dfrac{3}{14}+\dfrac{7}{30}\right) = 210\left(\dfrac{3}{14}\right)+210\left(\dfrac{7}{30}\right) = 15(3)+7(7) = 45+49 = 94$

81. Simplifying: $32\left(\dfrac{3}{4}\right)-16\left(\dfrac{3}{4}\right)^2 = 32\left(\dfrac{3}{4}\right)-16\left(\dfrac{9}{16}\right) = 24-9 = 15$

83. Simplifying the expression: $5a+7+8a+a = (5a+8a+a)+7 = 14a+7$

85. Simplifying the expression: $2(5x+1)+2x = 10x+2+2x = 12x+2$

87. Simplifying the expression: $3+4(5a+3)+4a = 3+20a+12+4a = 24a+15$

89. Simplifying the expression: $5x+3(x+2)+7 = 5x+3x+6+7 = 8x+13$

91. Simplifying the expression: $5(x+2y)+4(3x+y) = 5x+10y+12x+4y = 17x+14y$

93. Simplifying the expression: $5b+3(4b+a)+6a = 5b+12b+3a+6a = 17b+9a$

95. Solving the equation:
$$x+\frac{x}{4} = 15$$
$$4\left(x+\frac{x}{4}\right) = 4(15)$$
$$4x+x = 60$$
$$5x = 60$$
$$x = 12$$

97. Finding the difference: $814-47 = 767$ acres

99. Finding the percent: $\dfrac{47}{4,217} \approx 0.011 = 1.1\%$

101. A person with a blood-alcohol level of 0.20 is approximately 85 times more likely to get in an accident.

103. This is the commutative property of addition. The correct answer is c.

105. Applying the distributive property and simplifying: $3(2x+5)+4 = 3\cdot 2x+3\cdot 5+4 = 6x+15+4 = 6x+19$

The correct answer is a.

1.3 Arithmetic with Real Numbers

1. Finding the sum: $6+(-2)=6-2=4$

3. Finding the sum: $-6+2=-4$

5. Finding the difference: $-7-3=-7+(-3)=-10$

7. Finding the difference: $-7-(-3)=-7+3=-4$

9. Finding the difference: $\dfrac{3}{4}-\left(-\dfrac{5}{6}\right)=\dfrac{3}{4}+\dfrac{5}{6}=\dfrac{3}{4}\cdot\dfrac{3}{3}+\dfrac{5}{6}\cdot\dfrac{2}{2}=\dfrac{9}{12}+\dfrac{10}{12}=\dfrac{19}{12}=1\dfrac{7}{12}$

11. Finding the difference: $\dfrac{11}{42}-\dfrac{17}{30}=\dfrac{11}{42}\cdot\dfrac{5}{5}-\dfrac{17}{30}\cdot\dfrac{7}{7}=\dfrac{55}{210}-\dfrac{119}{210}=-\dfrac{64}{210}=-\dfrac{32}{105}$

13. Subtracting: $-3-5=-8$

15. Subtracting: $-4-8=-12$

17. Subtracting: $-3x-4x=-7x$

19. The number is 13, since $5-13=-8$.

21. Computing the value: $-7+(2-9)=-7+(-7)=-14$

23. Simplifying the value: $(8a+a)-3a=9a-3a=6a$

25. Finding the product: $3(-5)=-15$

27. Finding the product: $-3(-5)=15$

29. Finding the product: $2(-3)(4)=-6(4)=-24$

31. Finding the product: $-2(5x)=-10x$

33. Finding the product: $-\dfrac{1}{3}(-3x)=\dfrac{3}{3}x=x$

35. Finding the product: $-\dfrac{2}{3}\left(-\dfrac{3}{2}y\right)=\dfrac{6}{6}y=y$

37. Simplifying: $1(-2)-2(-16)+1(9)=-2+32+9=39$

39. Simplifying: $1(1)-3(-2)+(-2)(-2)=1+6+4=11$

41. Simplifying: $-4(0)(-2)-(-1)(1)(1)-1(2)(3)=0+1-6=-5$

43. Simplifying: $1[0-(-1)]-3(2-4)+(-2)(-2-0)=1(1)-3(-2)-2(-2)=1+6+4=11$

45. Simplifying: $3(-2)^2+2(-2)-1=3(4)+2(-2)-1=12-4-1=7$

47. Simplifying: $2(-2)^3-3(-2)^2+4(-2)-8=2(-8)-3(4)+4(-2)-8=-16-12-8-8=-44$

49. Simplifying: $\dfrac{0-4}{0-2}=\dfrac{-4}{-2}=2$

51. Simplifying: $\dfrac{-4-4}{-4-2}=\dfrac{-8}{-6}=\dfrac{4}{3}$

53. Simplifying: $\dfrac{-6+6}{-6-3}=\dfrac{0}{-9}=0$

55. Simplifying: $\dfrac{2-4}{2-2}=\dfrac{-2}{0}$, which is undefined

57. Simplifying: $\dfrac{3-(-1)}{-3-3}=\dfrac{4}{-6}=-\dfrac{2}{3}$

59. Simplifying: $\dfrac{-3^2+9}{-4-4}=\dfrac{-9+9}{-8}=0$

61. Simplifying: $|8-2|=|6|=6$

63. Simplifying: $\left|5\cdot2^3-2\cdot3^2\right|=|5\cdot8-2\cdot9|=|40-18|=|22|=22$

65. Simplifying: $|7-2|-|4-2|=|5|-|2|=5-2=3$

67. Simplifying: $10-|7-2(5-3)|=10-|7-2(2)|=10-|7-4|=10-|3|=10-3=7$

69. Simplifying:
$$15-|8-2(3\cdot4-9)|-10=15-|8-2(12-9)|-10$$
$$=15-|8-2(3)|-10$$
$$=15-|8-6|-10$$
$$=15-|2|-10$$
$$=15-2-10$$
$$=3$$

71. Finding the product: $-2(4x-3)=-8x+6$

73. Finding the product: $-\dfrac{1}{2}(6a-8)=-3a+4$

75. Simplifying: $3(5x+4)-x=15x+12-x=14x+12$

77. Simplifying: $6-7(3-m)=6-21+7m=7m-15$

79. Simplifying: $7-2(3x-1)+4x=7-6x+2+4x=-2x+9$

81. Simplifying: $5(3y+1)-(8y-5)=15y+5-8y+5=7y+10$

83. Simplifying: $4(2-6x)-(3-4x)=8-24x-3+4x=-20x+5$

85. Simplifying: $10-4(2x+1)-(3x-4)=10-8x-4-3x+4=-11x+10$

87. Simplifying: $3x-5(x-3)-2(1-3x)=3x-5x+15-2+6x=4x+13$

89. $\dfrac{4}{0}$ is undefined

91. Dividing: $\dfrac{0}{-3}=0\cdot\left(-\dfrac{1}{3}\right)=0$

93. Dividing: $-\dfrac{3}{4}\div\dfrac{9}{8}=-\dfrac{3}{4}\cdot\dfrac{8}{9}=-\dfrac{2}{3}$

95. Dividing: $-8\div\left(-\dfrac{1}{4}\right)=-8\cdot\left(-\dfrac{4}{1}\right)=32$

97. Dividing: $-40\div\left(-\dfrac{5}{8}\right)=-40\cdot\left(-\dfrac{8}{5}\right)=64$

99. Dividing: $\dfrac{4}{9}\div(-8)=\dfrac{4}{9}\cdot\left(-\dfrac{1}{8}\right)=-\dfrac{1}{18}$

101. Simplifying: $\dfrac{3(-1)-4(-2)}{8-5}=\dfrac{-3+8}{3}=\dfrac{5}{3}$

103. Simplifying: $8-(-6)\left[\dfrac{2(-3)-5(4)}{-8(6)-4}\right]=8+6\left(\dfrac{-6-20}{-48-4}\right)=8+6\left(\dfrac{-26}{-52}\right)=8+6\left(\dfrac{1}{2}\right)=8+3=11$

105. Simplifying: $6-(-3)\left[\dfrac{2-4(3-8)}{1-5(1-3)}\right]=6-(-3)\left[\dfrac{2-4(-5)}{1-5(-2)}\right]=6-(-3)\left(\dfrac{2+20}{1+10}\right)=6-(-3)\left(\dfrac{22}{11}\right)=6+6=12$

107. Completing the table:

a	b	Sum $a+b$	Difference $a-b$	Product ab	Quotient a/b
3	12	15	−9	36	$\frac{1}{4}$
−3	12	9	−15	−36	$-\frac{1}{4}$
3	−12	−9	15	−36	$-\frac{1}{4}$
−3	−12	−15	9	36	$\frac{1}{4}$

109. Completing the table:

x	$3(5x-2)$	$15x-6$	$15x-2$
−2	−36	−36	−32
−1	−21	−21	−17
0	−6	−6	−2
1	9	9	13
2	24	24	28

111. a. Evaluating when $a=3$ and $b=-6$: $-\dfrac{b}{2a}=-\dfrac{-6}{2(3)}=-\dfrac{-6}{6}=1$

   b. Evaluating when $a=-2$ and $b=6$: $-\dfrac{b}{2a}=-\dfrac{6}{2(-2)}=-\dfrac{6}{-4}=\dfrac{3}{2}$

   c. Evaluating when $a=-1$ and $b=-2$: $-\dfrac{b}{2a}=-\dfrac{-2}{2(-1)}=-\dfrac{-2}{-2}=-1$

   d. Evaluating when $a=-0.1$ and $b=27$: $-\dfrac{b}{2a}=-\dfrac{27}{2(-0.1)}=-\dfrac{27}{-0.2}=135$

113. Using a calculator: $\dfrac{1.380}{0.903} \approx 1.5282$

115. Using a calculator: $\dfrac{1}{2}(-0.1587) \approx -0.0794$

117. Using a calculator: $\dfrac{1}{2}\left(\dfrac{1.2}{1.4}-1\right) \approx -0.0714$

119. Using a calculator: $\dfrac{(6.8)(3.9)}{7.8} = 3.4$

121. Using a calculator: $\dfrac{0.0005(200)}{(0.25)^2} = 1.6$

123. Using a calculator: $-500 + 27(100) - 0.1(100)^2 = -500 + 2,700 - 1,000 = 1,200$

125. Using a calculator: $-0.05(130)^2 + 9.5(130) - 200 = -845 + 1,235 - 200 = 190$

127. A loss of 8 yards corresponds to –8 on the number line. The total yards lost is $6 + (-8) = -2$ yards.

129. This temperature is –64°F. The new temperature is $-54 + 10 = -44°F$.

131. This is –100 feet. The new depth is $-100 - 5 = -105$ feet.

133. Finding the ratio: $\dfrac{16,094}{4,217} \approx 3.8$ times larger

135. **a.** Finding the ratio: $\dfrac{4,050}{59,424} \approx 0.068$ stores per mi^2

   b. Finding the ratio: $\dfrac{9,143}{268,580} \approx 0.034$ stores per mi^2

   c. Georgia has a higher concentration of convenience stors.

137. Simplifying: $-4 - 9 - (-5) = -13 + 5 = -8$. The correct answer is d.

139. Dividing: $\dfrac{5}{6} \div \left(-\dfrac{7}{12}\right) = \dfrac{5}{6} \cdot \left(-\dfrac{12}{7}\right) = -\dfrac{10}{7}$. The correct answer is b.

1.4 Exponents and Scientific Notation

1. Evaluating: $4^2 = 4 \cdot 4 = 16$

3. Evaluating: $-4^2 = -(4 \cdot 4) = -16$

5. Evaluating: $-0.3^3 = -(0.3 \cdot 0.3 \cdot 0.3) = -0.027$

7. Evaluating: $2^5 = 2 \cdot 2 \cdot 2 \cdot 2 \cdot 2 = 32$

9. Evaluating: $\left(\dfrac{1}{2}\right)^3 = \dfrac{1}{2} \cdot \dfrac{1}{2} \cdot \dfrac{1}{2} = \dfrac{1}{8}$

11. Evaluating: $\left(\dfrac{5}{6}\right)^2 = \dfrac{5}{6} \cdot \dfrac{5}{6} = \dfrac{25}{36}$

13. Evaluating: $\left(\dfrac{1}{10}\right)^4 = \dfrac{1}{10} \cdot \dfrac{1}{10} \cdot \dfrac{1}{10} \cdot \dfrac{1}{10} = \dfrac{1}{10,000}$

15. Evaluating: $\left(-\dfrac{5}{6}\right)^2 = \left(-\dfrac{5}{6}\right)\left(-\dfrac{5}{6}\right) = \dfrac{25}{36}$

17. Evaluating: $\left(-\dfrac{3}{7}\right)^2 = \left(-\dfrac{3}{7}\right)\left(-\dfrac{3}{7}\right) = \dfrac{9}{49}$

19. Using properties of exponents: $x^5 \cdot x^4 = x^{5+4} = x^9$

21. Using properties of exponents: $\left(2^3\right)^2 = 2^{3 \cdot 2} = 2^6 = 64$

23. Using properties of exponents: $-3a^2\left(2a^4\right) = -6a^{2+4} = -6a^6$

25. Using properties of exponents: $\left(4x^2\right)^2 = 4^2\left(x^2\right)^2 = 16x^4$

27. Writing with positive exponents: $3^{-2} = \dfrac{1}{3^2} = \dfrac{1}{9}$

29. Writing with positive exponents: $(-2)^{-5} = \dfrac{1}{(-2)^5} = -\dfrac{1}{32}$

31. Writing with positive exponents: $\left(\dfrac{3}{4}\right)^{-2} = \left(\dfrac{4}{3}\right)^2 = \dfrac{16}{9}$

33. Writing with positive exponents: $\left(\frac{1}{3}\right)^{-2} + \left(\frac{1}{2}\right)^{-3} = 3^2 + 2^3 = 9 + 8 = 17$

35. Multiplying: $8x^3 \cdot 10y^6 = 80x^3y^6$

37. Multiplying: $8x^3 \cdot 9y^3 = 72x^3y^3$

39. Multiplying: $3x \cdot 5y = 15xy$

41. Multiplying: $4x^6y^6 \cdot 3x = 12x^7y^6$

43. Multiplying: $27a^6c^3 \cdot 2b^2c = 54a^6b^2c^4$

45. Multiplying: $12x^3y^4 \cdot 3xy^2 = 36x^4y^6$

47. Dividing: $\dfrac{10x^5}{5x^2} = 2x^{5-2} = 2x^3$

49. Dividing: $\dfrac{20x^3}{5x^2} = 4x^{3-2} = 4x$

51. Dividing: $\dfrac{8x^3y^5}{-2x^2y} = -4x^{3-2}y^{5-1} = -4xy^4$

53. Dividing: $\dfrac{4x^4y^3}{-2x^2y} = -2x^{4-2}y^{3-1} = -2x^2y^2$

55. Simplifying: $\dfrac{x^{-1}}{x^9} = x^{-1-9} = x^{-10} = \dfrac{1}{x^{10}}$

57. Simplifying: $\dfrac{a^4}{a^{-6}} = a^{4-(-6)} = a^{4+6} = a^{10}$

59. Simplifying: $\dfrac{t^{-10}}{t^{-4}} = t^{-10-(-4)} = t^{-10+4} = t^{-6} = \dfrac{1}{t^6}$

61. Simplifying: $\left(\dfrac{x^5}{x^3}\right)^6 = \left(x^{5-3}\right)^6 = \left(x^2\right)^6 = x^{12}$

63. Simplifying: $\dfrac{\left(x^5\right)^6}{\left(x^3\right)^4} = \dfrac{x^{30}}{x^{12}} = x^{30-12} = x^{18}$

65. Simplifying: $\dfrac{\left(x^{-2}\right)^3\left(x^3\right)^{-2}}{x^{10}} = \dfrac{x^{-6}x^{-6}}{x^{10}} = \dfrac{x^{-12}}{x^{10}} = x^{-12-10} = x^{-22} = \dfrac{1}{x^{22}}$

67. Simplifying: $\dfrac{5a^8b^3}{20a^5b^{-4}} = \dfrac{5}{20}a^{8-5}b^{3-(-4)} = \dfrac{1}{4}a^3b^7 = \dfrac{a^3b^7}{4}$

69. Simplifying: $\dfrac{\left(3x^{-2}y^8\right)^4}{\left(9x^4y^{-3}\right)^2} = \dfrac{81x^{-8}y^{32}}{81x^8y^{-6}} = x^{-8-8}y^{32+6} = x^{-16}y^{38} = \dfrac{y^{38}}{x^{16}}$

71. Simplifying: $\left(\dfrac{8x^2y}{4x^4y^{-3}}\right)^4 = \left(2x^{2-4}y^{1+3}\right)^4 = \left(2x^{-2}y^4\right)^4 = 16x^{-8}y^{16} = \dfrac{16y^{16}}{x^8}$

73. Simplifying: $\left(\dfrac{x^{-5}y^2}{x^{-3}y^5}\right)^{-2} = \left(x^{-5+3}y^{2-5}\right)^{-2} = \left(x^{-2}y^{-3}\right)^{-2} = x^4y^6$

75. Simplifying: $\left(\dfrac{ab^{-3}c^{-2}}{a^{-3}b^0c^{-5}}\right)^0 = 1$

77. Simplifying: $\left(\dfrac{x^2}{x^{-3}}\right)^0 = 1$

79. **a.** Using the rule for order of operations: $3 \cdot 5 + 4 = 15 + 4 = 19$

   b. Using the rule for order of operations: $3(5+4) = 3 \cdot 9 = 27$

   c. Using the rule for order of operations: $3 \cdot 5 + 3 \cdot 4 = 15 + 12 = 27$

81. **a.** Using the rule for order of operations: $6 + 3 \cdot 4 - 2 = 6 + 12 - 2 = 16$

   b. Using the rule for order of operations: $6 + 3(4-2) = 6 + 3 \cdot 2 = 6 + 6 = 12$

   c. Using the rule for order of operations: $(6+3)(4-2) = 9 \cdot 2 = 18$

83. **a.** Using the rule for order of operations: $(5+7)^2 = 12^2 = 144$

   b. Using the rule for order of operations: $5^2 + 7^2 = 25 + 49 = 74$

   c. Using the rule for order of operations: $5^2 + 2 \cdot 5 \cdot 7 + 7^2 = 25 + 70 + 49 = 144$

85. **a.** Using the rule for order of operations: $2+3\cdot2^2+3^2 = 2+3\cdot4+9 = 2+12+9 = 23$

    b. Using the rule for order of operations: $2+3(2^2+3^2) = 2+3(4+9) = 2+3\cdot13 = 2+39 = 41$

    c. Using the rule for order of operations: $(2+3)(2^2+3^2) = (5)(4+9) = 5\cdot13 = 65$

87. Writing in scientific notation: $378,000 = 3.78\times10^5$ 89. Writing in scientific notation: $4,900 = 4.9\times10^3$

91. Writing in scientific notation: $0.00037 = 3.7\times10^{-4}$ 93. Writing in scientific notation: $0.00495 = 4.95\times10^{-3}$

95. Writing in expanded form: $5.34\times10^3 = 5,340$ 97. Writing in expanded form: $7.8\times10^6 = 7,800,000$

99. Writing in expanded form: $3.44\times10^{-3} = 0.00344$ 101. Writing in expanded form: $4.9\times10^{-1} = 0.49$

103. Simplifying: $(4\times10^{10})(2\times10^{-6}) = 8\times10^{10-6} = 8\times10^4$ 105. Simplifying: $\dfrac{8\times10^{14}}{4\times10^5} = 2\times10^{14-5} = 2\times10^9$

107. Simplifying: $\dfrac{(5\times10^6)(4\times10^{-8})}{8\times10^4} = \dfrac{20\times10^{-2}}{8\times10^4} = \dfrac{20}{8}\times10^{-2-4} = 2.5\times10^{-6}$

109. Simplifying: $\dfrac{(2.4\times10^{-3})(3.6\times10^{-7})}{(4.8\times10^6)(1\times10^{-9})} = \dfrac{8.64\times10^{-10}}{4.8\times10^{-3}} = \dfrac{8.64}{4.8}\times10^{-10+3} = 1.8\times10^{-7}$

111. Simplifying: $\dfrac{2.00\times10^8}{3.98\times10^6} = \dfrac{2.00}{3.98}\times10^2 \approx 50$

113. Using a calculator: $10^{-4.1} \approx 7.9\times10^{-5}$

115. Writing in scientific notation: $630,000,000 = 6.3\times10^8$ seconds

117. Multiplying to find the distance: $(1.7\times10^6 \text{ light-years})(5.9\times10^{12} \text{ miles/light-year}) \approx 1.003\times10^{19}$ miles

119. Finding the distance: $(4.2 \text{ light-years})(5.9\times10^{12} \text{ miles/light-year}) = 2.478\times10^{13}$ miles

121. Finding the time: $\dfrac{4.13\times10^{17} \text{ miles}}{5.9\times10^{12} \text{ miles/year}} = 70,000$ years

123. **a.** Writing in scientific notation: $4,204,000 = 4.204\times10^6$ viewers

    b. Writing in scientific notation: $7,995,000 = 7.995\times10^6$ viewers

    c. Writing in scientific notation: $6,761,000 = 6.761\times10^6$ viewers

125. **a.** Writing in scientific notation: $800,000,000,000 = 8.0\times10^{11}$

    b. Dividing to find the average: $\dfrac{8.0\times10^{11} \text{ dollars}}{1.8\times10^8 \text{ people}} \approx \$4.444\times10^3 = \$4,444$

127. Completing the table:

Unit	Exponential Form	Scientific Form
Kilobyte	$2^{10} = 1,024$	1.024×10^3
Megabyte	$2^{20} \approx 1,048,000$	1.048×10^6
Gigabyte	$2^{30} \approx 1,074,000,000$	1.074×10^9
Terabyte	$2^{40} \approx 1,099,500,000,000$	1.0995×10^{12}

129. Writing in scientific notation: $0.0000357 = 3.57\times10^{-5}$. The correct answer is a.

Chapter 1 Test

1. Converting the fraction: $\dfrac{1}{2} \cdot \dfrac{9}{9} = \dfrac{9}{18}$

2. Converting the fraction: $\dfrac{5}{6} \cdot \dfrac{3}{3} = \dfrac{15}{18}$

3. The correct statement is: $-6 < -4$

4. The correct statement is: $7 < 9$

5. The correct statement is: $3 > -6$

6. The correct statement is: $-\dfrac{6}{7} < -\dfrac{2}{5}$

7. Simplifying: $|-16| = 16$

8. Simplifying: $-|-9| = -9$

9. The opposite of $\dfrac{2}{7}$ is $-\dfrac{2}{7}$ and the reciprocal is $\dfrac{7}{2}$.

10. Factoring: $588 = 12 \cdot 49 = 2 \cdot 2 \cdot 3 \cdot 7 \cdot 7 = 2^2 \cdot 3 \cdot 7^2$

11. Reducing the fraction: $\dfrac{192}{312} = \dfrac{24 \cdot 8}{24 \cdot 13} = \dfrac{8}{13}$

12. Reducing the fraction: $\dfrac{162}{459} = \dfrac{27 \cdot 6}{27 \cdot 17} = \dfrac{6}{17}$

13. Simplifying: $4(3x+2) - 6 = 12x + 8 - 6 = 12x + 2$

14. Simplifying: $6x - 3 + 4x + 5 = 10x + 2$

15. Simplifying: $4x + 3(2x + 4y) - 6y = 4x + 6x + 12y - 6y = 10x + 6y$

16. Simplifying: $3a + 2(5b + 4) - 1 = 3a + 10b + 8 - 1 = 3a + 10b + 7$

17. Simplifying: $6y + 3(x + 3) - 4y = 6y + 3x + 9 - 4y = 3x + 2y + 9$

18. Simplifying: $18\left(\dfrac{5}{6}y - \dfrac{2}{3}x\right) - 5y = 18 \cdot \dfrac{5}{6}y - 18 \cdot \dfrac{2}{3}x - 5y = 15y - 12x - 5y = 10y - 12x$

19. Adding the fractions: $\dfrac{7}{18} + \dfrac{7}{9} = \dfrac{7}{18} + \dfrac{7}{9} \cdot \dfrac{2}{2} = \dfrac{7}{18} + \dfrac{14}{18} = \dfrac{21}{18} = \dfrac{3 \cdot 7}{3 \cdot 6} = \dfrac{7}{6}$

20. Adding the fractions: $\dfrac{7}{12} + \dfrac{13}{34} = \dfrac{7}{12} \cdot \dfrac{17}{17} + \dfrac{13}{34} \cdot \dfrac{6}{6} = \dfrac{119}{204} + \dfrac{78}{204} = \dfrac{197}{204}$

21. Simplifying: $4 - (2x - 7) + 4x = 4 - 2x + 7 + 4x = 2x + 11$

22. Simplifying: $(5 - 4x) - (3 - 2x) = 5 - 4x - 3 + 2x = -2x + 2$

23. Simplifying: $5x - 3(2x + 4) + 15 = 5x - 6x - 12 + 15 = -x + 3$

24. Simplifying: $\dfrac{(8)(-9) - (6)(-2)}{-(12 - 8)} = \dfrac{-72 + 12}{-4} = \dfrac{-60}{-4} = 15$

25. Simplifying: $|7 - 10| - |3 - 5| = |-3| - |-2| = 3 - 2 = 1$

26. Simplifying: $6^2 + |3 \cdot 2 - 4| - 3^3 = 36 + |6 - 4| - 27 = 36 + |2| - 27 = 36 + 2 - 27 = 11$

27. Using properties of exponents: $\left(-3x^4\right)^{-3} = (-3)^{-3}\left(x^4\right)^{-3} = \dfrac{1}{(-3)^3\left(x^4\right)^3} = -\dfrac{1}{27x^{12}}$

28. Using properties of exponents: $\left(4x^2 y\right)^3 = (4)^3\left(x^2\right)^3(y)^3 = 64x^6 y^3$

29. Using properties of exponents: $\left(\dfrac{5}{9}\right)^{-2} = \left(\dfrac{9}{5}\right)^2 = \dfrac{81}{25}$

30. Using properties of exponents: $-5x^2 y \cdot -7x^3 y = 35x^5 y^2$

31. Using properties of exponents: $-6xy^3 \cdot 3x^{-2}y^4 = -18x^{-1}y^7 = -\dfrac{18y^7}{x}$

32. Using properties of exponents: $\dfrac{18a^4 b}{3ab^3} = 6a^{4-1}b^{1-3} = 6a^3 b^{-2} = \dfrac{6a^3}{b^2}$

33. Using properties of exponents: $\dfrac{18a^5 b^9}{24a^7 b^4} = \dfrac{3}{4}a^{5-7}b^{9-4} = \dfrac{3}{4}a^{-2}b^5 = \dfrac{3b^5}{4a^2}$

34. Using properties of exponents: $\left(\dfrac{3x^{-2}y}{9xy^2}\right)^{-3} = \left(\dfrac{1}{3x^3y}\right)^{-3} = \left(3x^3y\right)^3 = 27x^9y^3$

35. Writing in scientific notation: $12{,}530{,}000 = 1.253 \times 10^7$

36. Writing in scientific notation: $0.0052 = 5.2 \times 10^{-3}$

37. Writing in expanded form: $5.26 \times 10^{-3} = 0.00526$

38. Writing in expanded form: $4.9 \times 10^5 = 490{,}000$

39. Simplifying: $\dfrac{\left(1.4 \times 10^7\right)\left(6.5 \times 10^{-4}\right)}{7.0 \times 10^2} = \dfrac{9.1 \times 10^3}{7.0 \times 10^2} = \dfrac{9.1}{7.0} \times 10^{3-2} = 1.3 \times 10^1$

40. Simplifying: $\dfrac{\left(1.8 \times 10^7\right)\left(6.8 \times 10^6\right)}{\left(2.4 \times 10^9\right)\left(3.0 \times 10^{-4}\right)} = \dfrac{12.24 \times 10^{13}}{7.2 \times 10^5} = \dfrac{12.24}{7.2} \times 10^{13-5} = 1.7 \times 10^8$

Chapter 2
Equations and Inequalities in One Variable

2.1 Linear Equations

1. Solving the equation:

$$7y - 4 = 2y + 11$$
$$5y - 4 = 11$$
$$5y = 15$$
$$y = 3$$

3. Solving the equation:

$$-\frac{2}{5}x + \frac{2}{15} = \frac{2}{3}$$
$$15\left(-\frac{2}{5}x + \frac{2}{15}\right) = 15\left(\frac{2}{3}\right)$$
$$-6x + 2 = 10$$
$$-6x = 8$$
$$x = -\frac{4}{3}$$

5. Solving the equation:

$$0.14x + 0.08(10{,}000 - x) = 1{,}220$$
$$0.14x + 800 - 0.08x = 1{,}220$$
$$0.06x + 800 = 1{,}220$$
$$0.06x = 420$$
$$x = 7{,}000$$

7. Solving the equation:

$$5(y + 2) - 4(y + 1) = 3$$
$$5y + 10 - 4y - 4 = 3$$
$$y + 6 = 3$$
$$y = -3$$

9. Solving the equation:

$$2(4x + 5) = 11 + 8x$$
$$8x + 10 = 8x + 11$$
$$10 = 11$$

False!
There is no solution.

11. Solving the equation:

$$4(x + 1) = 7 + 4x - 3$$
$$4x + 4 = 4x + 4$$
$$4 = 4$$

True!
The solution set is all real numbers.

13. **a.** Distributing: $3(x - 4) = 3x - 12$

b. Simplifying: $3x - 4x = -x$

c. Solving:

$$3(x - 4) = 0$$
$$x - 4 = 0$$
$$x = 4$$

d. Solving:

$$3x - 4 = 0$$
$$3x = 4$$
$$x = \frac{4}{3}$$

15. **a.** Solving the equation:
$$9x - 5 = 0$$
$$9x = 5$$
$$x = \frac{5}{9}$$

b. Solving the equation:
$$9(x - 5) = 0$$
$$x - 5 = 0$$
$$x = 5$$

c. Solving the equation:
$$9x - 5 = 13$$
$$9x = 18$$
$$x = 2$$

d. Solving the equation:
$$9(x - 5) = 9x$$
$$9x - 45 = 9x$$
$$-45 = 0$$
False!
There is no solution.

17. Solving the equation:
$$-3 - 4x = 15$$
$$-4x = 18$$
$$x = -\frac{9}{2}$$

19. Solving the equation:
$$0 = 6,400a + 70$$
$$-70 = 6,400a$$
$$a = -\frac{70}{6,400} = -\frac{7}{640}$$

21. Solving the equation:
$$5(2x + 1) = 12$$
$$10x + 5 = 12$$
$$10x = 7$$
$$x = \frac{7}{10}$$

23. Solving the equation:
$$100P = 2,400$$
$$P = \frac{2,400}{100} = 24$$

25. Solving the equation:
$$5\left(-\frac{19}{15}\right) + 5y = 9$$
$$-\frac{19}{3} + 5y = 9$$
$$5y = \frac{46}{3}$$
$$y = \frac{46}{15}$$

27. Solving the equation:
$$\frac{3}{4}x - \frac{1}{6} = \frac{2}{3}$$
$$12\left(\frac{3}{4}x - \frac{1}{6}\right) = 12\left(\frac{2}{3}\right)$$
$$9x - 2 = 8$$
$$9x = 10$$
$$x = \frac{10}{9}$$

29. Solving the equation:
$$\frac{x}{2} - \frac{5}{6} = \frac{x}{3} + 1$$
$$6\left(\frac{x}{2} - \frac{5}{6}\right) = 6\left(\frac{x}{3} + 1\right)$$
$$3x - 5 = 2x + 6$$
$$x = 11$$

31. Solving the equation:
$$5(x + 4) - 3x = 14$$
$$5x + 20 - 3x = 14$$
$$2x + 20 = 14$$
$$2x = -6$$
$$x = -3$$

33. Solving the equation:
$$15 - 3(x - 1) = x - 2$$
$$15 - 3x + 3 = x - 2$$
$$-3x + 18 = x - 2$$
$$-4x + 18 = -2$$
$$-4x = -20$$
$$x = 5$$

35. Solving the equation:
$$2(20 + x) = 3(20 - x)$$
$$40 + 2x = 60 - 3x$$
$$40 + 5x = 60$$
$$5x = 20$$
$$x = 4$$

37. Solving the equation:

$$0.08x + 0.09(9{,}000 - x) = 750$$
$$0.08x + 810 - 0.09x = 750$$
$$-0.01x + 810 = 750$$
$$-0.01x = -60$$
$$x = 6{,}000$$

39. Solving the equation:

$$\frac{1}{2}(4x + 11) = 5x - \frac{2}{3}$$
$$2x + \frac{11}{2} = 5x - \frac{2}{3}$$
$$6\left(2x + \frac{11}{2}\right) = 6\left(5x - \frac{2}{3}\right)$$
$$12x + 33 = 30x - 4$$
$$-18x = -37$$
$$x = \frac{37}{18}$$

41. Solving the equation:

$$\frac{1}{6}(2x - 3) = \frac{7}{12} - \frac{1}{4}(x + 5)$$
$$\frac{1}{3}x - \frac{1}{2} = \frac{7}{12} - \frac{1}{4}x - \frac{5}{4}$$
$$12\left(\frac{1}{3}x - \frac{1}{2}\right) = 12\left(\frac{7}{12} - \frac{1}{4}x - \frac{5}{4}\right)$$
$$4x - 6 = 7 - 3x - 15$$
$$4x - 6 = -3x - 8$$
$$7x = -2$$
$$x = -\frac{2}{7}$$

43. Solving the equation:
$$3x - 6 = 3(x + 4)$$
$$3x - 6 = 3x + 12$$
$$-6 = 12$$
Since this statement is false, there is no solution.

45. Solving the equation:
$$2(4t - 1) + 3 = 5t + 4 + 3t$$
$$8t - 2 + 3 = 8t + 4$$
$$8t + 1 = 8t + 4$$
$$1 = 4$$
Since this statement is false, there is no solution.

47. Solving the equation:
$$7(x + 2) - 4(2x - 1) = 18 - x$$
$$7x + 14 - 8x + 4 = 18 - x$$
$$-x + 18 = -x + 18$$
$$18 = 18$$
Since this statement is true, the solution is all real numbers.

49. Solving the equation:
$$-0.0035A + 70 = -35$$
$$-0.0035A = -105$$
$$A = \frac{-105}{-0.0035}$$
$$A = 30{,}000$$
The altitude is 30,000 feet.

51. Solving the equation:

$$11 + 4x = 2x - 3$$
$$11 + 2x = -3$$
$$2x = -14$$
$$x = -7$$

The correct answer is d.

53. Since $2(x+1)+1 = 2x+2+1 = 2x+3$, the correct answer is a.

55. Solving the equation:

$$x \cdot 42 = 21$$

$$x = \frac{21}{42} = \frac{1}{2}$$

57. Solving the equation:

$$25 = 0.4x$$

$$x = \frac{25}{0.4} = 62.5$$

59. Solving the equation:

$$12 - 4y = 12$$

$$-4y = 0$$

$$y = 0$$

61. Solving the equation:

$$525 = 900 - 300p$$

$$-375 = -300p$$

$$p = \frac{-375}{-300} = \frac{5}{4}$$

63. Solving the equation:

$$486.7 = 78.5 + 31.4h$$

$$408.2 = 31.4h$$

$$h = \frac{408.2}{31.4} = 13$$

2.2 Formulas

1. Substituting $x = 0$:

$$3(0) - 4y = 12$$

$$-4y = 12$$

$$y = -3$$

3. Substituting $x = 4$:

$$3(4) - 4y = 12$$

$$12 - 4y = 12$$

$$-4y = 0$$

$$y = 0$$

5. Substituting $y = 0$:

$$2x - 3 = 0$$

$$2x = 3$$

$$x = \frac{3}{2}$$

7. Substituting $y = 5$:

$$2x - 3 = 5$$

$$2x = 8$$

$$x = 4$$

9. Substituting $y = -\frac{6}{5}$:

$$x - 2\left(-\frac{6}{5}\right) = 4$$

$$x + \frac{12}{5} = 4$$

$$x = \frac{8}{5}$$

11. Substituting $x = 160$ and $y = 0$:

$$0 = a(160 - 80)^2 + 70$$

$$-70 = a(80)^2$$

$$6,400a = -70$$

$$a = -\frac{70}{6,400} = -\frac{7}{640}$$

13. Substituting $d = 30, r = 12,$ and $t = 3$:

$$30 = (12 - c) \cdot 3$$

$$30 = 36 - 3c$$

$$-6 = -3c$$

$$c = 2$$

15. Substituting $x = 5$ and $y = 15$:

$$15 = k(5)$$

$$k = 3$$

17. Substituting $P = 48$ and $V = 50$:

$$50 = \frac{k}{48}$$
$$k = 50 \cdot 48 = 2{,}400$$

19. Substituting $x = 2$:

$$5(2) - 3y = -15$$
$$10 - 3y = -15$$
$$-3y = -25$$
$$y = \frac{25}{3}$$

21. Substituting $x = -\frac{1}{5}$:

$$5\left(-\frac{1}{5}\right) - 3y = -15$$
$$-1 - 3y = -15$$
$$-3y = -14$$
$$y = \frac{14}{3}$$

23. Solving for r:

$$d = rt$$
$$r = \frac{d}{t}$$

25. Solving for t:
$$d = (r + c)t$$
$$t = \frac{d}{r + c}$$

27. Solving for l:
$$A = lw$$
$$l = \frac{A}{w}$$

29. Solving for t:
$$I = prt$$
$$t = \frac{I}{pr}$$

31. Solving for T:
$$PV = nRT$$
$$T = \frac{PV}{nR}$$

33. Solving for x:

$$y = mx + b$$
$$y - b = mx$$
$$x = \frac{y - b}{m}$$

35. Solving for F:
$$C = \frac{5}{9}(F - 32)$$
$$\frac{9}{5}C = F - 32$$
$$F = \frac{9}{5}C + 32$$

37. Solving for v:
$$h = vt + 16t^2$$
$$h - 16t^2 = vt$$
$$v = \frac{h - 16t^2}{t}$$

39. Solving for d:
$$A = a + (n - 1)d$$
$$A - a = (n - 1)d$$
$$d = \frac{A - a}{n - 1}$$

41. Solving for y:
$$2x + 3y = 6$$
$$3y = -2x + 6$$
$$y = \frac{-2x + 6}{3}$$
$$y = -\frac{2}{3}x + 2$$

43. Solving for y:
$$-3x + 5y = 15$$
$$5y = 3x + 15$$
$$y = \frac{3x + 15}{5}$$
$$y = \frac{3}{5}x + 3$$

45. Solving for y:
$$2x - 6y + 12 = 0$$
$$-6y = -2x - 12$$
$$y = \frac{-2x - 12}{-6}$$
$$y = \frac{1}{3}x + 2$$

47. Solving for x:
$$ax + 4 = bx + 9$$
$$ax - bx + 4 = 9$$
$$ax - bx = 5$$
$$x(a - b) = 5$$
$$x = \frac{5}{a - b}$$

49. Solving for h:
$$S = \pi r^2 + 2\pi rh$$
$$2\pi rh = S - \pi r^2$$
$$h = \frac{S - \pi r^2}{2\pi r}$$

51. Solving for x:
$$-3x + 4y = 12$$
$$-3x = -4y + 12$$
$$x = \frac{-4y + 12}{-3} = \frac{4}{3}y - 4$$

53. Solving for x:
$$ax + 3 = cx - 7$$
$$ax - cx = -10$$
$$x(a - c) = -10$$
$$x = -\frac{10}{a - c}$$

55. Solving for y:
$$x = 2y - 3$$
$$2y = x + 3$$
$$y = \frac{x + 3}{2} = \frac{1}{2}x + \frac{3}{2}$$

57. Solving for y:
$$y - 3 = -2(x + 4)$$
$$y - 3 = -2x - 8$$
$$y = -2x - 5$$

59. Solving for y:
$$y - 3 = -\frac{2}{3}(x + 3)$$
$$y - 3 = -\frac{2}{3}x - 2$$
$$y = -\frac{2}{3}x + 1$$

61. Solving for y:
$$y - 4 = -\frac{1}{2}(x + 1)$$
$$y - 4 = -\frac{1}{2}x - \frac{1}{2}$$
$$y = -\frac{1}{2}x + \frac{7}{2}$$

63. **a.** Solving for y:

$$\frac{y+1}{x-0} = 4$$
$$y+1 = 4(x-0)$$
$$y+1 = 4x$$
$$y = 4x-1$$

b. Solving for y:

$$\frac{y+2}{x-4} = -\frac{1}{2}$$
$$y+2 = -\frac{1}{2}(x-4)$$
$$y+2 = -\frac{1}{2}x+2$$
$$y = -\frac{1}{2}x$$

c. Solving for y:

$$\frac{y+3}{x-7} = 0$$
$$y+3 = 0(x-7)$$
$$y+3 = 0$$
$$y = -3$$

65. Solving for y:

$$\frac{x}{8}+\frac{y}{2} = 1$$
$$8\left(\frac{x}{8}+\frac{y}{2}\right) = 8(1)$$
$$x+4y = 8$$
$$4y = -x+8$$
$$y = -\frac{1}{4}x+2$$

67. Solving for y:

$$\frac{x}{5}+\frac{y}{-3} = 1$$
$$15\left(\frac{x}{5}+\frac{y}{-3}\right) = 15(1)$$
$$3x-5y = 15$$
$$-5y = -3x+15$$
$$y = \frac{3}{5}x-3$$

69. **a.** Solving the equation:

$$-4x+5 = 20$$
$$-4x = 15$$
$$x = -\frac{15}{4}$$

b. Substituting $x = 3$: $-4x+5 = -4(3)+5 = -7$

c. Solving for y:

$$-4x+5y = 20$$
$$5y = 4x+20$$
$$y = \frac{4}{5}x+4$$

d. Solving for x:

$$-4x+5y = 20$$
$$-4x = -5y+20$$
$$x = \frac{5}{4}y-5$$

71. Finding the weight: $W = \dfrac{(6\cdot5)(30)(4)}{2,000} = \dfrac{9}{5}$ tons

73. Let c represent the rate of the current. The equation is:

$$2(15-c) = 18$$
$$30-2c = 18$$
$$-2c = -12$$
$$c = 6$$

The speed of the current is 6 mph.

75. Let w represent the rate of the wind. The equation is:

$$4(258-w) = 864$$
$$1032-4w = 864$$
$$-4w = -168$$
$$w = 42$$

The speed of the wind is 42 mph.

77. The distance traveled by the rider is the circumference: $C = \pi(65) \approx (3.14)(65) \approx 204.1$ feet

Finding the rate: $\dfrac{204.1 \text{ feet}}{30 \text{ seconds}} \approx 6.8$ feet per second

79. Substituting $F = 95$:

$$95 = \frac{9}{5}C + 32$$

$$63 = \frac{9}{5}C$$

$$\frac{5}{9}(63) = \frac{5}{9}\left(\frac{9}{5}C\right)$$

$$C = 35$$

81. Finding the size: $S = \dfrac{480 \cdot 216 \cdot 30 \cdot 150}{35,000} \approx 13,330$ KB

83. Substituting $n = 1$, $y = 7$, and $z = 15$:

$$x^1 + 7^1 = 15^1$$

$$x + 7 = 15$$

$$x = 8$$

85. For Shar, $M = 220 - 46 = 174$ and $R = 60$: $T = R + 0.6(M - R) = 60 + 0.6(174 - 60) = 128.4$ beats per minute

For Sara, $M = 220 - 26 = 194$ and $R = 60$: $T = R + 0.6(M - R) = 60 + 0.6(194 - 60) = 140.4$ beats per minute

87. Substituting $x = 2$:

$$4(2) - 3y = 5$$

$$8 - 3y = 5$$

$$-3y = -3$$

$$y = 1$$

The correct answer is b.

89. Solving for y:

$$4x - 3y = 6$$

$$-3y = -4x + 6$$

$$y = \frac{-4x + 6}{-3} = \frac{4}{3}x - 2$$

The correct answer is c.

91. Translating into symbols: $2x - 3$

93. Translating into symbols: $x + y = 180$

95. Solving the equation:

$$x + 2x = 90$$

$$3x = 90$$

$$x = 30$$

97. Solving the equation:

$$2(2x - 3) + 2x = 45$$

$$4x - 6 + 2x = 45$$

$$6x - 6 = 45$$

$$6x = 51$$

$$x = \frac{51}{6} = 8.5$$

99. Solving the equation:

$$0.06x + 0.05(10,000 - x) = 560$$

$$100\big(0.06x + 0.05(10,000 - x)\big) = 100(560)$$

$$6x + 5(10,000 - x) = 56,000$$

$$6x + 50,000 - 5x = 56,000$$

$$x + 50,000 = 56,000$$

$$x = 6,000$$

2.3 Applications

1. Let w represent the width and $2w$ represent the length. Using the perimeter formula:
$$2w + 2(2w) = 60$$
$$2w + 4w = 60$$
$$6w = 60$$
$$w = 10$$
The dimensions are 10 feet by 20 feet.

3. Let s represent the side of the square. Using the perimeter formula:
$$4s = 28$$
$$s = 7$$
The length of each side is 7 feet.

5. Let x represent the shortest side, $x + 3$ represent the medium side, and $2x$ represent the longest side. Using the perimeter formula:
$$x + x + 3 + 2x = 23$$
$$4x + 3 = 23$$
$$4x = 20$$
$$x = 5$$
The shortest side is 5 inches.

7. Let w represent the width and $2w - 3$ represent the length. Using the perimeter formula:
$$2w + 2(2w - 3) = 18$$
$$2w + 4w - 6 = 18$$
$$6w - 6 = 18$$
$$6w = 24$$
$$w = 4$$
The width is 4 meters.

9. Let w represent the width and $2w$ represent the length. Using the perimeter formula:
$$2w + 2(2w) = 48$$
$$2w + 4w = 48$$
$$6w = 48$$
$$w = 8$$
The width is 8 feet and the length is 16 feet. Finding the cost: $C = 1.75(32) + 2.25(16) = 56 + 36 = 92$
The cost to build the pen is $92.00.

11. Let b represent the amount of money Eric had at the beginning of the trip. Using the percent increase:
$$b + 0.50b = 300$$
$$1.5b = 300$$
$$b = 200$$
Eric had $200.00 at the beginning of the trip.

13. Let c represent the cost for the bookstore. Using the markup equation:
$$c + 0.33c = 115$$
$$1.33c = 115$$
$$c \approx 86.47$$
The cost to the bookstore was approximately $86.47.

15. Let T represent the total box office receipts that weekend. The equation is:
$$0.53R = 52.8$$
$$R = \frac{52.8}{0.53} \approx \$99.6 \text{ million}$$
The total box office receipts that weekend were $99.6 million.

17. Let x represent one angle and $8x$ represent the other angle. Since the angles are supplementary:

$$x + 8x = 180$$
$$9x = 180$$
$$x = 20$$

The two angles are 20° and 160°.

19. **a.** Let x represent one angle and $4x - 12$ represent the other angle. Since the angles are complementary:

$$x + 4x - 12 = 90$$
$$5x - 12 = 90$$
$$5x = 102$$
$$x = 20.4$$
$$4x - 12 = 4(20.4) - 12 = 69.6$$

The two angles are 20.4° and 69.6°.

b. Let x represent one angle and $4x - 12$ represent the other angle. Since the angles are supplementary:

$$x + 4x - 12 = 180$$
$$5x - 12 = 180$$
$$5x = 192$$
$$x = 38.4$$
$$4x - 12 = 4(38.4) - 12 = 141.6$$

The two angles are 38.4° and 141.6°.

21. Let x represent the smallest angle, $3x$ represent the largest angle, and $3x - 9$ represent the third angle. The equation is:

$$x + 3x + 3x - 9 = 180$$
$$7x - 9 = 180$$
$$7x = 189$$
$$x = 27$$

The three angles are 27°, 72° and 81°.

23. Let x represent the largest angle, $\frac{1}{3}x$ represent the smallest angle, and $\frac{1}{3}x + 10$ represent the third angle.

The equation is:

$$\frac{1}{3}x + x + \frac{1}{3}x + 10 = 180$$
$$\frac{5}{3}x + 10 = 180$$
$$\frac{5}{3}x = 170$$
$$x = 102$$

The three angles are 34°, 44° and 102°.

25. Let x represent the measure of the two base angles, and $2x + 8$ represent the third angle. The equation is:

$$x + x + 2x + 8 = 180$$
$$4x + 8 = 180$$
$$4x = 172$$
$$x = 43$$

The base angles are 43° and the third angle is 94°.

27. Let x represent the amount invested at 8% and $9{,}000 - x$ represent the amount invested at 9%. The equation is:

$$0.08x + 0.09(9{,}000 - x) = 750$$
$$0.08x + 810 - 0.09x = 750$$
$$-0.01x + 810 = 750$$
$$-0.01x = -60$$
$$x = 6{,}000$$

The woman invested $6,000 at 8% and $3,000 at 9%.

29. Let x represent the amount invested at 12% and $15{,}000 - x$ represent the amount invested at 10%. The equation is:

$$0.12x + 0.10(15{,}000 - x) = 1{,}600$$
$$0.12x + 1{,}500 - 0.10x = 1{,}600$$
$$0.02x + 1{,}500 = 1{,}600$$
$$0.02x = 100$$
$$x = 5{,}000$$

The investment was $5,000 at 12% and $10,000 at 10%.

31. Let x represent the amount invested at 8% and $6{,}000 - x$ represent the amount invested at 9%. The equation is:

$$0.08x + 0.09(6{,}000 - x) = 500$$
$$0.08x + 540 - 0.09x = 500$$
$$-0.01x + 540 = 500$$
$$-0.01x = -40$$
$$x = 4{,}000$$

Stacey invested $4,000 at 8% and $2,000 at 9%.

33. Let s represent the speed for Allegra, and $s + 4$ represent the speed for Eliana. Since the distances are equal:

$$2(s + 4) = 2.5(s)$$
$$2s + 8 = 2.5s$$
$$8 = 0.5s$$
$$s = 16$$
$$s + 4 = 20$$

Allegra can ride 16 mph and Eliana can ride 20 mph.

35. Completing the table:

Speed (miles per hour)	Distance (miles)
20	10
30	15
40	20
50	25
60	30
70	35

37. Completing the table:

Time (hours)	Distance upstream (miles)	Distance downstream (miles)
1	6	14
2	12	28
3	18	42
4	24	56
5	30	70
6	36	84

39. Let x represent the number of father tickets sold and $75 - x$ the number of son tickets sold. The equation is:

$$5(x) + 3.50(75 - x) = 307.50$$
$$5x + 262.5 - 3.5x = 307.5$$
$$1.5x + 262.5 = 307.5$$
$$1.5x = 45$$
$$x = 30$$
$$75 - x = 45$$

There were 30 fathers tickets and 45 sons tickets sold.

41. The total money collected is: $1204 - $250 = $954

Let x represent the amount of her sales (not including tax). Since this amount includes the tax collected, the equation is:

$$x + 0.06x = 954$$
$$1.06x = 954$$
$$x = 900$$

The woman's sales were $900, so the sales tax is: $0.06(900) = $54

43. Let x represent the length of Patrick's call. He talks 1 minute at 40 cents and $x - 1$ minutes at 30 cents, so the equation (in cents) is:

$$40(1) + 30(x - 1) + 50 = 1380$$
$$40 + 30x - 30 + 50 = 1380$$
$$30x + 60 = 1380$$
$$30x = 1320$$
$$x = 44$$

Patrick talked for 44 minutes.

45. Completing the table:

x	2,000	3,000	4,000	5,000
y	160	240	320	400

47. Completing the table:

Year	Sales (billions of dollars)
2005	7
2006	7.5
2007	8
2008	8.6
2009	9.2

49. Completing the table:

w (ft)	l (ft)	A (ft^2)
2	22	44
4	20	80
6	18	108
8	16	128
10	14	140
12	12	144

51. Completing the table:

Age (years)	Maximum Heart Rate (beats per minute)
18	202
19	201
20	200
21	199
22	198
23	197

53. Completing the table:

Maximum Heart Rate (beats per minute)	Training Heart Rate (beats per minute)
60	144.0
62	144.8
64	145.6
68	147.2
70	148.0
72	148.8

55. Let w represent the width and $3w + 2$ represent the length. Using the perimeter formula:

$$2w + 2(3w + 2) = 36$$
$$2w + 6w + 4 = 36$$
$$8w + 4 = 36$$
$$8w = 32$$
$$w = 4$$

The width is 4 inches. The correct answer is b.

57. Let s represent Vance's skateboard speed and $s - 9$ represent his running speed. Since the distances are equal:

$$2(s) = 5(s - 9)$$
$$2s = 5s - 45$$
$$-3s = -45$$
$$s = 15$$

Vance can skateboard at 15 mph. The correct answer is a.

59. Graphing the inequality:

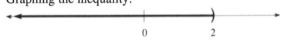

61. Graphing the inequality:

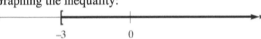

63. Solving the equation:

$$-2x - 3 = 7$$
$$-2x = 10$$
$$x = -5$$

65. Solving the equation:

$$3(2x - 4) - 7x = -3x$$
$$6x - 12 - 7x = -3x$$
$$-x - 12 = -3x$$
$$-12 = -2x$$
$$x = 6$$

2.4 Linear Inequalities in One Variable and Interval Notation

1. The set-builder notation is $\{x \mid x < 6\}$ and the interval notation is $(-\infty, 6)$. Sketching the graph:

3. The set-builder notation is $\{x \mid x \geq -1\}$ and the interval notation is $[-1, \infty)$. Sketching the graph:

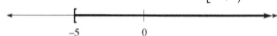

5. The set-builder notation is $\left\{x \mid x > \dfrac{3}{2}\right\}$ and the interval notation is $\left(\dfrac{3}{2}, \infty\right)$. Sketching the graph:

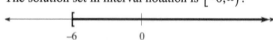

7. The set-builder notation is $\left\{x \mid x \leq -\dfrac{5}{4}\right\}$ and the interval notation is $\left(-\infty, -\dfrac{5}{4}\right]$. Sketching the graph:

9. The interval notation is $(-\infty, -3]$.

11. The interval notation is $(20, \infty)$.

13. The interval notation is $\left(-\infty, \dfrac{1}{2}\right)$.

15. The interval notation is $\left[-\dfrac{17}{4}, \infty\right)$.

17. Solving the inequality:
$$2x \leq 3$$
$$x \leq \frac{3}{2}$$

The solution set in interval notation is $\left(-\infty, \dfrac{3}{2}\right]$:

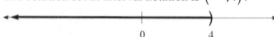

19. Solving the inequality:
$$\frac{1}{2}x > 2$$
$$x > 4$$

The solution set in interval notation is $(4, \infty)$:

21. Solving the inequality:

$$-5x \leq 25$$
$$x \geq -5$$

The solution set in interval notation is $[-5, \infty)$:

23. Solving the inequality:
$$-\frac{3}{2}x > -6$$
$$-3x > -12$$
$$x < 4$$

The solution set in interval notation is $(-\infty, 4)$:

25. Solving the inequality:
$$-12 \leq 2x$$
$$x \geq -6$$

The solution set in interval notation is $[-6, \infty)$:

27. Solving the inequality:
$$-1 \geq -\frac{1}{4}x$$
$$x \geq 4$$

The solution set in interval notation is $[4, \infty)$:

29. Solving the inequality:

$$-3x + 1 > 10$$
$$-3x > 9$$
$$x < -3$$

The solution set in interval notation is $(-\infty, -3)$:

31. Solving the inequality:

$$\frac{1}{2} - \frac{m}{12} \le \frac{7}{12}$$
$$12\left(\frac{1}{2} - \frac{m}{12}\right) \le 12\left(\frac{7}{12}\right)$$
$$6 - m \le 7$$
$$-m \le 1$$
$$m \ge -1$$

The solution set in interval notation is $[-1, \infty)$:

33. Solving the inequality:

$$\frac{1}{2} \ge -\frac{1}{6} - \frac{2}{9}x$$
$$18\left(\frac{1}{2}\right) \ge 18\left(-\frac{1}{6} - \frac{2}{9}x\right)$$
$$9 \ge -3 - 4x$$
$$12 \ge -4x$$
$$x \ge -3$$

The solution set in interval notation is $[-3, \infty)$:

35. Solving the inequality:

$$-40 \le 30 - 20y$$
$$-70 \le -20y$$
$$y \le \frac{7}{2}$$

The solution set in interval notation is $\left(-\infty, \frac{7}{2}\right]$:

37. Solving the inequality:

$$\frac{2}{3}x - 3 < 1$$
$$\frac{2}{3}x < 4$$
$$2x < 12$$
$$x < 6$$

The solution set in interval notation is $(-\infty, 6)$:

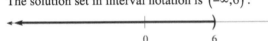

39. Solving the inequality:

$$10 - \frac{1}{2}y \le 36$$
$$-\frac{1}{2}y \le 26$$
$$y \ge -52$$

The solution set in interval notation is $[-52, \infty)$:

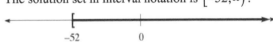

41. Solving the inequality:

$$4 - \frac{1}{2}x < \frac{2}{3}x - 5$$
$$6\left(4 - \frac{1}{2}x\right) < 6\left(\frac{2}{3}x - 5\right)$$
$$24 - 3x < 4x - 30$$
$$-7x < -54$$
$$x > \frac{54}{7}$$

The solution set in interval notation is $\left(\frac{54}{7}, \infty\right)$:

43. Solving the inequality:

$$0.03x - 0.4 \le 0.08x + 1.2$$
$$100(0.03x - 0.4) \le 100(0.08x + 1.2)$$
$$3x - 40 \le 8x + 120$$
$$-5x \le 160$$
$$x \ge -32$$

The solution set in interval notation is $[-32, \infty)$:

45. Solving the inequality:

$$3 - \frac{x}{5} < 5 - \frac{x}{4}$$

$$20\left(3 - \frac{x}{5}\right) < 20\left(5 - \frac{x}{4}\right)$$

$$60 - 4x < 100 - 5x$$

$$x < 40$$

The solution set in interval notation is $(-\infty, 40)$:

47. Solving the inequality:

$$2(3y+1) \le -10$$

$$6y + 2 \le -10$$

$$6y \le -12$$

$$y \le -2$$

The solution set is $(-\infty, -2]$.

49. Solving the inequality:

$$-(a+1) - 4a \le 2a - 8$$

$$-a - 1 - 4a \le 2a - 8$$

$$-5a - 1 \le 2a - 8$$

$$-7a \le -7$$

$$a \ge 1$$

The solution set is $[1, \infty)$.

51. Solving the inequality:

$$\frac{1}{3}t - \frac{1}{2}(5 - t) < 0$$

$$6\left(\frac{1}{3}t - \frac{1}{2}(5 - t)\right) < 6(0)$$

$$2t - 3(5 - t) < 0$$

$$2t - 15 + 3t < 0$$

$$5t - 15 < 0$$

$$5t < 15$$

$$t < 3$$

The solution set is $(-\infty, 3)$.

53. Solving the inequality:

$$-2 \le 5 - 7(2a + 3)$$

$$-2 \le 5 - 14a - 21$$

$$-2 \le -16 - 14a$$

$$14 \le -14a$$

$$a \le -1$$

The solution set is $(-\infty, -1]$.

55. Solving the inequality:

$$-\frac{1}{3}(x+5) \le -\frac{2}{9}(x-1)$$

$$9\left[-\frac{1}{3}(x+5)\right] \le 9\left[-\frac{2}{9}(x-1)\right]$$

$$-3(x+5) \le -2(x-1)$$

$$-3x - 15 \le -2x + 2$$

$$-x - 15 \le 2$$

$$-x \le 17$$

$$x \ge -17$$

The solution set is $[-17, \infty)$.

57. Solving the inequality:

$$5(x-2) - 7(x+1) \le -4x + 3$$

$$5x - 10 - 7x - 7 \le -4x + 3$$

$$-2x - 17 \le -4x + 3$$

$$2x - 17 \le 3$$

$$2x \le 20$$

$$x \le 10$$

The solution set is $(-\infty, 10]$.

59. Solving the inequality:

$$\frac{2}{3}x - \frac{1}{3}(4x-5) < 1$$

$$2x - 1(4x-5) < 3$$

$$2x - 4x + 5 < 3$$

$$-2x + 5 < 3$$

$$-2x < -2$$

$$x > 1$$

The solution set is $(1,\infty)$.

61. Solving the inequality:

$$20x + 9,300 > 18,000$$

$$20x > 8,700$$

$$x > 435$$

The solution set is $(435,\infty)$.

63. **a.** Evaluating when $x = 0$: $-\frac{1}{2}x + 1 = -\frac{1}{2}(0) + 1 = 1$

b. Solving the equation:

$$-\frac{1}{2}x + 1 = -7$$

$$-\frac{1}{2}x = -8$$

$$x = 16$$

c. Substituting $x = 0$: $-\frac{1}{2}x + 1 = -\frac{1}{2}(0) + 1 = 1$

No, 0 is not a solution to the inequality.

d. Solving the inequality:

$$-\frac{1}{2}x + 1 < -7$$

$$-\frac{1}{2}x < -8$$

$$x > 16$$

The solution set in interval notation is $(16,\infty)$.

65. **a.** Solving the inequality:
$$900 - 300p \geq 300$$
$$-300p \geq -600$$
$$p \leq 2.00$$
They should charge at most $2.00.

b. Solving the inequality:
$$900 - 300p > 600$$
$$-300p > -300$$
$$p < 1.00$$
They should charge less than $1.00.

c. Solving the inequality:
$$900 - 300p < 525$$
$$-300p < -375$$
$$p > 1.25$$
They should charge more than $1.25.

d. Solving the inequality:
$$900 - 300p \leq 375$$
$$-300p \leq -525$$
$$p \geq 1.75$$
They should charge at least $1.75.

67. Solving the inequality:

$$x \leq 0.08I$$

$$x \leq 0.08\left(\frac{24,000}{12}\right)$$

$$x \leq 160$$

The amount of monthly debt should be less than or equal to $160.

69. Solving the inequality:

$$11 - 3x \leq 20$$
$$-3x \leq 9$$
$$x \geq -3$$

The solution set in interval notation is $[-3, \infty)$. The correct answer is b.

71. This corresponds to the inequality $x < 4$, so the correct answer is a.

73. Graphing the interval $(-\infty, 4)$:

75. Graphing the interval $[-2, \infty)$:

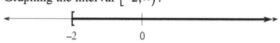

77. Graphing the interval $[-2, \infty)$:

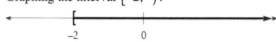

79. Graphing the interval $(-\infty, 2)$:

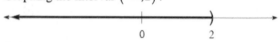

81. Solving the inequality:

$$3(1 - 4x) \leq 27$$
$$3 - 12x \leq 27$$
$$-12x \leq 24$$
$$x \geq -2$$

The solution set in interval notation is $[-2, \infty)$.

83. Solving the inequality:

$$3x + 7 \geq 4$$
$$3x \geq -3$$
$$x \geq -1$$

The solution set in interval notation is $[-1, \infty)$.

85. Solving the inequality:

$$-3 \leq 2x - 5$$
$$2 \leq 2x$$
$$x \geq 1$$

The solution set in interval notation is $[1, \infty)$.

87. Solving the inequality:

$$\frac{9}{5}x + 32 \leq 104$$
$$\frac{9}{5}x \leq 72$$
$$x \leq \frac{5}{9}(72)$$
$$x \leq 40$$

The solution set in interval notation is $(-\infty, 40]$.

2.5 Union, Intersection, and Compound Inequalities

1. The union is $A \cup B = \{1, 2, 3, 4, 5, 6\}$.

3. The union is $A \cup B = \{2, 4, 5, 6, 7, 8\}$.

5. The union is $A \cup B = (1, \infty)$.

7. The union is $A \cup B = (-\infty, -3]$.

9. The union is $A \cup B = (-\infty, -7) \cup (7, \infty)$.

11. The union is $A \cup B = (-\infty, \infty)$.

13. The intersection is $A \cap B = \varnothing$.

15. The intersection is $A \cap B = \{6, 8\}$.

17. The intersection is $A \cap B = (6, \infty)$.

19. The intersection is $A \cap B = (-\infty, -4)$.

21. The intersection is $A \cap B = \varnothing$.

23. The intersection is $A \cap B = \left(-2, \frac{3}{5}\right]$.

25. The interval notation is $(-\infty, \infty)$:

27. The interval notation is $[-9, \infty)$:

29. Solving each inequality:

$$2x - 9 < 5 \qquad\qquad 5x + 1 \le 6$$
$$2x < 14 \qquad\qquad 5x \le 5$$
$$x < 7 \qquad\qquad x \le 1$$

The solution is the interval $(-\infty, 7)$. Graphing the solution set:

31. Solving each inequality:

$$10 - x \le 15 \qquad\qquad 7 + x \ge 4$$
$$-x \le 5 \qquad\qquad x \ge -3$$
$$x \ge -5$$

The solution is the interval $[-5, \infty)$. Graphing the solution set:

33. Solving each inequality:

$$x + 5 \le -2 \qquad\qquad x + 5 \ge 2$$
$$x \le -7 \qquad\qquad x \ge -3$$

The solution set is $(-\infty, -7] \cup [-3, \infty)$. Graphing the solution set:

35. Solving each inequality:

$$5y + 1 \le -4 \qquad\qquad 5y + 1 \ge 4$$
$$5y \le -5 \qquad\qquad 5y \ge 3$$
$$y \le -1 \qquad\qquad y \ge \frac{3}{5}$$

The solution set is $(-\infty, -1] \cup \left[\frac{3}{5}, \infty\right)$. Graphing the solution set:

37. Solving each inequality:

$$5 - 3x > 3x \qquad\qquad 8x + 1 \ge 2x$$
$$5 > 6x \qquad\qquad 6x \ge -1$$
$$x < \frac{5}{6} \qquad\qquad x \ge -\frac{1}{6}$$

The solution set is $(-\infty, \infty)$. Graphing the solution set:

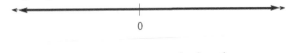

39. Solving each inequality:

$$2x + 5 < 3x - 1 \qquad\qquad x - 4 < 2x + 6$$
$$-x + 5 < -1 \qquad\qquad -x - 4 < 6$$
$$-x < -6 \qquad\qquad -x < 10$$
$$x > 6 \qquad\qquad x > -10$$

The solution set is $(-10, \infty)$. Graphing the solution set:

41. Solving each inequality:

$$2(3y+1) \geq 3(y-4)$$
$$6y+2 \geq 3y-12$$
$$3y \geq -14$$
$$y \geq -\frac{14}{3}$$

$$7(2y+3) \geq 4(3y-1)$$
$$14y+21 \geq 12y-4$$
$$2y \geq -25$$
$$y \geq -\frac{25}{2}$$

The solution set is $\left[-\dfrac{25}{2}, \infty\right)$. Graphing the solution set:

43. Solving each inequality:

$$\frac{1}{2} \geq -\frac{1}{6} - \frac{2}{9}x$$
$$18\left(\frac{1}{2}\right) \geq 18\left(-\frac{1}{6} - \frac{2}{9}x\right)$$
$$9 \geq -3 - 4x$$
$$4x \geq -12$$
$$x \geq -3$$

$$4 - \frac{1}{2}x < \frac{2}{3}x - 5$$
$$6\left(4 - \frac{1}{2}x\right) < 6\left(\frac{2}{3}x - 5\right)$$
$$24 - 3x < 9x - 30$$
$$-12x < -54$$
$$x > \frac{9}{2}$$

The solution set is $[-3, \infty)$. Graphing the solution set:

45. The interval notation is $(1,3)$:

47. The interval notation is $[-3, \infty)$:

49. Solving each inequality:

$$3x - 4 > 2$$
$$3x > 6$$
$$x > 2$$

$$6x + 2 > -10$$
$$6x > -12$$
$$x > -2$$

The solution set is $(2, \infty)$. Graphing the solution set:

51. Solving each inequality:

$$3x + 1 < -8$$
$$3x < -9$$
$$x < -3$$

$$-2x + 1 \leq -3$$
$$-2x \leq -4$$
$$x \geq 2$$

The solution set is $\varnothing$.

53. Solving each inequality:

$$x + 3 \geq -1$$
$$x \geq -4$$

$$x + 3 \leq 1$$
$$x \leq -2$$

The solution set is $[-4, -2]$. Graphing the solution set:

55. Solving each inequality:

$$4y - 1 > -2 \qquad\qquad 4y - 1 < 2$$
$$4y > -1 \qquad\qquad 4y < 3$$
$$y > -\frac{1}{4} \qquad\qquad y < \frac{3}{4}$$

The solution set is $\left(-\frac{1}{4}, \frac{3}{4}\right)$. Graphing the solution set:

$$-1/4 \qquad\qquad 3/4$$

57. Solving each inequality:

$$4 - 2x \leq x \qquad\qquad 7x > x - 5$$
$$-3x \leq -4 \qquad\qquad 6x > -5$$
$$x \geq \frac{4}{3} \qquad\qquad x > -\frac{5}{6}$$

The solution set is $\left[\frac{4}{3}, \infty\right)$. Graphing the solution set:

$$0 \qquad\qquad 4/3$$

59. Solving each inequality:

$$3(y - 5) < 4(2y + 3)$$
$$3y - 15 < 8y + 12 \qquad\qquad 2(5y + 1) < 9(y + 2)$$
$$-5y < 27 \qquad\qquad 10y + 2 < 9y + 18$$
$$y > -\frac{27}{5} \qquad\qquad y < 16$$

The solution set is $\left(-\frac{27}{5}, 16\right)$. Graphing the solution set:

$$-27/5 \qquad\qquad 16$$

61. Solving each inequality:

$$\frac{1}{2} - \frac{x}{12} \leq \frac{7}{12}$$
$$12\left(\frac{1}{2} - \frac{x}{12}\right) \leq 12\left(\frac{7}{12}\right) \qquad\qquad 3 - \frac{x}{5} < 5 - \frac{x}{4}$$
$$6 - x \leq 7 \qquad\qquad 20\left(3 - \frac{x}{5}\right) < 20\left(5 - \frac{x}{4}\right)$$
$$-x \leq 1 \qquad\qquad 60 - 4x < 100 - 5x$$
$$x \geq -1 \qquad\qquad x < 40$$

The solution set is $[-1, 40)$. Graphing the solution set:

$$-1 \qquad\qquad 40$$

63. Solving the inequality:

$$-2 \le m - 5 \le 2$$
$$3 \le m \le 7$$

The solution set is $[3,7]$. Graphing the solution set:

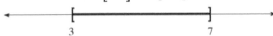

65. Solving the inequality:

$$-60 < 20a + 20 < 60$$
$$-80 < 20a < 40$$
$$-4 < a < 2$$

The solution set is $(-4,2)$. Graphing the solution set:

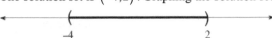

67. Solving the inequality:

$$0.5 \le 0.3a - 0.7 \le 1.1$$
$$1.2 \le 0.3a \le 1.8$$
$$4 \le a \le 6$$

The solution set is $[4,6]$. Graphing the solution set:

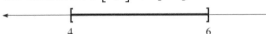

69. Solving the inequality:

$$3 < \frac{1}{2}x + 5 < 6$$
$$-2 < \frac{1}{2}x < 1$$
$$-4 < x < 2$$

The solution set is $(-4,2)$. Graphing the solution set:

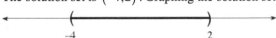

71. Solving the inequality:

$$4 < 6 + \frac{2}{3}x < 8$$
$$-2 < \frac{2}{3}x < 2$$
$$-6 < 2x < 6$$
$$-3 < x < 3$$

The solution set is $(-3,3)$. Graphing the solution set:

73. Writing as an inequality: $-2 < x \le 4$

75. Writing as an inequality: $x < -4$ or $x \ge 1$

77. **a.** Solving the inequality:

$$95 \le \frac{9}{5}C + 32 \le 113$$
$$63 \le \frac{9}{5}C \le 81$$
$$315 \le 9C \le 405$$
$$35° \le C \le 45°$$

b. Solving the inequality:

$$68 \le \frac{9}{5}C + 32 \le 86$$
$$36 \le \frac{9}{5}C \le 54$$
$$180 \le 9C \le 270$$
$$20° \le C \le 30°$$

c. Solving the inequality:

$$-13 \le \frac{9}{5}C + 32 \le 14$$
$$-45 \le \frac{9}{5}C \le -18$$
$$-225 \le 9C \le -90$$
$$-25° \le C \le -10°$$

d. Solving the inequality:

$$-4 \le \frac{9}{5}C + 32 \le 23$$
$$-36 \le \frac{9}{5}C \le -9$$
$$-180 \le 9C \le -45$$
$$-20° \le C \le -5°$$

79. For adults, the inequality is $0.72 - 0.11 \le r \le 0.72 + 0.11$, or $0.61 \le r \le 0.83$. The survival rate for adults is between 61% and 83%. For juveniles, the inequality is $0.13 - 0.07 \le r \le 0.13 + 0.07$, or $0.06 \le r \le 0.20$. The survival rate for juveniles is between 6% and 20%.

81. The union is $[-2,\infty)$. The correct answer is d.

83. Solving each inequality:

$$2x+5 \leq 3$$
$$2x \leq 2$$
$$x \leq 1$$

$$4-x \leq 9$$
$$-x \leq 5$$
$$x \geq -5$$

The union is $(-\infty, \infty)$. The correct answer is c.

85. Solving the equation:

$$2a-1 = -7$$
$$2a = -6$$
$$a = -3$$

87. Solving the equation:

$$\frac{2}{3}x - 3 = 7$$
$$\frac{2}{3}x = 10$$
$$x = 15$$

89. Solving the equation:

$$x-5 = x-7$$
$$-5 = -7$$

The equation has no solution $(\varnothing)$.

91. Solving the equation:

$$x-5 = -x-7$$
$$2x-5 = -7$$
$$2x = -2$$
$$x = -1$$

2.6 Equations with Absolute Value

1. Solving the equation:

$$|x| = 4$$
$$x = -4, 4$$

3. Solving the equation:

$$2 = |a|$$
$$a = -2, 2$$

5. The equation $|x| = -3$ has no solution, or $\varnothing$.

7. Solving the equation:

$$|a|+2 = 3$$
$$|a| = 1$$
$$a = -1, 1$$

9. Solving the equation:

$$|y|+4 = 3$$
$$|y| = -1$$

The equation $|y| = -1$ has no solution, or $\varnothing$.

11. Solving the equation:

$$|a-4| = \frac{5}{3}$$
$$a-4 = -\frac{5}{3}, \frac{5}{3}$$
$$a = \frac{7}{3}, \frac{17}{3}$$

13. Solving the equation:

$$\left|\frac{3}{5}a + \frac{1}{2}\right| = 1$$
$$\frac{3}{5}a + \frac{1}{2} = -1, 1$$
$$\frac{3}{5}a = -\frac{3}{2}, \frac{1}{2}$$
$$a = -\frac{5}{2}, \frac{5}{6}$$

15. Solving the equation:

$$60 = |20x - 40|$$
$$20x - 40 = -60, 60$$
$$20x = -20, 100$$
$$x = -1, 5$$

17. Since $|2x+1| = -3$ is impossible, there is no solution, or $\varnothing$.

19. Solving the equation:

$$\left|\frac{3}{4}x - 6\right| = 9$$

$$\frac{3}{4}x - 6 = -9, 9$$

$$\frac{3}{4}x = -3, 15$$

$$3x = -12, 60$$

$$x = -4, 20$$

21. Solving the equation:

$$\left|1 - \frac{1}{2}a\right| = 3$$

$$1 - \frac{1}{2}a = -3, 3$$

$$-\frac{1}{2}a = -4, 2$$

$$a = -4, 8$$

23. Solving the equation:

$$|2x - 5| = 3$$

$$2x - 5 = -3, 3$$

$$2x = 2, 8$$

$$x = 1, 4$$

25. Solving the equation:

$$|4 - 7x| = 5$$

$$4 - 7x = -5, 5$$

$$-7x = -9, 1$$

$$x = -\frac{1}{7}, \frac{9}{7}$$

27. Solving the equation:

$$\left|3 - \frac{2}{3}y\right| = 5$$

$$3 - \frac{2}{3}y = -5, 5$$

$$-\frac{2}{3}y = -8, 2$$

$$-2y = -24, 6$$

$$y = -3, 12$$

29. Solving the equation:

$$|3x + 12| = 0$$

$$3x + 12 = 0$$

$$3x = -12$$

$$x = -4$$

31. Solving the equation:

$$|3x + 4| + 1 = 7$$

$$|3x + 4| = 6$$

$$3x + 4 = -6, 6$$

$$3x = -10, 2$$

$$x = -\frac{10}{3}, \frac{2}{3}$$

33. Solving the equation:

$$|3 - 2y| + 4 = 3$$

$$|3 - 2y| = -1$$

Since this equation is impossible, there is no solution, or $\varnothing$.

35. Solving the equation:

$$3 + |4t - 1| = 8$$

$$|4t - 1| = 5$$

$$4t - 1 = -5, 5$$

$$4t = -4, 6$$

$$t = -1, \frac{3}{2}$$

37. Solving the equation:

$$5 + |3a + 2| = 5$$

$$|3a + 2| = 0$$

$$3a + 2 = 0$$

$$3a = -2$$

$$a = -\frac{2}{3}$$

39. Solving the equation:

$$\left|9 - \frac{3}{5}x\right| + 6 = 12$$

$$\left|9 - \frac{3}{5}x\right| = 6$$

$$9 - \frac{3}{5}x = -6, 6$$

$$-\frac{3}{5}x = -15, -3$$

$$-3x = -75, -15$$

$$x = 5, 25$$

41. Solving the equation:

$$5 = \left|\frac{2x}{7} + \frac{4}{7}\right| - 3$$

$$\left|\frac{2x}{7} + \frac{4}{7}\right| = 8$$

$$\frac{2x}{7} + \frac{4}{7} = -8, 8$$

$$2x + 4 = -56, 56$$

$$2x = -60, 52$$

$$x = -30, 26$$

43. Solving the equation:

$$2 = -8 + \left|4 - \frac{1}{2}y\right|$$

$$\left|4 - \frac{1}{2}y\right| = 10$$

$$4 - \frac{1}{2}y = -10, 10$$

$$-\frac{1}{2}y = -14, 6$$

$$y = -12, 28$$

45. Solving the equation:

$$\left|3(x+1)\right| - 4 = -1$$

$$\left|3(x+1)\right| = 3$$

$$3(x+1) = -3, 3$$

$$x + 1 = -1, 1$$

$$x = -2, 0$$

47. Solving the equation:

$$\left|1 + 3(2x-1)\right| = 5$$

$$1 + 3(2x-1) = -5, 5$$

$$3(2x-1) = -6, 4$$

$$2x - 1 = -2, \frac{4}{3}$$

$$2x = -1, \frac{7}{3}$$

$$x = -\frac{1}{2}, \frac{7}{6}$$

49. Solving the equation:

$$3 = -2 + \left|5 - \frac{2}{3}a\right|$$

$$\left|5 - \frac{2}{3}a\right| = 5$$

$$5 - \frac{2}{3}a = -5, 5$$

$$-\frac{2}{3}a = -10, 0$$

$$-2a = -30, 0$$

$$a = 0, 15$$

51. Solving the equation:

$$6 = \left|7(k+3) - 4\right|$$

$$7(k+3) - 4 = -6, 6$$

$$7(k+3) = -2, 10$$

$$k + 3 = -\frac{2}{7}, \frac{10}{7}$$

$$k = -\frac{23}{7}, -\frac{11}{7}$$

53. Solving the equation:

$$|3a+1| = |2a-4|$$

$3a+1 = 2a-4$	or	$3a+1 = -2a+4$
$a+1 = -4$		$5a = 3$
$a = -5$		$a = \dfrac{3}{5}$

55. Solving the equation:

$$\left|x - \frac{1}{3}\right| = \left|\frac{1}{2}x + \frac{1}{6}\right|$$

$x - \dfrac{1}{3} = \dfrac{1}{2}x + \dfrac{1}{6}$	or	$x - \dfrac{1}{3} = -\dfrac{1}{2}x - \dfrac{1}{6}$
$6x - 2 = 3x + 1$		$6x - 2 = -3x - 1$
$3x - 2 = 1$		$9x - 2 = -1$
$3x = 3$		$9x = 1$
$x = 1$		$x = \dfrac{1}{9}$

57. Solving the equation:

$$|y-2| = |y+3|$$

$y-2 = y+3$	or	$y-2 = -y-3$
$-2 = -3$		$2y = -1$
$y = $impossible		$y = -\dfrac{1}{2}$

59. Solving the equation:

$$|3x-1| = |3x+1|$$

$3x-1 = 3x+1$	or	$3x-1 = -3x-1$
$-1 = 1$		$6x = 0$
$x = $impossible		$x = 0$

61. Solving the equation:

$$|0.03 - 0.01x| = |0.04 + 0.05x|$$

$0.03 - 0.01x = 0.04 + 0.05x$	or	$0.03 - 0.01x = -0.04 - 0.05x$
$-0.06x = 0.01$		$0.04x = -0.07$
$x = -\dfrac{1}{6}$		$x = -\dfrac{7}{4}$

63. Since $|x-2| = |2-x|$ is always true, the solution set is all real numbers.

65. Since $\left|\dfrac{x}{5} - 1\right| = \left|1 - \dfrac{x}{5}\right|$ is always true, the solution set is all real numbers.

67. Solving the equation:

$$\left|\frac{2}{3}b - \frac{1}{4}\right| = \left|\frac{1}{6}b + \frac{1}{2}\right|$$

$$\frac{2}{3}b - \frac{1}{4} = \frac{1}{6}b + \frac{1}{2} \qquad \text{or} \qquad \frac{2}{3}b - \frac{1}{4} = -\frac{1}{6}b - \frac{1}{2}$$

$$8b - 3 = 2b + 6 \qquad\qquad\qquad 8b - 3 = -2b - 6$$

$$6b - 3 = 6 \qquad\qquad\qquad\quad 10b - 3 = -6$$

$$6b = 9 \qquad\qquad\qquad\qquad 10b = -3$$

$$b = \frac{3}{2} \qquad\qquad\qquad\qquad b = -\frac{3}{10}$$

69. Solving the equation:

$$|0.1a - 0.04| = |0.3a + 0.08|$$

$$0.1a - 0.04 = 0.3a + 0.08 \qquad \text{or} \qquad 0.1a - 0.04 = -0.3a - 0.08$$

$$-0.2a - 0.04 = 0.08 \qquad\qquad\qquad 0.4a - 0.04 = -0.08$$

$$-0.2a = 0.12 \qquad\qquad\qquad\qquad 0.4a = -0.04$$

$$-20a = 12 \qquad\qquad\qquad\qquad 40a = -4$$

$$a = -\frac{3}{5} \qquad\qquad\qquad\qquad a = -\frac{1}{10}$$

71. **a.** Solving the equation:

$$4x - 5 = 0$$

$$4x = 5$$

$$x = \frac{5}{4}$$

b. Solving the equation:

$$|4x - 5| = 0$$

$$4x - 5 = 0$$

$$4x = 5$$

$$x = \frac{5}{4}$$

c. Solving the equation:

$$4x - 5 = 3$$

$$4x = 8$$

$$x = 2$$

d. Solving the equation:

$$|4x - 5| = 3$$

$$4x - 5 = -3, 3$$

$$4x = 2, 8$$

$$x = \frac{1}{2}, 2$$

e. Solving the equation:

$$|4x - 5| = |2x + 3|$$

$$4x - 5 = 2x + 3 \qquad \text{or} \qquad 4x - 5 = -2x - 3$$

$$2x - 5 = 3 \qquad\qquad\qquad 6x - 5 = -3$$

$$2x = 8 \qquad\qquad\qquad\quad 6x = 2$$

$$x = 4 \qquad\qquad\qquad\qquad x = \frac{1}{3}$$

73. Solving the equation:

$$-60|x - 11| + 962 = 722$$

$$-60|x - 11| = -240$$

$$|x - 11| = 4$$

$$x - 11 = -4, 4$$

$$x = 7, 15$$

The revenue was \$722 million in 1987 and 1995.

75. Solving the equation:
$$|x+9|-3=5$$
$$|x+9|=8$$
$$x+9=-8,8$$
$$x=-17,-1$$
The correct answer is b.

77. Solving the equation:
$$|2a+3|=|a-4|$$

$$2a+3=a-4 \qquad \text{or} \qquad 2a+3=-a+4$$
$$a+3=-4 \qquad\qquad\qquad 3a=1$$
$$a=-7 \qquad\qquad\qquad\qquad a=\frac{1}{3}$$

The correct answer is c.

79. Solving the inequality:
$$-3<2x-5$$
$$2<2x$$
$$x>1$$

81. Solving the inequality:
$$3a+2\le 4$$
$$3a\le 2$$
$$a\le\frac{2}{3}$$

83. Solving the inequality:
$$4t-3\ge 9$$
$$4t\ge 12$$
$$t\ge 3$$

2.7 Inequalities Involving Absolute Value

1. Solving the inequality:
$$|x|<3$$
$$-3<x<3$$
The solution set is $(-3,3)$:

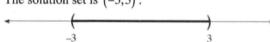

3. Solving the inequality:
$$|x|\ge 2$$
$$x\le -2 \text{ or } x\ge 2$$
The solution set is $(-\infty,-2]\cup[2,\infty)$:

5. Solving the inequality:
$$|x|+2<5$$
$$|x|<3$$
$$-3<x<3$$
The solution set is $(-3,3)$:

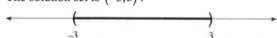

7. Solving the inequality:
$$|t|-3>4$$
$$|t|>7$$
$$t<-7 \text{ or } t>7$$
The solution set is $(-\infty,-7)\cup(7,\infty)$:

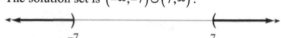

9. Since the inequality $|y|<-5$ is never true, the solution set is $\varnothing$:

11. Since the inequality $|x|\ge -2$ is always true, the solution set is all real numbers, or $(-\infty,\infty)$:

13. Solving the inequality:
$$|x-3| < 7$$
$$-7 < x-3 < 7$$
$$-4 < x < 10$$
The solution set is $(-4, 10)$:

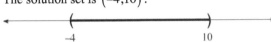

15. Solving the inequality:
$$|a+5| \geq 4$$
$$a+5 \leq -4 \text{ or } a+5 \geq 4$$
$$a \leq -9 \text{ or } \quad a \geq -1$$
The solution set is $(-\infty, -9] \cup [-1, \infty)$:

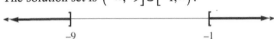

17. Since the inequality $|b+1| < 0$ is never true, the solution set is $\varnothing$:

19. Since the inequality $|b-2| \geq 0$ is always true, the solution set is all real numbers, or $(-\infty, \infty)$:

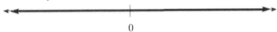

21. Since the inequality $|a-1| < -3$ is never true, the solution set is $\varnothing$:

23. Solving the inequality:
$$|2x-4| < 6$$
$$-6 < 2x-4 < 6$$
$$-2 < 2x < 10$$
$$-1 < x < 5$$
The solution set is $(-1, 5)$:

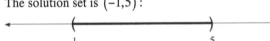

25. Solving the inequality:
$$|3y+9| \geq 6$$
$$3y+9 \leq -6 \qquad \text{or} \qquad 3y+9 \geq 6$$
$$3y \leq -15 \qquad\qquad 3y \geq -3$$
$$y \leq -5 \qquad\qquad y \geq -1$$
The solution set is $(-\infty, -5] \cup [-1, \infty)$:

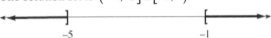

27. Solving the inequality:
$$|2k+3| \geq 7$$
$$2k+3 \leq -7 \qquad \text{or} \qquad 2k+3 \geq 7$$
$$2k \leq -10 \qquad\qquad 2k \geq 4$$
$$k \leq -5 \qquad\qquad k \geq 2$$
The solution set is $(-\infty, -5] \cup [2, \infty)$:

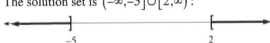

29. Solving the inequality:
$$|x-3| + 2 < 6$$
$$|x-3| < 4$$
$$-4 < x-3 < 4$$
$$-1 < x < 7$$
The solution set is $(-1, 7)$:

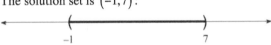

31. Solving the inequality:
$$|2a+1| + 4 \geq 7$$
$$|2a+1| \geq 3$$
$$2a+1 \leq -3 \qquad \text{or} \qquad 2a+1 \geq 3$$
$$2a \leq -4 \qquad\qquad 2a \geq 2$$
$$a \leq -2 \qquad\qquad a \geq 1$$
The solution set is $(-\infty, -2] \cup [1, \infty)$:

33. Solving the inequality:
$$|3x+5| - 8 < 5$$
$$|3x+5| < 13$$
$$-13 < 3x+5 < 13$$
$$-18 < 3x < 8$$
$$-6 < x < \frac{8}{3}$$
The solution set is $\left(-6, \frac{8}{3}\right)$:

35. Solving the inequality:
$$9 + |5y - 6| < 4$$
$$|5y - 6| < -5$$
The solution set is $\varnothing$:

37. Solving the inequality:

$$|x - 3| \leq 5$$
$$-5 \leq x - 3 \leq 5$$
$$-2 \leq x \leq 8$$

The solution set is $[-2, 8]$.

39. Solving the inequality:
$$|3y + 1| < 5$$
$$-5 < 3y + 1 < 5$$
$$-6 < 3y < 4$$
$$-2 < y < \frac{4}{3}$$
The solution set is $\left(-2, \frac{4}{3}\right)$.

41. Solving the inequality:

$$|a + 4| \geq 1$$
$$a + 4 \leq -1 \quad \text{or} \quad a + 4 \geq 1$$
$$a \leq -5 \qquad\qquad a \geq -3$$

The solution set is $(-\infty, -5] \cup [3, \infty)$.

43. Solving the inequality:
$$|2x + 5| > 2$$
$$2x + 5 < -2 \quad \text{or} \quad 2x + 5 > 2$$
$$2x < -7 \qquad\qquad 2x > -3$$
$$x < -\frac{7}{2} \qquad\qquad x > -\frac{3}{2}$$
The solution set is $\left(-\infty, -\frac{7}{2}\right) \cup \left(-\frac{3}{2}, \infty\right)$.

45. Solving the inequality:
$$|-5x + 3| \leq 8$$
$$-8 \leq -5x + 3 \leq 8$$
$$-11 \leq -5x \leq 5$$
$$\frac{11}{5} \geq x \geq -1$$
The solution set is $\left[-1, \frac{11}{5}\right]$.

47. Solving the inequality:
$$|-3x + 7| < 2$$
$$-2 < -3x + 7 < 2$$
$$-9 < -3x < -5$$
$$3 > x > \frac{5}{3}$$
The solution set is $\left(\frac{5}{3}, 3\right)$.

49. Solving the inequality:

$$|5 - x| > 3$$
$$5 - x < -3 \quad \text{or} \quad 5 - x > 3$$
$$-x < -8 \qquad\qquad -x > -2$$
$$x > 8 \qquad\qquad x < 2$$

The solution set is $(-\infty, 2) \cup (8, \infty)$:

51. Solving the inequality:

$$\left|3 - \frac{2}{3}x\right| \geq 5$$
$$3 - \frac{2}{3}x \leq -5 \quad \text{or} \quad 3 - \frac{2}{3}x \geq 5$$
$$-\frac{2}{3}x \leq -8 \qquad\qquad -\frac{2}{3}x \geq 2$$
$$-2x \leq -24 \qquad\qquad -2x \geq 6$$
$$x \geq 12 \qquad\qquad x \leq -3$$

The solution set is $(-\infty, -3] \cup [12, \infty)$:

53. Solving the inequality:

$$\left|2-\frac{1}{2}x\right|>1$$

$$2-\frac{1}{2}x<-1 \qquad \text{or} \qquad 2-\frac{1}{2}x>1$$

$$-\frac{1}{2}x<-3 \qquad\qquad -\frac{1}{2}x>-1$$

$$x>6 \qquad\qquad\qquad x<2$$

The solution set is $(-\infty,2)\cup(6,\infty)$:

55. Solving the inequality:

$$|x-1|<0.01$$

$$-0.01<x-1<0.01$$

$$0.99<x<1.01$$

The solution set is $(0.99,1.01)$.

57. Solving the inequality:

$$|2x+1|\geq\frac{1}{5}$$

$$2x+1\leq-\frac{1}{5} \qquad \text{or} \qquad 2x+1\geq\frac{1}{5}$$

$$2x\leq-\frac{6}{5} \qquad\qquad 2x\geq-\frac{4}{5}$$

$$x\leq-\frac{3}{5} \qquad\qquad x\geq-\frac{2}{5}$$

The solution set is $\left(-\infty,-\frac{3}{5}\right]\cup\left[-\frac{2}{5},\infty\right)$.

59. Solving the inequality:

$$|3x-2|\leq\frac{1}{3}$$

$$-\frac{1}{3}\leq 3x-2\leq\frac{1}{3}$$

$$\frac{5}{3}\leq 3x\leq\frac{7}{3}$$

$$\frac{5}{9}\leq x\leq\frac{7}{9}$$

The solution set is $\left[\frac{5}{9},\frac{7}{9}\right]$.

61. Solving the inequality:

$$\left|\frac{3x+1}{2}\right|>\frac{1}{2}$$

$$\frac{3x+1}{2}<-\frac{1}{2} \qquad \text{or} \qquad \frac{3x+1}{2}>\frac{1}{2}$$

$$3x+1<-1 \qquad\qquad 3x+1>1$$

$$3x<-2 \qquad\qquad\qquad 3x>0$$

$$x<-\frac{2}{3} \qquad\qquad\qquad x>0$$

The solution set is $\left(-\infty,-\frac{2}{3}\right)\cup(0,\infty)$.

63. Solving the inequality:

$$\left|\frac{4-3x}{2}\right|\geq1$$

$$\frac{4-3x}{2}\leq-1 \qquad \text{or} \qquad \frac{4-3x}{2}\geq1$$

$$4-3x\leq-2 \qquad\qquad 4-3x\geq2$$

$$-3x\leq-6 \qquad\qquad -3x\geq-2$$

$$x\geq2 \qquad\qquad\qquad x\leq\frac{2}{3}$$

The solution set is $\left(-\infty,\frac{2}{3}\right]\cup[2,\infty)$.

65. Solving the inequality:

$$\left|\frac{3x-2}{5}\right|\leq\frac{1}{2}$$

$$-\frac{1}{2}\leq\frac{3x-2}{5}\leq\frac{1}{2}$$

$$-\frac{5}{2}\leq 3x-2\leq\frac{5}{2}$$

$$-\frac{1}{2}\leq 3x\leq\frac{9}{2}$$

$$-\frac{1}{6}\leq x\leq\frac{3}{2}$$

The solution set is $\left[-\frac{1}{6},\frac{3}{2}\right]$.

67. Solving the inequality:

$$\left|2x - \frac{1}{5}\right| < 0.3$$

$$-0.3 < 2x - 0.2 < 0.3$$

$$-0.1 < 2x < 0.5$$

$$-0.05 < x < 0.25$$

The solution set is $(-0.05, 0.25)$.

69. Writing as an absolute value inequality: $|x| \le 4$

71. Writing as an absolute value inequality: $|x - 5| \le 1$

73. **a.** Evaluating when $x = 0$: $|5x + 3| = |5(0) + 3| = |3| = 3$

b. Solving the equation:

$$|5x + 3| = 7$$

$$5x + 3 = -7, 7$$

$$5x = -10, 4$$

$$x = -2, \frac{4}{5}$$

c. No, it is not a solution.

d. Solving the inequality:

$$|5x + 3| > 7$$

$5x + 3 < -7$	or	$5x + 3 > 7$
$5x < -10$		$5x > 4$
$x < -2$		$x > \frac{4}{5}$

The solution set is $(-\infty, -2) \cup \left(\frac{4}{5}, \infty\right)$.

75. The inequality is $55 \le x \le 75$.

77. Solving the inequality:

$$|x - 9| + 5 \le 10$$

$$|x - 9| \le 5$$

$$-5 \le x - 9 \le 5$$

$$4 \le x \le 14$$

The solution set is $[4, 14]$. The correct answer is d.

79. Since the inequality $|5 - y| < -7$ is never true, the solution set is $\varnothing$. The correct answer is a.

81. Writing with positive exponents: $3^{-2} = \frac{1}{3^2} = \frac{1}{9}$

83. Dividing: $\frac{15x^3 y^8}{5xy^{10}} = 3x^{3-1}y^{8-10} = 3x^2 y^{-2} = \frac{3x^2}{y^2}$

85. Simplifying: $\frac{\left(3x^{-3}y^5\right)^{-2}}{\left(9xy^{-2}\right)^{-1}} = \frac{3^{-2}x^6 y^{-10}}{9^{-1}x^{-1}y^2} = \frac{9}{3^2}x^{6+1}y^{-10-2} = x^7 y^{-12} = \frac{x^7}{y^{12}}$

87. Writing in scientific notation: $54,000 = 5.4 \times 10^4$

89. Writing in expanded form: $6.44 \times 10^3 = 6,440$

91. Simplifying: $\left(3 \times 10^8\right)\left(4 \times 10^{-5}\right) = 12 \times 10^3 = 1.2 \times 10^4$

Chapter 2 Test

1. Solving the equation:

$$5 - \frac{4}{7}a = -11$$

$$-\frac{4}{7}a = -16$$

$$a = -\frac{7}{4}(-16)$$

$$a = 28$$

2. Solving the equation:

$$10\left(\frac{1}{5}x - \frac{1}{2} - \frac{1}{10}x + \frac{2}{5}\right) = 10\left(\frac{3}{10}x + \frac{1}{2}\right)$$

$$2x - 5 - x + 4 = 3x + 5$$

$$x - 1 = 3x + 5$$

$$-2x = 6$$

$$x = -3$$

3. Solving the equation:

$$5(x-1) - 2(2x+3) = 5x - 4$$

$$5x - 5 - 4x - 6 = 5x - 4$$

$$x - 11 = 5x - 4$$

$$-4x = 7$$

$$x = -\frac{7}{4}$$

4. Solving the equation:

$$0.07 - 0.02(3x+1) = -0.04x + 0.01$$

$$0.07 - 0.06x - 0.02 = -0.04x + 0.01$$

$$-0.06x + 0.05 = -0.04x + 0.01$$

$$-0.02x = -0.04$$

$$x = 2$$

5. Solving for w:

$$P = 2l + 2w$$

$$P - 2l = 2w$$

$$w = \frac{P - 2l}{2}$$

6. Solving for B:

$$A = \frac{1}{2}h(b + B)$$

$$2A = hb + hB$$

$$2A - hb = hB$$

$$B = \frac{2A - hb}{h}$$

7. Solving for y:

$$5x - 2y = 10$$

$$-2y = -5x + 10$$

$$y = \frac{5}{2}x - 5$$

8. Solving for x:

$$\frac{y - 5}{x - 4} = 3$$

$$y - 5 = 3x - 12$$

$$y = 3x - 7$$

9. Let x represent the width and $2x$ represent the length. Using the perimeter formula:

$$2(x) + 2(2x) = 36$$

$$2x + 4x = 36$$

$$6x = 36$$

$$x = 6$$

$$2x = 12$$

The width is 6 in. and the length is 12 in.

10. Let x and $2x + 15$ represent the two angles. Since they are supplementary:

$$x + 2x + 15 = 180$$

$$3x + 15 = 180$$

$$3x = 165$$

$$x = 55$$

$$2x + 15 = 125$$

The angles are 55° and 125°.

11.   Solving the inequality:

$$-5t \le 30$$
$$t \ge -6$$

The solution set is $[-6,\infty)$:

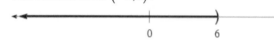

12.   Solving the inequality:

$$5 - \frac{3}{2}x > -1$$
$$-\frac{3}{2}x > -6$$
$$-3x > -12$$
$$x < 4$$

The solution set is $(-\infty,4)$:

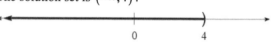

13.   Solving the inequality:

$$1.6x - 2 < 0.8x + 2.8$$
$$0.8x < 4.8$$
$$x < 6$$

The solution set is $(-\infty,6)$:

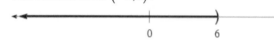

14.   Solving the inequality:

$$3(2y + 4) \ge 5(y - 8)$$
$$6y + 12 \ge 5y - 40$$
$$y \ge -52$$

The solution set is $[-52,\infty)$:

15.   The union is $\{1,2,3,4,6\}$.

16.   The union is $(-\infty,4]$.

17.   The intersection is $\{2\}$.

18.   The intersection is $(-\infty,-1)$.

19.   Solving each inequality:

$$x + 5 \le 9 \qquad\qquad x - 2 > -8$$
$$x \le 4 \qquad\qquad\quad x > -6$$

The solution set is all real numbers, or $(-\infty,\infty)$.

20.   Solving each inequality:

$$5x - 3 < 7 \qquad\qquad 4 - x > 7$$
$$5x < 10 \qquad\qquad\quad -x > 3$$
$$x < 2 \qquad\qquad\qquad x < -3$$

The solution set is $(-\infty,-3)$.

21.   Solving the equation:

$$|x + 6| - 3 = 1$$
$$|x + 6| = 4$$
$$x + 6 = -4, 4$$
$$x = -10, -2$$

22.   Solving the equation:

$$\left|\frac{1}{4}x - 1\right| = \frac{1}{2}$$
$$\frac{1}{4}x - 1 = -\frac{1}{2}, \frac{1}{2}$$
$$\frac{1}{4}x = \frac{1}{2}, \frac{3}{2}$$
$$x = 2, 6$$

23.   Solving the equation:

$$|3 - 2x| + 5 = 2$$
$$|3 - 2x| = -3$$

Since this equation is impossible, there is no solution, or $\varnothing$.

24. Solving the equation:

$$|x-1| = |5x+2|$$

$$x-1 = 5x+2 \qquad \text{or} \qquad x-1 = -5x-2$$

$$-4x = 3 \qquad\qquad\qquad\qquad 6x = -1$$

$$x = -\frac{3}{4} \qquad\qquad\qquad\qquad x = -\frac{1}{6}$$

25. Solving the inequality:

$$|6x-1| > 7$$

$$6x-1 < -7 \qquad \text{or} \qquad 6x-1 > 7$$

$$6x < -6 \qquad\qquad\qquad 6x > 8$$

$$x < -1 \qquad\qquad\qquad x > \frac{4}{3}$$

The solution set is $\left(-\infty, -1\right) \cup \left(\frac{4}{3}, \infty\right)$:

26. Solving the inequality:

$$|3x-5| - 4 \le 3$$

$$|3x-5| \le 7$$

$$-7 \le 3x - 5 \le 7$$

$$-2 \le 3x \le 12$$

$$-\frac{2}{3} \le x \le 4$$

The solution set is $\left[-\frac{2}{3}, 4\right]$:

27. Since the inequality $|5-4x| \ge -7$ is always true, the solution set is all real numbers, or $\left(-\infty, \infty\right)$:

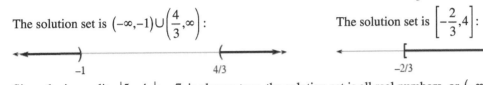

28. Since the inequality $|4t-1| < -3$ is never true, the solution set is $\varnothing$:

Chapter 3
Linear Equations in Two Variables and Functions

3.1 The Rectangular Coordinate System and Graphing Lines

1. Plotting the points:

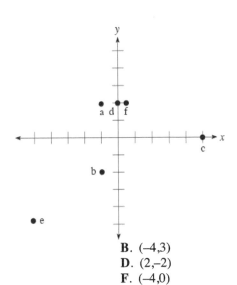

3. A. (4,1)   B. (−4,3)
    C. (−2,−5)   D. (2,−2)
    E. (0,5)   F. (−4,0)
    G. (1,0)

5. The correct chart is b.
7. Since the y-intercept is −2 and the x-intercept is 3, this is the graph of equation b.
9. Three points are (−1,−2), (0,0), and (1,2). Sketching the graph:

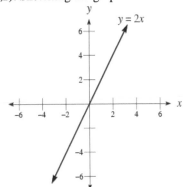

11. Three points are $(-4,3)$, $(0,0)$, and $(4,-3)$. Sketching the graph:

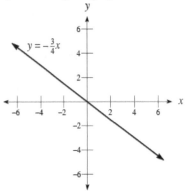

13. Three points are $(-1,-1)$, $(0,0)$, and $(1,1)$. Sketching the graph:

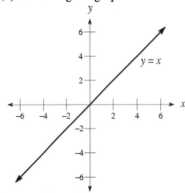

15. Three points are $(-3,0)$, $(0,1)$, and $(3,2)$. Sketching the graph:

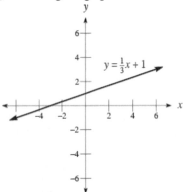

17. Three points are $(-1,1)$, $(0,-2)$, and $(1,-5)$. Sketching the graph:

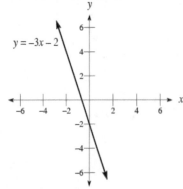

19. The *x*-intercept is (2,0) and the *y*-intercept is (0,–3):

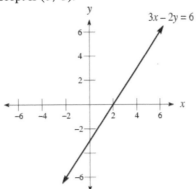

21. The *x*-intercept is (2,0) and the *y*-intercept is (0,4):

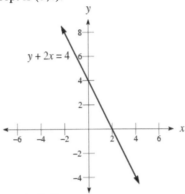

23. The *x*-intercept is (0,0) and the *y*-intercept is (0,0):

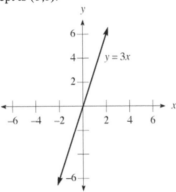

25. The *x*-intercept is (2,0) and the *y*-intercept is (0,–4):

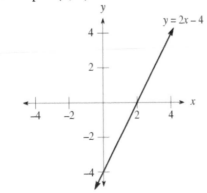

27. The *x*-intercept is (–2,0) and the *y*-intercept is (0,1):

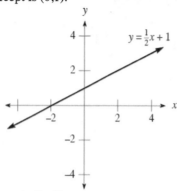

$$y = \tfrac{1}{2}x + 1$$

29. The *x*-intercept is (3,0) and the *y*-intercept is (0,–3):

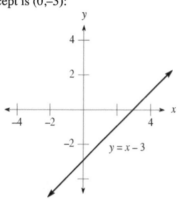

$$y = x - 3$$

31. The *x*-intercept is $\left(\dfrac{5}{2},0\right)$ and the *y*-intercept is $\left(0,\dfrac{5}{4}\right)$:

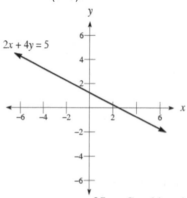

$$2x + 4y = 5$$

33. Graphing the line:

35. Graphing the line:

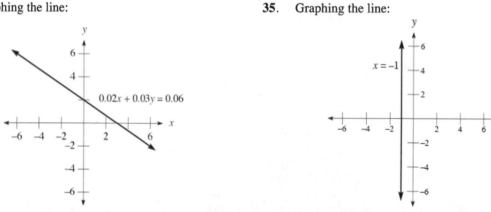

$$0.02x + 0.03y = 0.06$$

$$x = -1$$

37. Graphing the line:

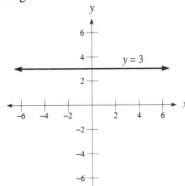

39. Graphing the line:

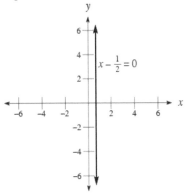

41. Graphing the line:

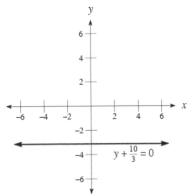

43. **a.** Graphing the line:

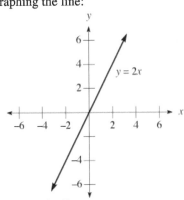

45. **a.** Graphing the line:

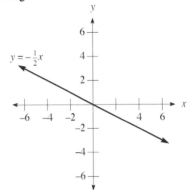

b. Graphing the line:

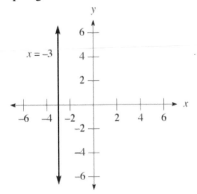

b. Graphing the line:

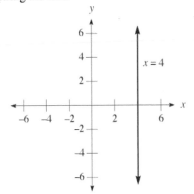

c. Graphing the line:

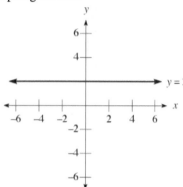

$y = 2$

c. Graphing the line:

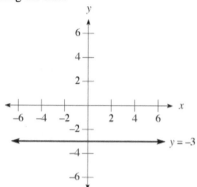

$y = -3$

47. **a.** Solving the equation:
$$4x + 12 = -16$$
$$4x = -28$$
$$x = -7$$

b. Substituting $y = 0$:
$$4x + 12(0) = -16$$
$$4x = -16$$
$$x = -4$$

c. Substituting $x = 0$:
$$4(0) + 12y = -16$$
$$12y = -16$$
$$y = -\frac{4}{3}$$

d. Graphing the line:

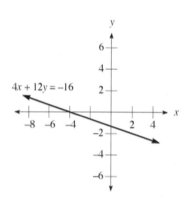

$4x + 12y = -16$

e. Solving for y:
$$4x + 12y = -16$$
$$12y = -4x - 16$$
$$y = -\frac{1}{3}x - \frac{4}{3}$$

49. **a.** Yes, the graph contains the point $(2000, 7500)$.
b. No, the graph does not contain the point $(2004, 15000)$.
c. Yes, the graph contains the point $(2005, 15000)$.

51. Constructing a line graph:

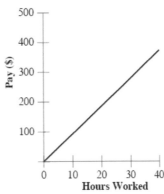

53. **a.** At 6:30 there are 60 people in line.   **b.** At 6:45 there are 70 people in line.
 c. At 7:30 there are 10 people in line.   **d.** There are 60 people in line at 6:30 and at 7:00.
 e. There is no one left in line about 22 minutes after the show starts.

55. The ordered pair (3,–5) lies in quadrant IV. The correct answer is a.

57. If $y = 0$, $x = -5$, so the x-intercept is –5. The correct answer is b.

59. Writing as a fraction: $-0.06 = -\dfrac{6}{100}$

61. Substituting $x = 2$: $y = 2(2) - 3 = 4 - 3 = 1$

63. Simplifying: $\dfrac{1-(-3)}{-5-(-2)} = \dfrac{1+3}{-5+2} = \dfrac{4}{-3} = -\dfrac{4}{3}$

65. Simplifying: $\dfrac{-1-4}{3-3} = \dfrac{-5}{0}$, which is undefined

67. **a.** The number is $\dfrac{3}{2}$.   **b.** The number is $-\dfrac{3}{2}$.

3.2 The Slope of a Line

1. The slope is $\dfrac{3}{2}$.

3. There is no slope (undefined).

5. The slope is $\dfrac{2}{3}$.

7. Finding the slope: $m = \dfrac{4-1}{4-2} = \dfrac{3}{2}$

Sketching the graph:

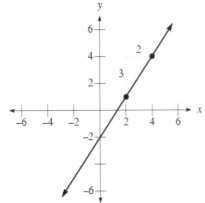

9. Finding the slope: $m = \dfrac{2-4}{5-1} = \dfrac{-2}{4} = -\dfrac{1}{2}$

Sketching the graph:

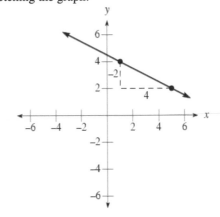

11. Finding the slope: $m = \dfrac{2-(-3)}{4-1} = \dfrac{2+3}{3} = \dfrac{5}{3}$

Sketching the graph:

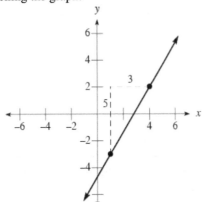

13. Finding the slope: $m = \dfrac{-1-5}{-1-(-3)} = \dfrac{-6}{2} = -3$

Sketching the graph:

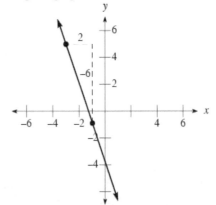

15. Finding the slope: $m = \dfrac{-1-5}{1-(-3)} = \dfrac{-6}{1+3} = \dfrac{-6}{4} = -\dfrac{3}{2}$

Sketching the graph:

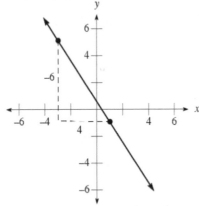

17. Finding the slope: $m = \dfrac{6-6}{2-(-4)} = \dfrac{0}{6} = 0$

Sketching the graph:

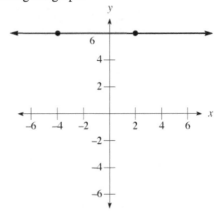

19. Finding the slope: $m = \dfrac{5-(-3)}{-1-(-1)} = \dfrac{5+3}{0}$, which is undefined

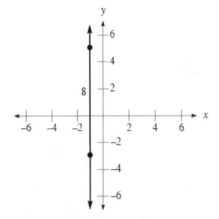

21. Using the slope formula:

$$\frac{3-6}{a-2}=-1$$
$$-3=-1(a-2)$$
$$-3=-a+2$$
$$-5=-a$$
$$a=5$$

23. Using the slope formula:

$$\frac{4b-b}{-1-2}=-2$$
$$3b=-2(-3)$$
$$3b=6$$
$$b=2$$

25. Completing the table:

x	y
0	2
3	0

Finding the slope: $m=\dfrac{2-0}{0-3}=-\dfrac{2}{3}$

27. Completing the table:

x	y
0	−5
3	−3

Finding the slope: $m=\dfrac{-5-(-3)}{0-3}=\dfrac{-5+3}{-3}=\dfrac{2}{3}$

29. The slope is $m=\dfrac{2}{3}$. Graphing the line:

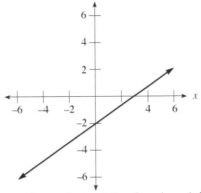

31. Since there is no y-intercept, the line must be vertical and the slope is undefined.

33. Finding each slope:

$$m_1=\frac{3-2}{1-(-1)}=\frac{3-2}{1+1}=\frac{1}{2}\qquad m_2=\frac{0-(-2)}{6-2}=\frac{0+2}{6-2}=\frac{2}{4}=\frac{1}{2}$$

Since these two slopes are equal, the two lines are parallel.

35. Finding each slope:

$$m_1=\frac{4-1}{2-1}=\frac{3}{1}=3\qquad m_2=\frac{5-3}{3-(-3)}=\frac{5-3}{3+3}=\frac{2}{6}=\frac{1}{3}$$

The two lines are neither parallel nor perpendicular.

37. Finding each slope:

$$m_1=\frac{-5-1}{5-(-4)}=\frac{-5-1}{5+4}=\frac{-6}{9}=-\frac{2}{3}\qquad m_2=\frac{7-4}{0-(-2)}=\frac{7-4}{0+2}=\frac{3}{2}$$

Since these two slopes are negative reciprocals, the two lines are perpendicular.

39. Finding the slope of this line: $m=\dfrac{1-3}{-8-2}=\dfrac{-2}{-10}=\dfrac{1}{5}$. Since the parallel slope is the same, its slope is $\dfrac{1}{5}$.

41. Finding the slope of this line: $m=\dfrac{2-(-6)}{5-5}=\dfrac{8}{0}$, which is undefined

Since the perpendicular slope is a horizontal line, its slope is 0.

43. Finding the slope of this line: $m=\dfrac{-5-1}{4-(-2)}=\dfrac{-6}{6}=-1$. Since the parallel slope is the same, its slope is -1.

45. Finding the slope of this line: $m = \dfrac{-3-(-5)}{1-(-2)} = \dfrac{2}{3}$

Since the perpendicular slope is the negative reciprocal, its slope is $-\dfrac{3}{2}$.

47. **a.** Since the slopes between each successive pairs of points is 2, this could represent ordered pairs from a line.

b. Since the slopes between each successive pairs of points is not the same, this could not represent ordered pairs from a line.

49. Finding the slope: $m = \dfrac{105-0}{6-0} = 17.5$ miles/hour

51. Finding the slope: $m = \dfrac{3600-0}{30-0} = 120$ feet/second

53. **a.** It takes 10 minutes for all the ice to melt. **b.** It takes 20 minutes before the water boils.

c. The slope of A is 20°C per minute. **d.** The slope of C is 10°C per minute.

e. It is changing faster during the first minute, since its slope is greater.

55. Computing the slope: $m = \dfrac{20{,}000-8{,}000}{2006-1997} = \dfrac{12{,}000}{9} \approx 1{,}333$

Between 1997 and 2006, the number of solar thermal collector shipments increased at an average of 1,333 shipments per year.

57. **a.** Computing the slope: $m = \dfrac{150-40}{2600-450} = \dfrac{110}{2150} \approx 0.05$

For each additional lumen of output, the incandescent light bulb uses an average of 0.05 watts of energy.

b. Computing the slope: $m = \dfrac{40-10}{2600-450} = \dfrac{30}{2150} \approx 0.014$

For each additional lumen of output, the energy efficient bulb uses an average of 0.014 watts of energy.

c. The energy efficient bulb is better, since it uses an average amount of energy which is less per lumen of output.

59. Finding the slope: $m = \dfrac{1-3}{2-(-3)} = \dfrac{1-3}{2+3} = -\dfrac{2}{5}$. The correct answer is d.

61. First find the given slope: $m = \dfrac{2-0}{0-(-4)} = \dfrac{2}{4} = \dfrac{1}{2}$. Then the perpendicular line must have a slope of –2. The correct answer is a.

63. Simplifying: $2\left(-\dfrac{1}{2}\right) = -1$

65. Simplifying: $-\dfrac{5-(-3)}{2-6} = -\dfrac{8}{-4} = 2$

67. Solving for y:
$$\dfrac{y-b}{x-0} = m$$
$$y-b = mx$$
$$y = mx+b$$

69. Solving for y:
$$y-3 = -2(x+4)$$
$$y-3 = -2x-8$$
$$y = -2x-5$$

71. Solving for y: $y = -\dfrac{4}{3}(0)+5 = 0+5 = 5$

3.3 The Equation of a Line

1. Using the slope-intercept formula: $y = -4x - 3$

3. Using the slope-intercept formula: $y = -\frac{2}{3}x$

5. Using the slope-intercept formula: $y = -\frac{2}{3}x + \frac{1}{4}$

7. a. The parallel slope will be the same, which is 3.

   b. The perpendicular slope will be the negative reciprocal, which is $-\frac{1}{3}$.

9. a. First solve for y to find the slope:
   $$3y + y = -2$$
   $$y = -3x - 2$$
   The parallel slope will be the same, which is –3.

   b. The perpendicular slope will be the negative reciprocal, which is $\frac{1}{3}$.

11. a. First solve for y to find the slope:
    $$2x + 5y = -11$$
    $$5y = -2x - 11$$
    $$y = -\frac{2}{5}x - \frac{11}{5}$$
    The parallel slope will be the same, which is $-\frac{2}{5}$.

    b. The perpendicular slope will be the negative reciprocal, which is $\frac{5}{2}$.

13. The slope is 3, the y-intercept is –2, and the perpendicular slope is $-\frac{1}{3}$.

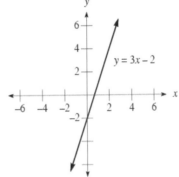

$y = 3x - 2$

15. The slope is $\frac{2}{3}$, the y-intercept is –4, and the perpendicular slope is $-\frac{3}{2}$.

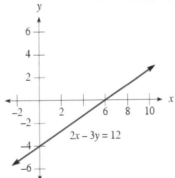

$2x - 3y = 12$

17. The slope is $-\dfrac{4}{5}$, the y-intercept is 4, and the perpendicular slope is $\dfrac{5}{4}$.

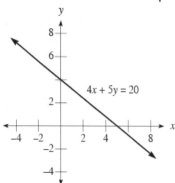

$4x + 5y = 20$

19. The slope is $\dfrac{1}{2}$ and the y-intercept is -4. Using the slope-intercept form, the equation is $y = \dfrac{1}{2}x - 4$.

21. The slope is $-\dfrac{2}{3}$ and the y-intercept is 3. Using the slope-intercept form, the equation is $y = -\dfrac{2}{3}x + 3$.

23. Using the point-slope formula:

$$y - (-5) = 2(x - (-2))$$
$$y + 5 = 2(x + 2)$$
$$y + 5 = 2x + 4$$
$$y = 2x - 1$$

25. Using the point-slope formula:

$$y - 1 = -\dfrac{1}{2}(x - (-4))$$
$$y - 1 = -\dfrac{1}{2}(x + 4)$$
$$y - 1 = -\dfrac{1}{2}x - 2$$
$$y = -\dfrac{1}{2}x - 1$$

27. Using the point-slope formula:

$$y - 2 = -3\left(x - \left(-\dfrac{1}{3}\right)\right)$$
$$y - 2 = -3\left(x + \dfrac{1}{3}\right)$$
$$y - 2 = -3x - 1$$
$$y = -3x + 1$$

29. Using the point-slope formula:

$$y - 2 = \dfrac{2}{3}(x - (-4))$$
$$y - 2 = \dfrac{2}{3}(x + 4)$$
$$y - 2 = \dfrac{2}{3}x + \dfrac{8}{3}$$
$$y = \dfrac{2}{3}x + \dfrac{14}{3}$$

31. Using the point-slope formula:

$$y - (-2) = -\dfrac{1}{4}(x - (-5))$$
$$y + 2 = -\dfrac{1}{4}(x + 5)$$
$$y + 2 = -\dfrac{1}{4}x - \dfrac{5}{4}$$
$$y = -\dfrac{1}{4}x - \dfrac{13}{4}$$

33. Since the line is horizontal, its equation is $y = 6$.

35. First find the slope: $m = \dfrac{1-(-2)}{-2-3} = \dfrac{1+2}{-5} = -\dfrac{3}{5}$. Using the point-slope formula:

$$y-(-2) = -\dfrac{3}{5}(x-3)$$
$$5(y+2) = -3(x-3)$$
$$5y+10 = -3x+9$$
$$3x+5y = -1$$

37. First find the slope: $m = \dfrac{\dfrac{1}{3}-\dfrac{1}{2}}{-4-(-2)} = \dfrac{-\dfrac{1}{6}}{-4+2} = \dfrac{-\dfrac{1}{6}}{-2} = \dfrac{1}{12}$. Using the point-slope formula:

$$y-\dfrac{1}{2} = \dfrac{1}{12}(x-(-2))$$
$$12\left(y-\dfrac{1}{2}\right) = 1(x+2)$$
$$12y-6 = x+2$$
$$x-12y = -8$$

39. First find the slope: $m = \dfrac{-1-\left(-\dfrac{1}{5}\right)}{-\dfrac{1}{3}-\dfrac{1}{3}} = \dfrac{-1+\dfrac{1}{5}}{-\dfrac{2}{3}} = \dfrac{-\dfrac{4}{5}}{-\dfrac{2}{3}} = \dfrac{4}{5}\cdot\dfrac{3}{2} = \dfrac{6}{5}$. Using the point-slope formula:

$$y-(-1) = \dfrac{6}{5}\left(x-\left(-\dfrac{1}{3}\right)\right)$$
$$y+1 = \dfrac{6}{5}\left(x+\dfrac{1}{3}\right)$$
$$5(y+1) = 6\left(x+\dfrac{1}{3}\right)$$
$$5y+5 = 6x+2$$
$$6x-5y = 3$$

41. First find the slope: $m = \dfrac{2-2}{\dfrac{1}{6}-\dfrac{3}{4}} = \dfrac{0}{-\dfrac{11}{12}} = 0$. Since the line is horizontal, its equation is $y = 2$.

43. First find the slope: $m = \dfrac{3-1}{-\dfrac{4}{3}-\left(-\dfrac{4}{3}\right)} = \dfrac{2}{0}$, which is undefined. Since the line is vertical, its equation is $x = -\dfrac{4}{3}$,

or $3x = -4$.

45. Two points on the line are (0,–4) and (2,0). Finding the slope: $m = \dfrac{0-(-4)}{2-0} = \dfrac{4}{2} = 2$

Using the slope-intercept form, the equation is $y = 2x-4$.

47. Two points on the line are (0,4) and (–2,0). Finding the slope: $m = \dfrac{0-4}{-2-0} = \dfrac{-4}{-2} = 2$

Using the slope-intercept form, the equation is $y = 2x+4$.

49. **a.** For the *x*-intercept, substitute $y = 0$:
$$3x - 2(0) = 10$$
$$3x = 10$$
$$x = \frac{10}{3}$$

For the *y*-intercept, substitute $x = 0$:
$$3(0) - 2y = 10$$
$$-2y = 10$$
$$y = -5$$

b. Substituting $y = 1$:
$$3x - 2(1) = 10$$
$$3x - 2 = 10$$
$$3x = 12$$
$$x = 4$$
Another solution is (4,1). Other answers are possible.

c. Solving for *y*:
$$3x - 2y = 10$$
$$-2y = -3x + 10$$
$$y = \frac{3}{2}x - 5$$

d. Substituting $x = 2$: $y = \frac{3}{2}(2) - 5 = 3 - 5 = -2$. No, the point (2,2) is not a solution to the equation.

51. **a.** Solving for *x*:
$$-2x + 1 = -3$$
$$-2x = -4$$
$$x = 2$$

b. Substituting $y = 0$:
$$-2x + 0 = -3$$
$$-2x = -3$$
$$x = \frac{3}{2}$$

c. Substituting $x = 0$:
$$-2(0) + y = -3$$
$$y = -3$$

d. Sketching the graph:

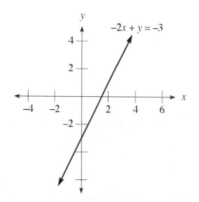

e. Solving for *y*:
$$-2x + y = -3$$
$$y = 2x - 3$$

53. **a.** The slope is $\dfrac{1}{2}$, the x-intercept is 0, and the y-intercept is 0.

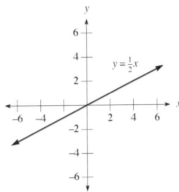

b. There is no slope, the x-intercept is 3, and there is no y-intercept.

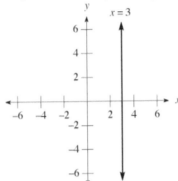

c. The slope is 0, there is no x-intercept, and the y-intercept is –2.

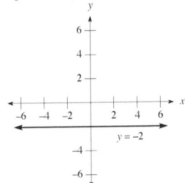

55. First find the slope:
$$3x - y = 5$$
$$-y = -3x + 5$$
$$y = 3x - 5$$
So the slope is 3. Using $(-1, 4)$ in the point-slope formula:
$$y - 4 = 3\big(x - (-1)\big)$$
$$y - 4 = 3(x + 1)$$
$$y - 4 = 3x + 3$$
$$-3x + y = 7$$
$$3x - y = -7$$

57. First find the slope:

$$2x - 5y = 10$$
$$-5y = -2x + 10$$
$$y = \frac{2}{5}x - 2$$

So the perpendicular slope is $-\frac{5}{2}$. Using $(-4,-3)$ in the point-slope formula:

$$y - (-3) = -\frac{5}{2}(x - (-4))$$
$$y + 3 = -\frac{5}{2}(x + 4)$$
$$2(y + 3) = -5(x + 4)$$
$$2y + 6 = -5x - 20$$
$$5x + 2y = -26$$

59. The perpendicular slope is $\frac{1}{4}$. Using $(-1,0)$ in the point-slope formula:

$$y - 0 = \frac{1}{4}(x - (-1))$$
$$y = \frac{1}{4}(x + 1)$$
$$4y = x + 1$$
$$-x + 4y = 1$$
$$x - 4y = -1$$

61. Using the points $(3,0)$ and $(0,2)$, first find the slope: $m = \frac{2-0}{0-3} = -\frac{2}{3}$

Using the slope-intercept formula, the equation is:

$$y = -\frac{2}{3}x + 2$$
$$3y = -2x + 6$$
$$2x + 3y = 6$$

63. **a.** Using the points $(0,32)$ and $(25,77)$, first find the slope: $m = \frac{77-32}{25-0} = \frac{45}{25} = \frac{9}{5}$

Using the slope-intercept formula, the equation is: $F = \frac{9}{5}C + 32$

b. Substituting $C = 30$: $F = \frac{9}{5}(30) + 32 = 54 + 32 = 86°$

65. **a.** Using the points $(2, 2.8)$ and $(4, 5.6)$, first find the slope: $m = \frac{5.6-2.8}{4-2} = \frac{2.8}{2} = 1.4$

Using $(2, 2.8)$ in the point-slope formula:

$$s - 2.8 = 1.4(w - 2)$$
$$s - 2.8 = 1.4w - 2.8$$
$$s = 1.4w$$

b. Substituting $w = 11$: $s = 1.4(11) = 15.4$ cm

67. **a.** Substituting $n = 10{,}000$: $C = 125{,}000 + 6.5(10{,}000) = \$190{,}000$

  b. Finding the average cost: $\dfrac{\$190{,}000}{10{,}000} = \$19$ per textbook

  c. Since each textbook costs \$6.50 in materials, this is the cost to produce the next textbook.

69. Using the points $(2000, 65.4)$ and $(2005, 104)$, first find the slope: $m = \dfrac{104 - 65.4}{2005 - 2000} = \dfrac{38.6}{5} = 7.72$

  Using the point-slope formula:
  $$y - 65.4 = 7.72(x - 2000)$$
  $$y - 65.4 = 7.72x - 15{,}440$$
  $$y = 7.72x - 15{,}374.6$$

71. Since the slope is $\dfrac{2}{5}$ and the y-intercept is $(0,-1)$, the correct answer is c.

73. First find the slope: $m = \dfrac{-1 - 3}{1 - (-2)} = \dfrac{-4}{1 + 2} = -\dfrac{4}{3}$. Using the point $(1,-1)$ in the point-slope formula results in the equation

  $y - (-1) = -\dfrac{4}{3}(x - 1)$, or $y + 1 = -\dfrac{4}{3}(x - 1)$. The correct answer is d.

75. Since $0 + 0 \le 4$ and $4 + 0 \le 4$, but $2 + 3 > 4$, the points $(0,0)$ and $(4,0)$ are solutions.

77. Since $0 \le \dfrac{1}{2}(0)$ and $0 \le \dfrac{1}{2}(2)$, but $0 > \dfrac{1}{2}(-2)$, the points $(0,0)$ and $(2,0)$ are solutions.

3.4 Linear Inequalities in Two Variables

1. Graphing the solution set:

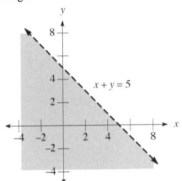

3. Graphing the solution set:

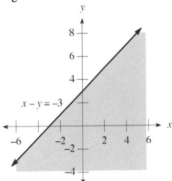

5. Graphing the solution set:

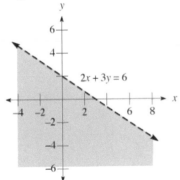

7. Graphing the solution set:

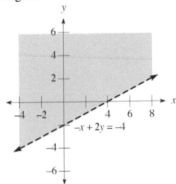

9. Graphing the solution set:

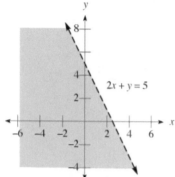

$2x + y = 5$

11. Graphing the solution set:

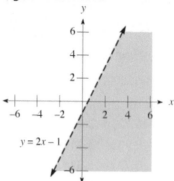

$y = 2x - 1$

13. Graphing the solution set:

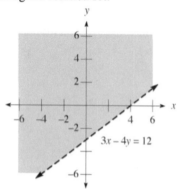

$3x - 4y = 12$

15. Graphing the solution set:

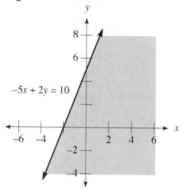

$-5x + 2y = 10$

17. The inequality is $x + y > 4$, or $y > -x + 4$.

19. The inequality is $-x + 2y \leq 4$ or $y \leq \frac{1}{2}x + 2$.

21. Graphing the solution set:

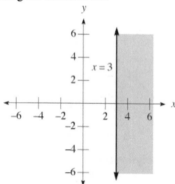

$x = 3$

23. Graphing the solution set:

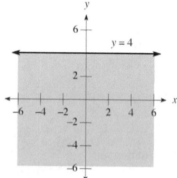

$y = 4$

25. Graphing the solution set:

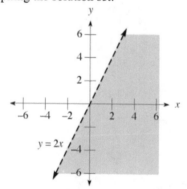

$y = 2x$

27. Graphing the solution set:

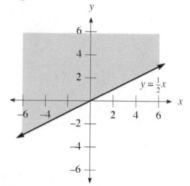

$y = \frac{1}{2}x$

29. Graphing the solution set:

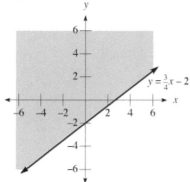

$y = \frac{3}{4}x - 2$

31. Graphing the solution set:

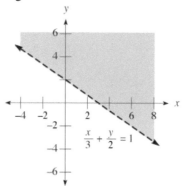

$\frac{x}{3} + \frac{y}{2} = 1$

33. Graphing the solution set:

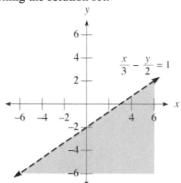

$\frac{x}{3} - \frac{y}{2} = 1$

35. Graphing the solution set:

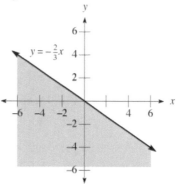

$y = -\frac{2}{3}x$

37. Graphing the solution set:

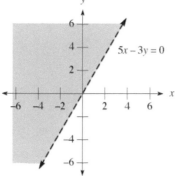

$5x - 3y = 0$

39. Graphing the solution set:

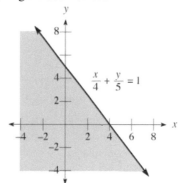

$\frac{x}{4} + \frac{y}{5} = 1$

41. Graphing the region:

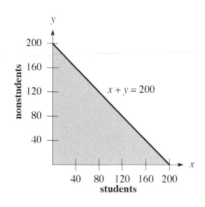

$x + y = 200$

43. Graphing the region:

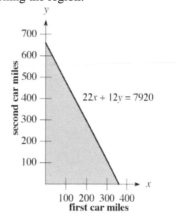

$22x + 12y = 7920$

45. Since this is a strict inequality, the boundary should be drawn as a broken line. The correct answer is b.

47. Completing the table:

x	y
0	0
10	75
20	150

49. Completing the table:

x	y
0	0
$\frac{1}{2}$	3.75
1	7.5

3.5 Introduction to Functions

1. The domain is {1,3,5,7} and the range is {2,4,6,8}. This is a function.

3. The domain is {0,1,2,3} and the range is {4,5,6}. This is a function.

5. The domain is {a,b,c,d} and the range is {3,4,5}. This is a function.

7. The domain is {a} and the range is {1,2,3,4}. This is not a function.

9. Yes, since it passes the vertical line test.   **11.** No, since it fails the vertical line test.

13. No, since it fails the vertical line test.   **15.** Yes, since it passes the vertical line test.

17. Yes, since it passes the vertical line test.   **19.** Yes, since it passes the vertical line test.

21. The domain is $\{x \mid -3 \le x \le 1\} = [-3,1]$ and the range is $\{y \mid -2 \le y \le 4\} = [-2,4]$.

23. The domain is $\{x \mid -5 \le x \le 3\} = [-5,3]$ and the range is $\{y \mid y = 3\}$.

25. The domain is $\{x \mid -5 \le x \le 5\} = [-5,5]$ and the range is $\{y \mid 0 \le y \le 5\} = [0,5]$.

27. The domain is $\{-4,-3,-1,0,2,5\}$ and the range is $\{-4,-1,1,3,4\}$.

29. The domain is all real numbers and the range is all real numbers. This is a function.

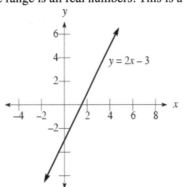

31. The domain is $\{4\}$ and the range is all real numbers. This is not a function.

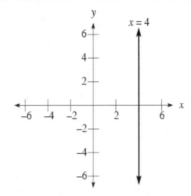

33. The domain is all real numbers and the range is $\{y \mid y \le 0\} = (-\infty, 0]$. This is a function.

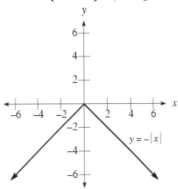

$$y = -|x|$$

35. The domain is all real numbers and the range is $\{y \mid y \ge -1\} = [-1, \infty)$. This is a function.

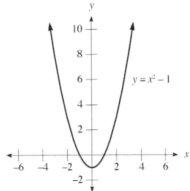

$$y = x^2 - 1$$

37. The domain is $\{x \mid x \le 3\}$ and the range is all real numbers. This is not a function.

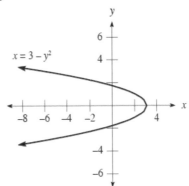

$$x = 3 - y^2$$

39. **a.** The equation is $y = 8.5x$ for $10 \le x \le 40$.

b. Completing the table:

Hours Worked	Function Rule	Gross Pay ($)
x	$y = 8.5x$	y
10	$y = 8.5(10) = 85$	85
20	$y = 8.5(20) = 170$	170
30	$y = 8.5(30) = 255$	255
40	$y = 8.5(40) = 340$	340

c. Constructing a line graph:

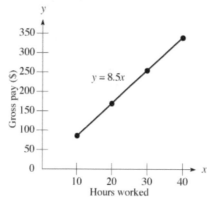

d. The domain is $\{x \mid 10 \le x \le 40\} = [10,40]$ and the range is $\{y \mid 85 \le y \le 340\} = [85,340]$.

e. The minimum is \$85 and the maximum is \$340.

41. The domain is $\{2004,2005,2006,2007,2008,2009,2010\}$ and the range is $\{680,730,800,900,920,1030\}$.

43. **a.** Figure III   **b.** Figure I

     c. Figure II   **d.** Figure IV

45. The correct answers are b and c.

47. Only the graph in b passes the vertical line test. The correct answer is b.

49. Simplifying: $4(3.14)(9) = 113.04 \approx 113$ **51.** Simplifying: $4(-2)-1 = -8-1 = -9$

53. **a.** Substituting $t = 10$: $s = \dfrac{60}{10} = 6$ **b.** Substituting $t = 8$: $s = \dfrac{60}{8} = 7.5$

55. **a.** Substituting $x = 5$: $(5)^2 + 2 = 25 + 2 = 27$ **b.** Substituting $x = -2$: $(-2)^2 + 2 = 4 + 2 = 6$

57. Substituting $x = 2$: $y = (2)^2 - 3 = 4 - 3 = 1$ **59.** Substituting $x = 0$: $y = (0)^2 - 3 = 0 - 3 = -3$

61. Solving for y:
$$\frac{8}{5} - 2y = 4$$
$$-2y = \frac{12}{5}$$
$$y = -\frac{6}{5}$$

63. Substituting $x = 0$ and $y = 0$:
$$0 = a(0-8)^2 + 70$$
$$0 = 64a + 70$$
$$64a = -70$$
$$a = -\frac{70}{64} = -\frac{35}{32}$$

64. Substituting $p = 2.5$: $R = (900 - 300 \cdot 2.5)(2.5) = (150)(2.5) = 375$

3.6 Evaluating Functions

1. The ordered pair is $(3,8)$.   **3.** The ordered pair is $(-1,5)$.

5. The function notation is $f(4) = 0$.   **7.** The function notation is $f(-1) = 9$.

9. The function notation is $f(10) = 0.1$.   **11.** The function notation is $f\left(-\dfrac{1}{5}\right) = -\dfrac{1}{10}$.

13. Evaluating the function: $f(2) = 2(2) - 5 = 4 - 5 = -1$

15. Evaluating the function: $f(-3) = 2(-3) - 5 = -6 - 5 = -11$

17. Evaluating the function: $g(-1) = (-1)^2 + 3(-1) + 4 = 1 - 3 + 4 = 2$

19. Evaluating the function: $g(-3) = (-3)^2 + 3(-3) + 4 = 9 - 9 + 4 = 4$

21. Evaluating the function: $g(a) = a^2 + 3a + 4$

23. Evaluating the function: $f(a+6) = 2(x+6) - 5 = 2a + 12 - 5 = 2a + 7$

25. Evaluating the function: $f(0) = 3(0)^2 - 4(0) + 1 = 0 - 0 + 1 = 1$

27. Evaluating the function: $g(-4) = 2(-4) - 1 = -8 - 1 = -9$

29. Evaluating the function: $f(-1) = 3(-1)^2 - 4(-1) + 1 = 3 + 4 + 1 = 8$

31. Evaluating the function: $g\left(\dfrac{1}{2}\right) = 2\left(\dfrac{1}{2}\right) - 1 = 1 - 1 = 0$

33. Evaluating the function: $f(a) = 3a^2 - 4a + 1$

35. Evaluating the function: $f(a+2) = 3(a+2)^2 - 4(a+2) + 1 = 3a^2 + 12a + 12 - 4a - 8 + 1 = 3a^2 + 8a + 5$

37. Evaluating the function: $f\left(\dfrac{1}{3}\right) = \dfrac{1}{\dfrac{1}{3} + 3} \cdot \dfrac{3}{3} = \dfrac{3}{1+9} = \dfrac{3}{10}$

39. Evaluating the function: $f\left(-\dfrac{1}{2}\right) = \dfrac{1}{-\dfrac{1}{2} + 3} \cdot \dfrac{2}{2} = \dfrac{2}{-1+6} = \dfrac{2}{5}$

41. Evaluating the function: $f(-1) = \dfrac{1}{-3+3} = \dfrac{1}{0}$, which is undefined

43. First evaluate each function:

$f(-2) = (-2)^2 - 2(-2) = 4 + 4 = 8$ $\qquad\qquad$ $g(-1) = 5(-1) - 4 = -5 - 4 = -9$

Now evaluating: $f(-2) + g(-1) = 8 - 9 = -1$

45. First evaluate each function:

$f(2) = (2)^2 - 2(2) = 4 - 4 = 0$ $\qquad\qquad$ $g(3) = 5(3) - 4 = 15 - 4 = 11$

Now evaluating: $f(2) - g(3) = 0 - 11 = -11$

47. Evaluating the function: $f[g(3)] = f[5(3) - 4] = f(11) = (11)^2 - 2(11) = 121 - 22 = 99$

49. $f(1) = 4$ $\qquad\qquad\qquad\qquad\qquad\qquad$ **51.** $g\left(\dfrac{1}{2}\right) = 0$

53. $g(-2) = 2$ $\qquad\qquad\qquad\qquad\qquad\qquad$ **55.** $f(0) = -2$

57. $f(3) = 2$ $\qquad\qquad\qquad\qquad\qquad\qquad\;$ **59.** $f(-1) = 1$

61. $3f(-2) = 3 \cdot 5 = 15$ $\qquad\qquad\qquad\qquad\;$ **63.** $f(3) = -1$

65. $f(-1) = 2$ $\qquad\qquad\qquad\qquad\qquad\qquad$ **67.** $g(0) = 0$

69. $g(-2) = -1$

71. **a.** Evaluating the function: $f(a) - 3 = (a^2 - 4) - 3 = a^2 - 7$

$\quad$ **b.** Evaluating the function: $f(a-3) = (a-3)^2 - 4 = a^2 - 6a + 9 - 4 = a^2 - 6a + 5$

$\quad$ **c.** Evaluating the function: $f(x) + 2 = (x^2 - 4) + 2 = x^2 - 2$

$\quad$ **d.** Evaluating the function: $f(x+2) = (x+2)^2 - 4 = x^2 + 4x + 4 - 4 = x^2 + 4x$

$\quad$ **e.** Evaluating the function: $f(a+b) = (a+b)^2 - 4 = a^2 + 2ab + b^2 - 4$

$\quad$ **f.** Evaluating the function: $f(x+h) = (x+h)^2 - 4 = x^2 + 2xh + h^2 - 4$

$\quad$ **g.** Evaluating the function: $f(3x) = (3x)^2 - 4 = 9x^2 - 4$

$\quad$ **h.** Evaluating the function: $3f(x) = 3(x^2 - 4) = 3x^2 - 12$

73. Graphing the function:

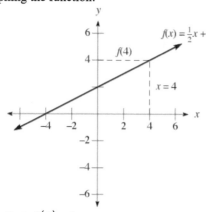

Note that $f(4)=4$.

75. Graphing the function:

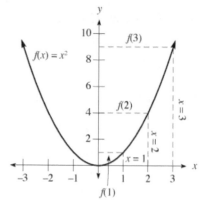

Note that $f(1)=1$, $f(2)=4$, and $f(3)=9$.

77. First find the slope: $m=\dfrac{0-2}{6-0}=\dfrac{-2}{6}=-\dfrac{1}{3}$. Since the y-intercept is 2, the function is $f(x)=-\dfrac{1}{3}x+2$.

79. Evaluating: $V(3)=150\cdot 2^{3/3}=150\cdot 2=300$; The painting is worth \$300 in 3 years.

Evaluating: $V(6)=150\cdot 2^{6/3}=150\cdot 4=600$; The painting is worth \$600 in 6 years.

81. **a.** This statement is true. **b.** This statement is false.
  c. This statement is true. **d.** This statement is false.
  e. This statement is true.

83. **a.** Evaluating when $x=2.5$: $S(2.5)=1.4(2.5)=3.5$ cm

  b. Finding when $S=5.6$:
  $1.4x=5.6$

  $x=4$ lb

  c. Sketching the graph:

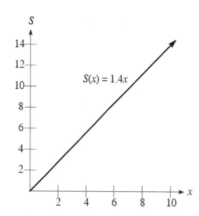

85. **a.** Evaluating: $V(3.75) = -3300(3.75) + 18000 = \$5,625$

b. Evaluating: $V(5) = -3300(5) + 18000 = \$1,500$

c. The domain of this function is $\{t \mid 0 \le t \le 5\} = [0,5]$.

d. Sketching the graph:

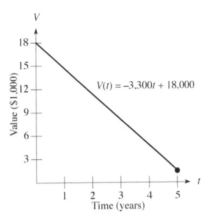

e. The range of this function is $\{V(t) \mid 1,500 \le V(t) \le 18,000\} = [1500, 18000]$.

f. Solving $V(t) = 10000$:
$$-3300t + 18000 = 10000$$
$$-3300t = -8000$$
$$t \approx 2.42$$
The copier will be worth $10,000 after approximately 2.42 years.

87. The function notation is $f(-2) = 6$. The correct answer is c.

89. Evaluating: $f(1) = -3$. The correct answer is a.

91. Multiplying: $x(35 - 0.1x) = 35x - 0.1x^2$

93. Multiplying: $(4x - 3)(x - 1) = 4x^2 - 3x - 4x + 3 = 4x^2 - 7x + 3$

95. Simplifying: $(35x - 0.1x^2) - (8x + 500) = 35x - 0.1x^2 - 8x - 500 = -0.1x^2 + 27x - 500$

97. Simplifying: $(4x^2 + 3x + 2) - (2x^2 - 5x - 6) = 4x^2 + 3x + 2 - 2x^2 + 5x + 6 = 2x^2 + 8x + 8$

99. Simplifying: $4(2)^2 - 3(2) = 16 - 6 = 10$

3.7 Algebra and Composition with Functions

1. Evaluating: $(f + g)(2) = f(2) + g(2) = (2 \cdot 2 + 1) + (4 \cdot 2 + 2) = 5 + 10 = 15$

3. Evaluating: $(f \cdot g)(3) = f(3) \cdot g(3) = (2 \cdot 3 + 1)(4 \cdot 3 + 2) = 7 \cdot 14 = 98$

5. Evaluating: $\left(\dfrac{h}{g}\right)(1) = \dfrac{h(1)}{g(1)} = \dfrac{4(1)^2 + 4(1) + 1}{4(1) + 2} = \dfrac{9}{6} = \dfrac{3}{2}$

7. Evaluating: $(f \cdot h)(0) = f(0) \cdot h(0) = (2(0) + 1)(4(0)^2 + 4(0) + 1) = (1)(1) = 1$

9. Evaluating: $(f + g + h)(2) = f(2) + g(2) + h(2) = (2(2) + 1) + (4(2) + 2) + (4(2)^2 + 4(2) + 1) = 5 + 10 + 25 = 40$

11. Evaluating:
$$(h + f \cdot g)(3) = h(3) + f(3) \cdot g(3) = (4(3)^2 + 4(3) + 1) + (2(3) + 1) \cdot (4(3) + 2) = 49 + 7 \cdot 14 = 49 + 98 = 147$$

13. Writing the formula: $(f + g)(x) = f(x) + g(x) = (4x - 3) + (2x + 5) = 6x + 2$

15. Writing the formula: $(g - f)(x) = g(x) - f(x) = (2x + 5) - (4x - 3) = -2x + 8$

17. Writing the formula: $(f \cdot g)(x) = f(x) \cdot g(x) = (4x-3)(2x+5) = 8x^2 + 14x - 15$

19. Writing the formula: $\left(\dfrac{g}{f}\right)(x) = \dfrac{g(x)}{f(x)} = \dfrac{2x+5}{4x-3}$

21. Writing the formula: $(g+f)(x) = g(x) + f(x) = (x-2) + (3x-5) = 4x - 7$

23. Writing the formula: $(g+h)(x) = g(x) + h(x) = (x-2) + (3x^2 - 11x + 10) = 3x^2 - 10x + 8$

25. Writing the formula: $(g-f)(x) = g(x) - f(x) = (x-2) - (3x-5) = -2x + 3$

27. Writing the formula: $(f \cdot g)(x) = f(x) \cdot g(x) = (3x-5)(x-2) = 3x^2 - 11x + 10$

29. Writing the formula:
$$(f \cdot h)(x) = f(x) \cdot h(x) = (3x-5)(3x^2 - 11x + 10) = 9x^3 - 33x^2 + 30x - 15x^2 + 55x - 50 = 9x^3 - 48x^2 + 85x - 50$$

31. Writing the formula: $\left(\dfrac{h}{f}\right)(x) = \dfrac{h(x)}{f(x)} = \dfrac{3x^2 - 11x + 10}{3x-5} = \dfrac{(3x-5)(x-2)}{3x-5} = x - 2$

33. Writing the formula: $\left(\dfrac{f}{h}\right)(x) = \dfrac{f(x)}{h(x)} = \dfrac{3x-5}{3x^2 - 11x + 10} = \dfrac{3x-5}{(3x-5)(x-2)} = \dfrac{1}{x-2}$

35. Writing the formula: $(f+g+h)(x) = f(x) + g(x) + h(x) = (3x-5) + (x-2) + (3x^2 - 11x + 10) = 3x^2 - 7x + 3$

37. Writing the formula:
$$(h + f \cdot g)(x) = h(x) + f(x) \cdot g(x)$$
$$= (3x^2 - 11x + 10) + (3x-5)(x-2)$$
$$= 3x^2 - 11x + 10 + 3x^2 - 11x + 10$$
$$= 6x^2 - 22x + 20$$

39. a. Finding the values:
$$f(2) = (2)^2 + 3(2) = 4 + 6 = 10$$
$$g(2) = 4(2) - 1 = 8 - 1 = 7$$
$$(f+g)(2) = f(2) + g(2) = 10 + 7 = 17$$

b. Finding the function:
$$(f+g)(x) = f(x) + g(x) = (x^2 + 3x) + (4x-1) = x^2 + 7x - 1$$

c. Evaluating the function: $(f+g)(2) = (2)^2 + 7(2) - 1 = 4 + 14 - 1 = 17$
This matches our answer from **a**.

41. a. Finding the values:
$$f(-2) = 3(-2) - 2 = -6 - 2 = -8$$
$$g(-2) = 5(-2) + 4 = -10 + 4 = -6$$
$$(fg)(-2) = f(-2) \cdot g(-2) = (-8)(-6) = 48$$

b. Finding the function: $(fg)(x) = f(x) \cdot g(x) = (3x-2)(5x+4) = 15x^2 + 2x - 8$

c. Evaluating the function: $(fg)(-2) = 15(-2)^2 + 2(-2) - 8 = 60 - 4 - 8 = 48$
This matches our answer from **a**.

43. Evaluating: $(f \circ g)(-1) = f(g(-1)) = f(-4+2) = f(-2) = 2(-2) + 1 = -3$

45. Evaluating: $(g \circ h)(1) = g(h(1)) = g(4+4+1) = g(9) = 4(9) + 2 = 38$

47. Evaluating: $(h \circ f)(-3) = h(f(-3)) = h(-6+1) = h(-5) = 4(-5)^2 + 4(-5) + 1 = 81$

49. Evaluating: $(g \circ f)(0) = g(f(0)) = g(0+1) = g(1) = 4(1) + 2 = 6$

51.   a.   Evaluating: $(f \circ g)(5) = f(g(5)) = f(5+4) = f(9) = 9^2 = 81$

      b.   Evaluating: $(g \circ f)(5) = g(f(5)) = g(5^2) = g(25) = 25 + 4 = 29$

      c.   Evaluating: $(f \circ g)(x) = f(g(x)) = f(x+4) = (x+4)^2$

      d.   Evaluating: $(g \circ f)(x) = g(f(x)) = g(x^2) = x^2 + 4$

53.   a.   Evaluating: $(f \circ g)(0) = f(g(0)) = f(4 \cdot 0 - 1) = f(-1) = (-1)^2 + 3(-1) = 1 - 3 = -2$

      b.   Evaluating: $(g \circ f)(0) = g(f(0)) = g(0^2 + 3 \cdot 0) = g(0) = 4(0) - 1 = -1$

      c.   Evaluating: $(f \circ g)(x) = f(g(x)) = f(4x - 1) = (4x - 1)^2 + 3(4x - 1) = 16x^2 - 8x + 1 + 12x - 3 = 16x^2 + 4x - 2$

      d.   Evaluating: $(g \circ f)(x) = g(f(x)) = g(x^2 + 3x) = 4(x^2 + 3x) - 1 = 4x^2 + 12x - 1$

55.   Evaluating each composition:

$$(f \circ g)(x) = f(g(x)) = f\left(\frac{x+4}{5}\right) = 5\left(\frac{x+4}{5}\right) - 4 = x + 4 - 4 = x$$

$$(g \circ f)(x) = g(f(x)) = g(5x - 4) = \frac{5x - 4 + 4}{5} = \frac{5x}{5} = x$$

Thus $(f \circ g)(x) = (g \circ f)(x) = x$.

57.   Evaluating: $(f + g)(0) = f(0) + g(0) = -2 + (-4) = -6$ 59.   Evaluating: $(g - f)(-2) = g(-2) - f(-2) = 0 - 5 = -5$

61.   Evaluating: $(fg)(-3) = f(-3) \cdot g(-3) = (4)(3) = 12$ 63.   Evaluating: $(g / f)(3) = \frac{g(3)}{f(3)} = \frac{-1}{2} = -\frac{1}{2}$

65.   Evaluating: $(f \circ g)(-1) = f(g(-1)) = f(2) = 0$ 67.   Evaluating: $(g \circ f)(2) = g(f(2)) = g(0) = -4$

69.   Evaluating: $(f \circ f)(0) = f(f(0)) = f(-2) = 5$ 71.   Evaluating: $(f - g)(1) = f(1) - g(1) = 0 - (-3) = 0 + 3 = 3$

73.   Evaluating: $(g + f)(0) = g(0) + f(0) = -2 + (-1) = -3$ 75.   Evaluating: $(fg)(-3) = f(-3) \cdot g(-3) = (3)(0) = 0$

77.   Evaluating: $(g / f)(-2) = \frac{g(-2)}{f(-2)} = \frac{1}{4}$ 79.   Evaluating: $(f \circ g)(0) = f(g(0)) = f(-2) = 4$

81.   Evaluating: $(g \circ f)(2) = g(f(2)) = g(-2) = 1$ 83.   Evaluating: $(f \circ f)(4) = f(f(4)) = f(-3) = 3$

85.   a.   Finding the revenue: $R(x) = x(11.5 - 0.05x) = 11.5x - 0.05x^2$

      b.   Finding the cost: $C(x) = 2x + 200$

      c.   Finding the profit: $P(x) = R(x) - C(x) = (11.5x - 0.05x^2) - (2x + 200) = -0.05x^2 + 9.5x - 200$

      d.   Finding the average cost: $\overline{C}(x) = \frac{C(x)}{x} = \frac{2x + 200}{x} = 2 + \frac{200}{x}$

87.   a.   The function is $M(x) = 220 - x$.

      b.   Evaluating: $M(24) = 220 - 24 = 196$ beats per minute

      c.   The training heart rate function is: $T(M) = 62 + 0.6(M - 62) = 0.6M + 24.8$

         Finding the composition: $T(M(x)) = T(220 - x) = 0.6(220 - x) + 24.8 = 156.8 - 0.6x$

         Evaluating: $T(M(24)) = 156.8 - 0.6(24) \approx 142$ beats per minute

      d.   Evaluating: $T(M(36)) = 156.8 - 0.6(36) \approx 135$ beats per minute

      e.   Evaluating: $T(M(48)) = 156.8 - 0.6(48) \approx 128$ beats per minute

89.   Finding the value: $(f + g)(-1) = f(-1) + g(-1) = (-3 - 2) + (-4 + 5) = -5 + 1 = -4$. The correct answer is c.

91.   Finding the value: $(f \circ g)(-2) = f(g(-2)) = f(-8 + 5) = f(-3) = -9 - 2 = -11$. The correct answer is d.

93. Simplifying: $16(3.5)^2 = 16(12.25) = 196$

95. Simplifying: $\dfrac{180}{45} = 4$

97. Simplifying: $\dfrac{0.0005(200)}{(0.25)^2} = \dfrac{0.1}{0.0625} = 1.6$

99. Solving for k:
$$15 = k(5)$$
$$k = 3$$

101. Solving for k:
$$50 = \dfrac{k}{48}$$
$$k = 50 \cdot 48 = 2,400$$

3.8 Variation

1. This represents inverse variation with $K = 3$.

3. This represents direct variation with $K = 2\pi$.

5. This represents joint variation with $K = \dfrac{1}{2}$.

7. This represents direct variation with $K = 0.5$.

9. Writing the variation equation: $z = K\sqrt{x}$

11. Writing the variation equation: $F = \dfrac{Km^2}{d}$

13. Writing the variation equation: $A = Kh(a+b)$

15. The variation equation is $y = Kx$. Substituting $x = 2$ and $y = 10$:
$$10 = K \cdot 2$$
$$K = 5$$
So $y = 5x$. Substituting $x = 6$: $y = 5 \cdot 6 = 30$

17. The variation equation is $r = \dfrac{K}{s}$. Substituting $s = 4$ and $r = -3$:
$$-3 = \dfrac{K}{4}$$
$$K = -12$$
So $r = \dfrac{-12}{s}$. Substituting $s = 2$: $r = \dfrac{-12}{2} = -6$

19. The variation equation is $d = Kr^2$. Substituting $r = 5$ and $d = 10$:
$$10 = K \cdot 5^2$$
$$10 = 25K$$
$$K = \dfrac{2}{5}$$
So $d = \dfrac{2}{5}r^2$. Substituting $r = 10$: $d = \dfrac{2}{5}(10)^2 = \dfrac{2}{5} \cdot 100 = 40$

21. The variation equation is $y = \dfrac{K}{x^2}$. Substituting $x = 3$ and $y = 45$:
$$45 = \dfrac{K}{3^2}$$
$$45 = \dfrac{K}{9}$$
$$K = 405$$
So $y = \dfrac{405}{x^2}$. Substituting $x = 5$: $y = \dfrac{405}{5^2} = \dfrac{405}{25} = \dfrac{81}{5}$

23. The variation equation is $z = Kxy^2$. Substituting $x = 3, y = 3$, and $z = 54$:

$$54 = K(3)(3)^2$$
$$54 = 27K$$
$$K = 2$$

So $z = 2xy^2$. Substituting $x = 2$ and $y = 4$: $z = 2(2)(4)^2 = 64$

25. The variation equation is $I = \dfrac{K}{w^3}$. Substituting $w = \dfrac{1}{2}$ and $I = 32$:

$$32 = \frac{K}{\left(\dfrac{1}{2}\right)^3}$$
$$32 = \frac{K}{1/8}$$
$$K = 4$$

So $I = \dfrac{4}{w^3}$. Substituting $w = \dfrac{1}{3}$: $I = \dfrac{4}{\left(\dfrac{1}{3}\right)^3} = \dfrac{4}{1/27} = 108$

27. The variation equation is $z = Kyx^2$. Substituting $x = 3, y = 2$, and $z = 72$:

$$72 = K(2)(3)^2$$
$$72 = 18K$$
$$K = 4$$

So $z = 4yx^2$. Substituting $x = 5$ and $y = 3$: $z = 4(3)(5)^2 = 300$

29. The variation equation is $z = Kyx^2$. Substituting $x = 1, y = 5$, and $z = 25$:

$$25 = K(5)(1)^2$$
$$25 = 5K$$
$$K = 5$$

So $z = 5yx^2$. Substituting $z = 160$ and $y = 8$:

$$160 = 5(8)x^2$$
$$160 = 40x^2$$
$$x^2 = 4$$
$$x = \pm 2$$

31. The variation equation is $F = \dfrac{Km}{d^2}$. Substituting $F = 150, m = 240$, and $d = 8$:

$$150 = \frac{K(240)}{8^2}$$
$$150 = \frac{240K}{64}$$
$$240K = 9600$$
$$K = 40$$

So $F = \dfrac{40m}{d^2}$. Substituting $m = 360$ and $d = 3$: $F = \dfrac{40(360)}{3^2} = \dfrac{14400}{9} = 1600$

33. The variation equation is $F = \dfrac{Km}{d^2}$. Substituting $F = 24$, $m = 20$, and $d = 5$:

$$24 = \frac{K(20)}{5^2}$$

$$24 = \frac{20K}{25}$$

$$20K = 600$$

$$K = 30$$

So $F = \dfrac{30m}{d^2}$. Substituting $F = 18.75$ and $m = 40$:

$$18.75 = \frac{30(40)}{d^2}$$

$$18.75 = \frac{1200}{d^2}$$

$$18.75d^2 = 1200$$

$$d^2 = 64$$

$$d = \pm 8$$

35. Let l represent the length and f represent the force. The variation equation is $l = Kf$. Substituting $f = 5$ and $l = 7$:

$$7 = K \cdot 5$$

$$K = \frac{7}{5}$$

So $l = \dfrac{7}{5}f$. Substituting $l = 10$:

$$10 = \frac{7}{5}f$$

$$50 = 7f$$

$$f = \frac{50}{7}$$

The force required is $\dfrac{50}{7}$ pounds.

37. **a.** The variation equation is $T = 4P$.

b. Graphing the equation:

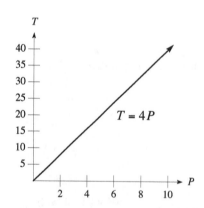

c. Substituting $T = 280$:

$$280 = 4P$$

$$P = 70$$

The pressure is 70 pounds per square inch.

39. Let v represent the volume and p represent the pressure. The variation equation is $v = \dfrac{K}{p}$.

Substituting $p = 36$ and $v = 25$:

$$25 = \dfrac{K}{36}$$
$$K = 900$$

The equation is $v = \dfrac{900}{p}$. Substituting $v = 75$:

$$75 = \dfrac{900}{p}$$
$$75p = 900$$
$$p = 12$$

The pressure is 12 pounds per square inch.

41. **a.** The variation equation is $f = \dfrac{80}{d}$.

b. Graphing the equation:

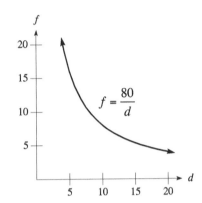

c. Substituting $d = 10$:

$$f = \dfrac{80}{10}$$
$$f = 8$$

The f-stop is 8.

43. Let A represent the surface area, h represent the height, and r represent the radius. The variation equation is $A = Khr$.
Substituting $A = 94$, $r = 3$, and $h = 5$:

$$94 = K(3)(5)$$
$$94 = 15K$$
$$K = \dfrac{94}{15}$$

The equation is $A = \dfrac{94}{15} hr$. Substituting $r = 2$ and $h = 8$: $A = \dfrac{94}{15}(8)(2) = \dfrac{1504}{15}$.

The surface area is $\dfrac{1504}{15}$ square inches .

45. Let R represent the resistance, l represent the length, and d represent the diameter. The variation equation is $R = \dfrac{Kl}{d^2}$.

Substituting $R = 10$, $l = 100$, and $d = 0.01$:

$$10 = \frac{K(100)}{(0.01)^2}$$
$$0.001 = 100K$$
$$K = 0.00001$$

The equation is $R = \dfrac{0.00001l}{d^2}$. Substituting $l = 60$ and $d = 0.02$: $R = \dfrac{0.00001(60)}{(0.02)^2} = 1.5$. The resistance is 1.5 ohms.

47. **a.** The variation equation is $P = 0.21\sqrt{L}$.

b. Graphing the equation:

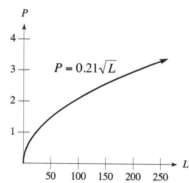

c. Substituting $L = 225$: $P = 0.21\sqrt{225} = 3.15$
The period is 3.15 seconds.

49. The variation equation is $y = Kx^2$. Substituting $x = 5$ and $y = 450$:

$$450 = K(5)^2$$
$$450 = 25K$$
$$K = 18$$

So $y = 18x^2$. Substituting $x = 3$: $y = 18(3)^2 = 162$. The correct answer is d.

51. The variation equation is $d = Kr\sqrt{x}$. Substituting $d = 36$, $r = 6$, and $x = 4$:

$$36 = K(6)\sqrt{4}$$
$$36 = 12K$$
$$K = 3$$

So $d = 3r\sqrt{x}$. Substituting $r = 5$ and $x = 9$: $d = 3(5)\sqrt{9} = 45$. The correct answer is a.

53. Solving the equation:

$$x - 5 = 7$$
$$x = 12$$

55. Solving the equation:

$$5 - \frac{4}{7}a = -11$$
$$7\left(5 - \frac{4}{7}a\right) = 7(-11)$$
$$35 - 4a = -77$$
$$-4a = -112$$
$$a = 28$$

57. Solving the equation:

$$5(x-1)-2(2x+3)=5x-4$$
$$5x-5-4x-6=5x-4$$
$$x-11=5x-4$$
$$-4x=7$$
$$x=-\frac{7}{4}$$

59. Solving the equation:

$$P=2l+2w$$
$$P-2l=2w$$
$$w=\frac{P-2l}{2}$$

61. Solving the inequality:

$$-5t\le 30$$
$$t\ge -6$$

The solution set is $[-6,\infty)$. Graphing:

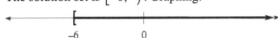

63. Solving the inequality:

$$1.6x-2<0.8x+2.8$$
$$0.8x-2<2.8$$
$$0.8x<4.8$$
$$x<6$$

The solution set is $(-\infty,6)$. Graphing:

65. Solving the equation:

$$\left|\frac{1}{4}x-1\right|=\frac{1}{2}$$
$$\frac{1}{4}x-1=-\frac{1}{2},\frac{1}{2}$$
$$\frac{1}{4}x=\frac{1}{2},\frac{3}{2}$$
$$x=2,6$$

67. Solving the equation:

$$|3-2x|+5=2$$
$$|3-2x|=-3$$

Since this statement is false, there is no solution, or $\varnothing$.

68. Solving the equation:

$$5=|3y+6|-4$$
$$9=|3y+6|$$
$$3y+6=-9,9$$
$$3y=-15,3$$
$$y=-5,1$$

Chapter 3 Test

1. The *x*-intercept is 3, the *y*-intercept is 6, and the slope is –2.

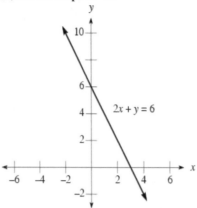

2. The *x*-intercept is $-\dfrac{3}{2}$, the *y*-intercept is –3, and the slope is –2.

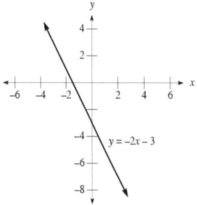

3. The *x*-intercept is $-\dfrac{8}{3}$, the *y*-intercept is 4, and the slope is $\dfrac{3}{2}$.

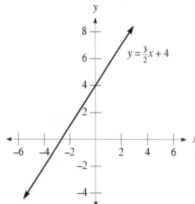

4. The *x*-intercept is –2, there is no *y*-intercept, and there is no slope.

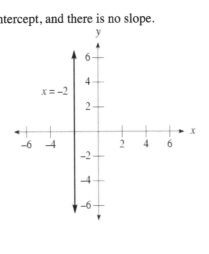

5. Using the point-slope formula:

$$y - 3 = 2(x + 1)$$
$$y - 3 = 2x + 2$$
$$y = 2x + 5$$

6. First find the slope: $m = \dfrac{-1 - 2}{4 - (-3)} = \dfrac{-3}{4 + 3} = -\dfrac{3}{7}$. Using the point-slope formula:

$$y - 2 = -\frac{3}{7}(x + 3)$$
$$y - 2 = -\frac{3}{7}x - \frac{9}{7}$$
$$y = -\frac{3}{7}x + \frac{5}{7}$$

7. First solve for *y* to find the slope:

$$2x - 5y = 10$$
$$-5y = -2x + 10$$
$$y = \frac{2}{5}x - 2$$

The parallel line will also have a slope of $\dfrac{2}{5}$. Now using the point-slope formula:

$$y - (-3) = \frac{2}{5}(x - 5)$$
$$y + 3 = \frac{2}{5}x - 2$$
$$y = \frac{2}{5}x - 5$$

8. The perpendicular slope is $-\dfrac{1}{3}$. Using the point-slope formula:

$$y - (-2) = -\frac{1}{3}(x - (-1))$$
$$y + 2 = -\frac{1}{3}x - \frac{1}{3}$$
$$y = -\frac{1}{3}x - \frac{7}{3}$$

9. Since the line is vertical, its equation is $x = 4$.

10. Graphing the inequality:

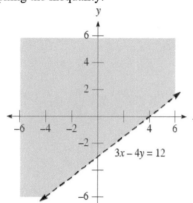

$3x - 4y = 12$

11. Graphing the inequality:

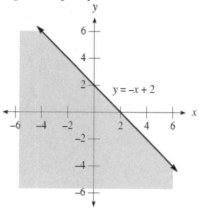

$y = -x + 2$

12. The domain is $\{-3,-2\}$ and the range is $\{0,1\}$. This is not a function.

13. The domain is all real numbers and the range is $\{y \mid y \geq -9\} = [-9, \infty)$. This is a function.

14. Evaluating the function: $f(3) + g(2) = [3-2] + [3 \cdot 2 + 4] = 1 + 10 = 11$

15. Evaluating the function: $h(x) - g(x) = (3x^2 - 2x - 8) - (3x + 4) = 3x^2 - 2x - 8 - 3x - 4 = 3x^2 - 5x - 12$

16. Evaluating the function: $(f \circ g)(2) = f(g(2)) = f(6 + 4) = f(10) = 10 - 2 = 8$

17. Evaluating the function: $(g \circ h)(x) = g(3x^2 - 2x - 8) = 3(3x^2 - 2x - 8) + 4 = 9x^2 - 6x - 20$

18. The variation equation is $y = Kx^2$. Substituting $x = 5$ and $y = 50$:

$$50 = K(5)^2$$
$$50 = 25K$$
$$K = 2$$

The equation is $y = 2x^2$. Substituting $x = 3$: $y = 2(3)^2 = 2 \cdot 9 = 18$

19. The variation equation is $z = Kxy^3$. Substituting $x = 5, y = 2$, and $z = 15$:

$$15 = K(5)(2)^3$$
$$15 = 40K$$
$$K = \frac{3}{8}$$

The equation is $z = \frac{3}{8}xy^3$. Substituting $x = 2$ and $y = 3$: $z = \frac{3}{8}(2)(3)^3 = \frac{3}{8} \cdot 54 = \frac{81}{4}$

20. The variation equation is $L = \frac{Kwd^2}{l}$. Substituting $l = 10, w = 3, d = 4$, and $L = 800$:

$$800 = \frac{K(3)(4)^2}{10}$$
$$8000 = 48K$$
$$K = \frac{500}{3}$$

The equation is $L = \frac{500wd^2}{3l}$. Substituting $l = 12, w = 3$, and $d = 4$: $L = \frac{500(3)(4)^2}{3(12)} = \frac{2000}{3}$

The beam can safely hold $\frac{2000}{3}$ pounds.

Chapter 4
Systems of Equations

4.1 Sysems of Linear Equations in Two Variables

1. The intersection point is (4,3).

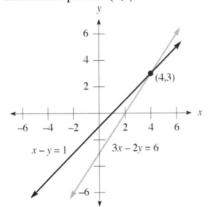

3. The intersection point is (–5,–6).

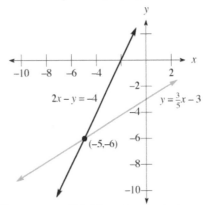

5. The intersection point is (4,2).

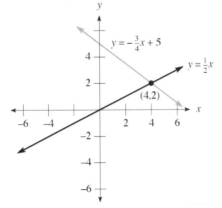

7. The lines are parallel. There is no solution to the system.

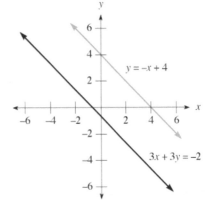

9. Adding the two equations:
$$6x = 8$$
$$x = \frac{4}{3}$$
Substituting into the first equation:
$$3\left(\frac{4}{3}\right) + y = 5$$
$$4 + y = 5$$
$$y = 1$$
The solution is $\left(\frac{4}{3}, 1\right)$.

11. Multiply the first equation by –2:
$$6x + 4y = 2$$
$$-6x + 4y = -2$$
Adding yields:
$$8y = 0$$
$$y = 0$$
Substituting into the first equation:
$$6x + 4(0) = 2$$
$$6x = 2$$
$$x = \frac{1}{3}$$
The solution is $\left(\frac{1}{3}, 0\right)$.

13. Multiply the first equation by –2:
$$-4x + 10y = -32$$
$$4x - 3y = 11$$
Adding yields:
$$7y = -21$$
$$y = -3$$
Substituting into the first equation:
$$2x - 5(-3) = 16$$
$$2x + 15 = 16$$
$$2x = 1$$
$$x = \frac{1}{2}$$
The solution is $\left(\frac{1}{2}, -3\right)$.

15. Multiply the first equation by 3 and the second equation by –2:

$$18x + 9y = -3$$
$$-18x - 10y = -2$$

Adding yields:

$$-y = -5$$
$$y = 5$$

Substituting into the second equation:

$$9x + 5(5) = 1$$
$$9x + 25 = 1$$
$$9x = -24$$
$$x = -\frac{8}{3}$$

The solution is $\left(-\frac{8}{3}, 5\right)$.

17. Multiply the first equation by 2 and the second equation by 3:

$$8x + 6y = 28$$
$$27x - 6y = 42$$

Adding yields:

$$35x = 70$$
$$x = 2$$

Substituting into the first equation:

$$4(2) + 3y = 14$$
$$8 + 3y = 14$$
$$3y = 6$$
$$y = 2$$

The solution is (2,2).

19. Multiply the first equation by 2:

$$4x - 10y = 6$$
$$-4x + 10y = 3$$

Adding yields $0 = 9$, which is false. There is no solution ($\varnothing$).

21. To clear each equation of fractions, multiply the first equation by 6 and the second equation by 20:

$$3x + 2y = 78$$
$$8x + 5y = 200$$

Multiply the first equation by 5 and the second equation by –2:

$$15x + 10y = 390$$
$$-16x - 10y = -400$$

Adding yields:

$$-x = -10$$
$$x = 10$$

The solution is (10,24).

23. To clear each equation of fractions, multiply the first equation by 4 and the second equation by 6:

$$2x - 3y = -2$$
$$2x - 3y = -2$$

Multiply the second equation by –1:

$$2x - 3y = -2$$
$$-2x + 3y = 2$$

Adding yields $0 = 0$. Since this statement is true, the two lines coincide. The solution is $\left\{(x,y) \mid \frac{1}{2}x - \frac{3}{4}y = -\frac{1}{2}\right\}$.

25. Substituting into the first equation:

$$7(2y+9)-y=24$$
$$14y+63-y=24$$
$$13y=-39$$
$$y=-3$$
$$x=2(-3)+9=3$$

The solution is $(3,-3)$.

27. Solving the second equation for y yields $y=-\frac{3}{4}x-1$. Substituting into the first equation:

$$6x-\left(-\frac{3}{4}x-1\right)=10$$
$$6x+\frac{3}{4}x+1=10$$
$$\frac{27}{4}x=9$$
$$27x=36$$
$$x=\frac{4}{3}$$
$$y=-\frac{3}{4}\left(\frac{4}{3}\right)-1=-1-1=-2$$

The solution is $\left(\frac{4}{3},-2\right)$.

29. Substituting into the first equation:

$$4x-4=3x-2$$
$$x-4=-2$$
$$x=2$$
$$y=4(2)-4=4$$

The solution is $(2,4)$.

31. Solving the first equation for y yields $y=2x-10$. Substituting into the second equation:

$$4x-2(2x-10)=10$$
$$4x-4x+20=10$$
$$20=10$$

Since this statement is false, there is no solution, or $\varnothing$.

33. Substituting into the first equation:

$$\frac{1}{3}\left(\frac{3}{2}y\right)-\frac{1}{2}y=0$$
$$\frac{1}{2}y-\frac{1}{2}y=0$$
$$0=0$$

Since this statement is true, the two lines coincide. The solution is $\left\{(x,y)\mid x=\frac{3}{2}y\right\}$.

35. Multiply the first equation by 2 and the second equation by 7:

$$8x - 14y = 6$$
$$35x + 14y = -21$$

Adding yields:

$$43x = -15$$
$$x = -\frac{15}{43}$$

Substituting into the original second equation:

$$5\left(-\frac{15}{43}\right) + 2y = -3$$
$$-\frac{75}{43} + 2y = -3$$
$$2y = -\frac{54}{43}$$
$$y = -\frac{27}{43}$$

The solution is $\left(-\frac{15}{43}, -\frac{27}{43}\right)$.

37. Multiply the first equation by 3 and the second equation by 8:

$$27x - 24y = 12$$
$$16x + 24y = 48$$

Adding yields:

$$43x = 60$$
$$x = \frac{60}{43}$$

Substituting into the original second equation:

$$2\left(\frac{60}{43}\right) + 3y = 6$$
$$\frac{120}{43} + 3y = 6$$
$$3y = \frac{138}{43}$$
$$y = \frac{46}{43}$$

The solution is $\left(\frac{60}{43}, \frac{46}{43}\right)$.

39. Multiply the first equation by 2 and the second equation by 5:
$$6x - 10y = 4$$
$$35x + 10y = 5$$
Adding yields:
$$41x = 9$$
$$x = \frac{9}{41}$$
Substituting into the original second equation:
$$7\left(\frac{9}{41}\right) + 2y = 1$$
$$\frac{63}{41} + 2y = 1$$
$$2y = -\frac{22}{41}$$
$$y = -\frac{11}{41}$$
The solution is $\left(\frac{9}{41}, -\frac{11}{41}\right)$.

41. Multiply the second equation by 3:
$$x - 3y = 7$$
$$6x + 3y = -18$$
Adding yields:
$$7x = -11$$
$$x = -\frac{11}{7}$$
Substituting into the original second equation:
$$2\left(-\frac{11}{7}\right) + y = -6$$
$$-\frac{22}{7} + y = -6$$
$$y = -\frac{20}{7}$$
The solution is $\left(-\frac{11}{7}, -\frac{20}{7}\right)$.

43. Substituting into the first equation:
$$-\frac{1}{3}x + 2 = \frac{1}{2}x + \frac{1}{3}$$
$$6\left(-\frac{1}{3}x + 2\right) = 6\left(\frac{1}{2}x + \frac{1}{3}\right)$$
$$-2x + 12 = 3x + 2$$
$$-5x = -10$$
$$x = 2$$
Substituting into the first equation: $y = \frac{1}{2}(2) + \frac{1}{3} = 1 + \frac{1}{3} = \frac{4}{3}$. The solution is $\left(2, \frac{4}{3}\right)$.

45. Substituting into the first equation:

$$3\left(\frac{2}{3}y-4\right)-4y=12$$
$$2y-12-4y=12$$
$$-2y-12=12$$
$$-2y=24$$
$$y=-12$$

Substituting into the second equation: $x=\frac{2}{3}(-12)-4=-8-4=-12$. The solution is $(-12,-12)$.

47. Multiply the first equation by 2:

$$8x-6y=-14$$
$$-8x+6y=-11$$
$$0=-25$$

Since this statement is false, there is no solution ($\varnothing$). The system is inconsistent.

49. Multiply the first equation by -20:

$$-60y-20z=-340$$
$$5y+20z=65$$

Adding yields:

$$-55y=-275$$
$$y=5$$

Substituting into the first equation:

$$3(5)+z=17$$
$$15+z=17$$
$$z=2$$

The solution is $y=5$, $z=2$.

51. Substitute into the first equation:

$$\frac{3}{4}x-\frac{1}{3}\left(\frac{1}{4}x\right)=1$$
$$\frac{3}{4}x-\frac{1}{12}x=1$$
$$\frac{2}{3}x=1$$
$$x=\frac{3}{2}$$

Substituting into the second equation: $y=\frac{1}{4}\left(\frac{3}{2}\right)=\frac{3}{8}$. The solution is $\left(\frac{3}{2},\frac{3}{8}\right)$.

53. To clear each equation of fractions, multiply the first equation by 12 and the second equation by 12:

$$3x-6y=4$$
$$4x-3y=-8$$

Multiply the second equation by -2:

$$3x-6y=4$$
$$-8x+6y=16$$

Adding yields:

$$-5x=20$$
$$x=-4$$

Substituting into the first equation:

$$3(-4) - 6y = 4$$
$$-12 - 6y = 4$$
$$-6y = 16$$
$$y = -\frac{8}{3}$$

The solution is $\left(-4, -\frac{8}{3}\right)$.

55.   **a.**   Simplifying: $(3x - 4y) - 3(x - y) = 3x - 4y - 3x + 3y = -y$

     b.   Substituting $x = 0$:
$$3(0) - 4y = 8$$
$$-4y = 8$$
$$y = -2$$

     c.   From part **b**, the y-intercept is $(0,-2)$.

     d.   Graphing the line:

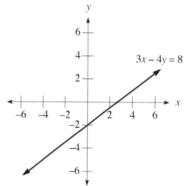

     e.   Multiply the second equation by -3:
$$3x - 4y = 8$$
$$-3x + 3y = -6$$
Adding yields:
$$-y = 2$$
$$y = -2$$
Substituting into the first equation:
$$3x - 4(-2) = 8$$
$$3x + 8 = 8$$
$$3x = 0$$
$$x = 0$$
The lines intersect at the point $(0,-2)$.

57.   Multiply the second equation by 100:
$$x + y = 10{,}000$$
$$6x + 5y = 56{,}000$$
Multiply the first equation by -5:
$$-5x - 5y = -50{,}000$$
$$6x + 5y = 56{,}000$$
Adding yields $x = 6000$. The solution is $(6000, 4000)$.

59. Substituting $x = 4 - y$ into the second equation:

$$(4 - y) - 2y = 4$$
$$4 - 3y = 4$$
$$-3y = 0$$
$$y = 0$$

The solution is $(4, 0)$.

61. The solution is in the third quadrant, so $(-3, 1)$ is the only possibility. The correct answer is c.

63. Solving the first equation for y yields $y = -5x + 2$. Substituting into the second equation:

$$2x - 3(-5x + 2) = 4$$
$$2x + 15x - 6 = 4$$
$$17x = 10$$
$$x = \frac{10}{17}$$

The correct answer is d.

65. Simplifying: $2 - 2(6) = 2 - 12 = -10$

67. Simplifying: $(x + 3y) - 1(x - 2z) = x + 3y - x + 2z = 3y + 2z$

69. Solving the equation:

$$-9y = -9$$
$$y = 1$$

71. Solving the equation:

$$3(1) + 2z = 9$$
$$3 + 2z = 9$$
$$2z = 6$$
$$z = 3$$

73. Applying the distributive property: $2(5x - z) = 10x - 2z$

75. Applying the distributive property: $3(3x + y - 2z) = 9x + 3y - 6z$

4.2 Systems of Linear Equations in Three Variables

1. **a.** Substituting $(2, 1, 3)$ into each equation:

$$2(2) + 1 - 3 = 4 + 1 - 3 = 2$$
$$2 + 1 + 3 = 6 \neq -1$$
$$3(2) - 2(1) + 2(3) = 6 - 2 + 6 = 10 \neq 3$$

Since $(2, 1, 3)$ does not check in each equation, it is not a solution.

b. Substituting $(1, -1, -1)$ into each equation:

$$2(1) - 1 + 1 = 2 - 1 + 1 = 2$$
$$1 - 1 - 1 = -1$$
$$3(1) - 2(-1) + 2(-1) = 3 + 2 - 2 = 3$$

Since $(1, -1, -1)$ checks in each equation, it is a solution.

3. Adding the first two equations and the first and third equations results in the system:

$$2x + 3z = 5$$
$$2x - 2z = 0$$

Solving the second equation yields $x = z$, now substituting:

$$2z + 3z = 5$$
$$5z = 5$$
$$z = 1$$

So $x = 1$, now substituting into the original first equation:

$$1 + y + 1 = 4$$
$$y + 2 = 4$$
$$y = 2$$

The solution is $(1, 2, 1)$.

5.   Adding the first two equations and the first and third equations results in the system:
$$2x + 3z = 13$$
$$3x - 3z = -3$$
Adding yields:
$$5x = 10$$
$$x = 2$$
Substituting to find z:
$$2(2) + 3z = 13$$
$$4 + 3z = 13$$
$$3z = 9$$
$$z = 3$$
Substituting into the original first equation:
$$2 + y + 3 = 6$$
$$y + 5 = 6$$
$$y = 1$$
The solution is (2,1,3).

7.   Adding the second and third equations:
$$5x + z = 11$$
Multiplying the second equation by 2:
$$x + 2y + z = 3$$
$$4x - 2y + 4z = 12$$
Adding yields:
$$5x + 5z = 15$$
$$x + z = 3$$
So the system becomes:
$$5x + z = 11$$
$$x + z = 3$$
Multiply the second equation by –1:
$$5x + z = 11$$
$$-x - z = -3$$
Adding yields:
$$4x = 8$$
$$x = 2$$
Substituting to find z:
$$5(2) + z = 11$$
$$z + 10 = 11$$
$$z = 1$$
Substituting into the original first equation:
$$2 + 2y + 1 = 3$$
$$2y + 3 = 3$$
$$2y = 0$$
$$y = 0$$
The solution is (2,0,1).

9. Multiply the second equation by –1 and add it to the first equation:
$$2x+3y-2z=4$$
$$-x-3y+3z=-4$$
Adding results in the equation $x+z=0$. Multiply the second equation by 2 and add it to the third equation:
$$2x+6y-6z=8$$
$$3x-6y+z=-3$$
Adding results in the equation:
$$5x-5z=5$$
$$x-z=1$$
So the system becomes:
$$x-z=1$$
$$x+z=0$$
Adding yields:
$$2x=1$$
$$x=\frac{1}{2}$$
Substituting to find z:
$$\frac{1}{2}+z=0$$
$$z=-\frac{1}{2}$$
Substituting into the original first equation:
$$2\left(\frac{1}{2}\right)+3y-2\left(-\frac{1}{2}\right)=4$$
$$1+3y+1=4$$
$$3y+2=4$$
$$3y=2$$
$$y=\frac{2}{3}$$
The solution is $\left(\frac{1}{2},\frac{2}{3},-\frac{1}{2}\right)$.

11. Multiply the first equation by 2 and add it to the second equation:
$$-2x+8y-6z=4$$
$$2x-8y+6z=1$$
Adding yields $0=5$, which is false. There is no solution (inconsistent system).

13. To clear the system of fractions, multiply the first equation by 2 and the second equation by 3:
$$x-2y+2z=0$$
$$6x+y+3z=6$$
$$x+y+z=-4$$
Multiply the third equation by 2 and add it to the first equation:
$$x-2y+2z=0$$
$$2x+2y+2z=-8$$
Adding yields the equation $3x+4z=-8$. Multiply the third equation by –1 and add it to the second equation:
$$6x+y+3z=6$$
$$-x-y-z=4$$
Adding yields the equation $5x+2z=10$. So the system becomes:
$$3x+4z=-8$$
$$5x+2z=10$$
Multiply the second equation by –2:
$$3x+4z=-8$$
$$-10x-4z=-20$$

Adding yields:
$$-7x = -28$$
$$x = 4$$
Substituting to find z:
$$3(4) + 4z = -8$$
$$12 + 4z = -8$$
$$4z = -20$$
$$z = -5$$
Substituting into the original third equation:
$$4 + y - 5 = -4$$
$$y - 1 = -4$$
$$y = -3$$
The solution is $(4,-3,-5)$.

15. Multiply the first equation by –2 and add it to the third equation:
$$-4x + 2y + 6z = -2$$
$$4x - 2y - 6z = 2$$

Adding yields $0 = 0$, which is true. Since there are now less equations than unknowns, there is no unique solution (dependent system).

17. Multiply the second equation by 3 and add it to the first equation:
$$2x - y + 3z = 4$$
$$3x + 6y - 3z = -9$$

Adding yields the equation $5x + 5y = -5$, or $x + y = -1$.

Multiply the second equation by 2 and add it to the third equation:
$$2x + 4y - 2z = -6$$
$$4x + 3y + 2z = -5$$

Adding yields the equation $6x + 7y = -11$. So the system becomes:
$$6x + 7y = -11$$
$$x + y = -1$$

Multiply the second equation by –6:
$$6x + 7y = -11$$
$$-6x - 6y = 6$$

Adding yields $y = -5$. Substituting to find x:
$$6x + 7(-5) = -11$$
$$6x - 35 = -11$$
$$6x = 24$$
$$x = 4$$
Substituting into the original first equation:
$$2(4) - (-5) + 3z = 4$$
$$13 + 3z = 4$$
$$3z = -9$$
$$z = -3$$
The solution is $(4,-5,-3)$.

19. Adding the second and third equations results in the equation $x + y = 9$. Since this is the same as the first equation, there are less equations than unknowns. There is no unique solution (dependent system).

21. Adding the second and third equations results in the equation $4x + y = 3$. So the system becomes:

$$4x + y = 3$$
$$2x + y = 2$$

Multiplying the second equation by –1:

$$4x + y = 3$$
$$-2x - y = -2$$

Adding yields:

$$2x = 1$$
$$x = \frac{1}{2}$$

Substituting to find y:

$$2\left(\frac{1}{2}\right) + y = 2$$
$$1 + y = 2$$
$$y = 1$$

Substituting into the original second equation:

$$1 + z = 3$$
$$z = 2$$

The solution is $\left(\frac{1}{2}, 1, 2\right)$.

23. Multiply the third equation by 2 and adding it to the second equation:

$$6y - 4z = 1$$
$$2x + 4z = 2$$

Adding yields the equation $2x + 6y = 3$. So the system becomes:

$$2x - 3y = 0$$
$$2x + 6y = 3$$

Multiply the first equation by 2:

$$4x - 6y = 0$$
$$2x + 6y = 3$$

Adding yields:

$$6x = 3$$
$$x = \frac{1}{2}$$

Substituting to find y:

$$2\left(\frac{1}{2}\right) + 6y = 3$$
$$1 + 6y = 3$$
$$6y = 2$$
$$y = \frac{1}{3}$$

Substituting into the original third equation to find z:

$$\frac{1}{2} + 2z = 1$$
$$2z = \frac{1}{2}$$
$$z = \frac{1}{4}$$

The solution is $\left(\frac{1}{2}, \frac{1}{3}, \frac{1}{4}\right)$.

25. Multiply the first equation by –2 and add it to the second equation:
$$-2x - 2y + 2z = -4$$
$$2x + y + 3z = 4$$

Adding yields $-y + 5z = 0$. Multiply the first equation by –1 and add it to the third equation:
$$-x - y + z = -2$$
$$x - 2y + 2z = 6$$

Adding yields $-3y + 3z = 4$. So the system becomes:
$$-y + 5z = 0$$
$$-3y + 3z = 4$$

Multiply the first equation by –3:
$$3y - 15z = 0$$
$$-3y + 3z = 4$$

Adding yields:
$$-12z = 4$$
$$z = -\frac{1}{3}$$

Substituting to find y:
$$-3y + 3\left(-\frac{1}{3}\right) = 4$$
$$-3y - 1 = 4$$
$$-3y = 5$$
$$y = -\frac{5}{3}$$

Substituting into the original first equation:
$$x - \frac{5}{3} + \frac{1}{3} = 2$$
$$x - \frac{4}{3} = 2$$
$$x = \frac{10}{3}$$

The solution is $\left(\frac{10}{3}, -\frac{5}{3}, -\frac{1}{3}\right)$.

27. Multiply the third equation by –1 and add it to the first equation:
$$2x + 3y = -\frac{1}{2}$$
$$-3y - 2z = \frac{3}{4}$$

Adding yields the equation $2x - 2z = \frac{1}{4}$. So the system becomes:
$$2x - 2z = \frac{1}{4}$$
$$4x + 8z = 2$$

Multiply the first equation by 4:
$$8x - 8z = 1$$
$$4x + 8z = 2$$

Adding yields:
$$12x = 3$$
$$x = \frac{1}{4}$$
Substituting to find z:
$$4\left(\frac{1}{4}\right) + 8z = 2$$
$$1 + 8z = 2$$
$$8z = 1$$
$$z = \frac{1}{8}$$
Substituting to find y:
$$2\left(\frac{1}{4}\right) + 3y = -\frac{1}{2}$$
$$\frac{1}{2} + 3y = -\frac{1}{2}$$
$$3y = -1$$
$$y = -\frac{1}{3}$$
The solution is $\left(\frac{1}{4}, -\frac{1}{3}, \frac{1}{8}\right)$.

29. To clear each equation of fractions, multiply the first equation by 6, the second equation by 4, and the third equation by 12:
$$2x + 3y - z = 24$$
$$x - 3y + 2z = 6$$
$$6x - 8y - 3z = -64$$
Multiply the first equation by 2 and add it to the second equation:
$$4x + 6y - 2z = 48$$
$$x - 3y + 2z = 6$$
Adding yields the equation $5x + 3y = 54$. Multiply the first equation by -3 and add it to the third equation:
$$-6x - 9y + 3z = -72$$
$$6x - 8y - 3z = -64$$
Adding yields:
$$-17y = -136$$
$$y = 8$$
Substituting to find x:
$$5x + 3(8) = 54$$
$$5x + 24 = 54$$
$$5x = 30$$
$$x = 6$$
Substituting to find z:
$$6 - 3(8) + 2z = 6$$
$$-18 + 2z = 6$$
$$2z = 24$$
$$z = 12$$
The solution is $(6, 8, 12)$.

31. To clear each equation of fractions, multiply the first equation by 6, the second equation by 6, and the third equation by 12:

$$6x - 3y - 2z = -8$$
$$2x - 3z = 30$$
$$-3x + 8y - 12z = -9$$

Multiply the first equation by 8 and the third equation by 3:

$$48x - 24y - 16z = -64$$
$$-9x + 24y - 36z = -27$$

Adding yields the equation:

$$39x - 52z = -91$$
$$3x - 4z = -7$$

So the system becomes:

$$2x - 3z = 30$$
$$3x - 4z = -7$$

Multiply the first equation by 3 and the second equation by –2:

$$6x - 9z = 90$$
$$-6x + 8z = 14$$

Adding yields:

$$-z = 104$$
$$z = -104$$

Substituting to find x:

$$2x - 3(-104) = 30$$
$$2x + 312 = 30$$
$$2x = -282$$
$$x = -141$$

Substituting to find y:

$$6(-141) - 3y - 2(-104) = -8$$
$$-846 - 3y + 208 = -8$$
$$-3y - 638 = -8$$
$$-3y = 630$$
$$y = -210$$

The solution is $(-141, -210, -104)$.

33. Divide the second equation by 5 and the third equation by 10 to produce the system:

$$x - y - z = 0$$
$$x + 4y = 16$$
$$2y - z = 5$$

Multiply the third equation by –1 and add it to the first equation:

$$x - y - z = 0$$
$$-2y + z = -5$$

Adding yields the equation $x - 3y = -5$. So the system becomes:

$$x + 4y = 16$$
$$x - 3y = -5$$

Multiply the second equation by –1:

$$x + 4y = 16$$
$$-x + 3y = 5$$

Adding yields:
$$7y = 21$$
$$y = 3$$
Substituting to find x:
$$x + 12 = 16$$
$$x = 4$$
Substituting to find z:
$$6 - z = 5$$
$$z = 1$$
The currents are 4 amps, 3 amps, and 1 amp.

35. The point $\left(5, 3, -\frac{1}{2}\right)$ satisfies all three equations, so it is a solution. The correct answer is c.

37. Multiplying the first equation by –2 and adding it to the second equation:
$$-2x - 4y + 2z = -6$$
$$2x + 4y - 2z = c$$
Adding yields:
$$0 = c - 6$$
$$c = 6$$
The correct answer is b.

39. Translating into symbols: $3x + 2$

41. Simplifying: $25 - \dfrac{385}{9} = \dfrac{225}{9} - \dfrac{385}{9} = -\dfrac{160}{9}$

43. Simplifying: $0.08(4,000) = 320$

45. Simplifying: $10(0.2x + 0.5y) = 2x + 5y$

47. Solving the equation:
$$x + (3x + 2) = 26$$
$$4x + 2 = 26$$
$$4x = 24$$
$$x = 6$$

49. Adding the two equations results in:
$$-9y = 9$$
$$y = -1$$
Substituting into the second equation:
$$-7(-1) + 4z = 27$$
$$7 + 4z = 27$$
$$4z = 20$$
$$z = 5$$
The solution is $y = -1$ and $z = 5$.

4.3 Applications

1. Let x and y represent the two numbers. The system of equations is:
    $$y = 2x + 3$$
    $$x + y = 18$$
    Substituting into the second equation:
    $$x + 2x + 3 = 18$$
    $$3x = 15$$
    $$x = 5$$
    $$y = 2(5) + 3 = 13$$
    The two numbers are 5 and 13.

3. Let x and y represent the two numbers. The system of equations is:
    $$y - x = 6$$
    $$2x = 4 + y$$
    The second equation is $y = 2x - 4$. Substituting into the first equation:
    $$2x - 4 - x = 6$$
    $$x = 10$$
    $$y = 2(10) - 4 = 16$$
    The two numbers are 10 and 16.

5. Let x, y, and z represent the three numbers. The system of equations is:
    $$x + y + z = 8$$
    $$2x = z - 2$$
    $$x + z = 5$$
    The third equation is $z = 5 - x$. Substituting into the second equation:
    $$2x = 5 - x - 2$$
    $$3x = 3$$
    $$x = 1$$
    $$z = 5 - 1 = 4$$
    Substituting into the first equation:
    $$1 + y + 4 = 8$$
    $$y = 3$$
    The three numbers are 1, 3, and 4.

7. Let a represent the number of adult tickets and c represent the number of children's tickets. The system of equations is:
    $$a + c = 925$$
    $$2a + c = 1150$$
    Multiply the first equation by -1:
    $$-a - c = -925$$
    $$2a + c = 1150$$
    Adding yields:
    $$a = 225$$
    $$c = 700$$
    There were 225 adult tickets and 700 children's tickets sold.

9.   Let x represent the amount invested at 6% and y represent the amount invested at 7%. The system of equations is:

$$x + y = 20{,}000$$
$$0.06x + 0.07y = 1{,}280$$

Multiplying the first equation by –0.06:

$$-0.06x - 0.06y = -1{,}200$$
$$0.06x + 0.07y = 1{,}280$$

Adding yields:

$$0.01y = 80$$
$$y = 8{,}000$$
$$x = 12{,}000$$

Mr. Jones invested $12,000 at 6% and $8,000 at 7%.

11. Let x represent the amount invested at 6% and $2x$ represent the amount invested at 7.5%. The equation is:

$$0.075(2x) + 0.06(x) = 840$$
$$0.21x = 840$$
$$x = 4{,}000$$
$$2x = 8{,}000$$

Susan invested $4,000 at 6% and $8,000 at 7.5%.

13. Let x, y and z represent the amounts invested in the three accounts. The system of equations is:

$$x + y + z = 2{,}200$$
$$z = 3x$$
$$0.06x + 0.08y + 0.09z = 178$$

Substituting into the first equation:

$$x + y + 3x = 2{,}200$$
$$4x + y = 2{,}200$$

Substituting into the third equation:

$$0.06x + 0.08y + 0.09(3x) = 178$$
$$0.33x + 0.08y = 178$$

The system of equations becomes:

$$4x + y = 2{,}200$$
$$0.33x + 0.08y = 178$$

Multiply the first equation by –0.08:

$$-0.32x - 0.08y = -176$$
$$0.33x + 0.08y = 178$$

Adding yields:

$$0.01x = 2$$
$$x = 200$$
$$z = 3(200) = 600$$
$$y = 2{,}200 - 4(200) = 1{,}400$$

The man invested $200 at 6%, $1,400 at 8%, and $600 at 9%.

15. Let x represent the amount of 20% alcohol and y represent the amount of 50% alcohol. The system of equations is:

$$x + y = 9$$
$$0.20x + 0.50y = 0.30(9)$$

Multiplying the first equation by –0.2:

$$-0.20x - 0.20y = -1.8$$
$$0.20x + 0.50y = 2.7$$

Adding yields:

$$0.30y = 0.9$$
$$y = 3$$
$$x = 6$$

The mixture contains 3 gallons of 50% alcohol and 6 gallons of 20% alcohol.

17. Let x represent the amount of 20% disinfectant and y represent the amount of 14% disinfectant. The system of equations is:
$$x + y = 15$$
$$0.20x + 0.14y = 0.16(15)$$
Multiplying the first equation by –0.14:
$$-0.14x - 0.14y = -2.1$$
$$0.20x + 0.14y = 2.4$$
Adding yields:
$$0.06x = 0.3$$
$$x = 5$$
$$y = 10$$
The mixture contains 5 gallons of 20% disinfectant and 10 gallons of 14% disinfectant.

19. Let x represent the amount of nuts and y represent the amount of oats. The system of equations is:
$$x + y = 25$$
$$1.55x + 1.35y = 1.45(25)$$
Multiplying the first equation by –1.35:
$$-1.35x - 1.35y = -33.75$$
$$1.55x + 1.35y = 36.25$$
Adding yields:
$$0.20x = 2.5$$
$$x = 12.5$$
$$y = 12.5$$
The mixture contains 12.5 pounds of oats and 12.5 pounds of nuts.

21. Let b represent the speed of the boat and c represent the speed of the current. The system of equations is:
$$2(b + c) = 24$$
$$3(b - c) = 18$$
The system of equations simplifies to:
$$b + c = 12$$
$$b - c = 6$$
Adding yields:
$$2b = 18$$
$$b = 9$$
$$c = 3$$
The speed of the boat is 9 mph and the speed of the current is 3 mph.

23. Let a represent the rate of the airplane and w represent the rate of the wind. The system of equations is:
$$2(a + w) = 600$$
$$\frac{5}{2}(a - w) = 600$$
The system of equations simplifies to:
$$a + w = 300$$
$$a - w = 240$$
Adding yields:
$$2a = 540$$
$$a = 270$$
$$w = 30$$
The rate of the airplane is 270 mph and the rate of the wind is 30 mph.

25. Let n represent the number of nickels and d represent the number of dimes. The system of equations is:

$$n + d = 20$$
$$0.05n + 0.10d = 1.40$$

Multiplying the first equation by –0.05:

$$-0.05n - 0.05d = -1$$
$$0.05n + 0.10d = 1.40$$

Adding yields:

$$0.05d = 0.40$$
$$d = 8$$
$$n = 12$$

Bob has 12 nickels and 8 dimes.

27. Let n, d, and q represent the number of nickels, dimes, and quarters. The system of equations is:

$$n + d + q = 9$$
$$0.05n + 0.10d + 0.25q = 1.20$$
$$d = n$$

Substituting into the first equation:

$$n + n + q = 9$$
$$2n + q = 9$$

Substituting into the second equation:

$$0.05n + 0.10n + 0.25q = 1.20$$
$$0.15n + 0.25q = 1.20$$

The system of equations becomes:

$$2n + q = 9$$
$$0.15n + 0.25q = 1.20$$

Multiplying the first equation by –0.25:

$$-0.50n - 0.25q = -2.25$$
$$0.15n + 0.25q = 1.20$$

Adding yields:

$$-0.35n = -1.05$$
$$n = 3$$
$$d = 3$$
$$q = 9 - 2(3) = 3$$

The collection contains 3 nickels, 3 dimes, and 3 quarters.

29. Let n, d, and q represent the number of nickels, dimes, and quarters. The system of equations is:

$$n + d + q = 140$$
$$0.05n + 0.10d + 0.25q = 10.00$$
$$d = 2q$$

Substituting into the first equation:

$$n + 2q + q = 140$$
$$n + 3q = 140$$

Substituting into the second equation:

$$0.05n + 0.10(2q) + 0.25q = 10.00$$
$$0.05n + 0.45q = 10.00$$

The system of equations becomes:

$$n + 3q = 140$$
$$0.05n + 0.45q = 10.00$$

Multiplying the first equation by –0.05:

$$-0.05n - 0.15q = -7$$
$$0.05n + 0.45q = 10$$

Adding yields:
$$0.30q = 3$$
$$q = 10$$
$$d = 2(10) = 20$$
$$n = 140 - 3(10) = 110$$

There are 110 nickels in the collection.

31. Let $x = mp + b$ represent the relationship. Using the points (2,300) and (1.5,400) results in the system:
$$300 = 2m + b$$
$$400 = 1.5m + b$$

Multiplying the second equation by –1:
$$300 = 2m + b$$
$$-400 = -1.5m - b$$

Adding yields:
$$-100 = 0.5m$$
$$m = -200$$
$$b = 300 - 2(-200) = 700$$

The equation is $x = -200p + 700$. Substituting $p = 3$: $x = -200(3) + 700 = 100$ items

33. The system of equations is:
$$a + b + c = 128$$
$$9a + 3b + c = 128$$
$$25a + 5b + c = 0$$

Multiply the first equation by –1 and add it to the second equation:
$$-a - b - c = -128$$
$$9a + 3b + c = 128$$

Adding yields:
$$8a + 2b = 0$$
$$4a + b = 0$$

Multiply the first equation by –1 and add it to the third equation:
$$-a - b - c = -128$$
$$25a + 5b + c = 0$$

Adding yields:
$$24a + 4b = -128$$
$$6a + b = -32$$

The system simplifies to:
$$4a + b = 0$$
$$6a + b = -32$$

Multiplying the first equation by –1:
$$-4a - b = 0$$
$$6a + b = -32$$

Adding yields:
$$2a = -32$$
$$a = -16$$

Substituting to find b:
$$4(-16) + b = 0$$
$$b = 64$$

Substituting to find c:
$$-16 + 64 + c = 128$$
$$c = 80$$

The equation for the height is $h = -16t^2 + 64t + 80$.

35. If x represents the amount of 25% salt solution and y represents the amount of 60% salt solution, the system of equations is:
$$x + y = 10$$
$$0.25x + 0.60y = 5$$
The correct answer is c.

37. No, the graph does not include the boundary line.

39. Substituting $x = 4 - y$ into the second equation:
$$(4 - y) - 2y = 4$$
$$4 - 3y = 4$$
$$-3y = 0$$
$$y = 0$$
The solution is (4,0).

41. Solving the inequality:
$$20x + 9,300 > 18,000$$
$$20x > 8,700$$
$$x > 435$$

4.4 Systems of Linear Inequalities

1. **a.** Since $0 - 0 = 0$, it does not satisfy the second equation. This is not a solution.
   b. Since $(-3,-1)$ satisfies both equations, this is a solution.
   c. Since $1 - (-4) = 5$, it does not satisfy the second equation. This is not a solution.
   d. Since $(-2,0)$ satisfies both equation, this is a solution.

3. Graphing the solution set:

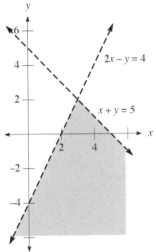

5. Graphing the solution set:

7. Graphing the solution set:

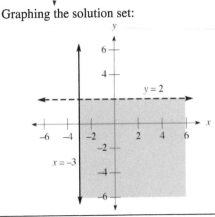

9. Graphing the solution set:

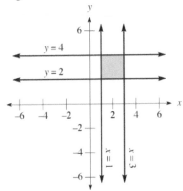

11. Graphing the solution set:

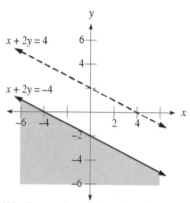

13. There is no solution, since it is impossible for $y > 1$ and also $y \le -3$.

15. Graphing the solution set:

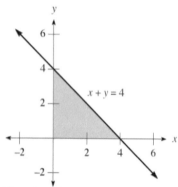

17. Graphing the solution set:

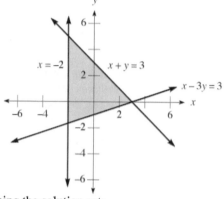

19. Graphing the solution set:

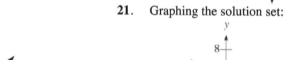

21. Graphing the solution set:

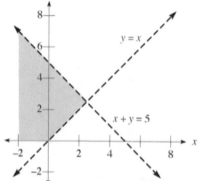

23. Graphing the solution set:

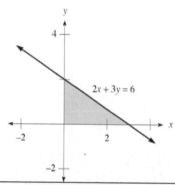

25. The system of inequalities is:
$$x + y \le 4$$
$$-x + y < 4$$

27. The system of inequalities is:
$$x + y \ge 4$$
$$-x + y < 4$$

29. The system of inequalities is:
$$x \ge -4$$
$$x \le -2$$

31. **a.** The system of inequalities is:
$$0.55x + 0.65y \le 40$$
$$x \ge 2y$$
$$x > 15$$
$$y \ge 0$$

Graphing the solution set:

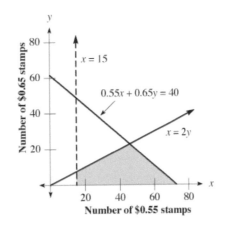

b. Substitute $x = 20$:
$$2y \le 20$$
$$y \le 10$$

The most he can purchase is ten 65-cent stamps.

33. Only the point $(3, -1)$ satisfies both inequalities, so the correct answer is d.

35. The correct answer is c.

37. The x-intercept is $-\dfrac{8}{3}$, the y-intercept is 4, and the slope is $\dfrac{3}{2}$.

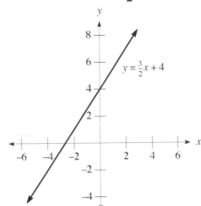

39. Using the point-slope formula:
$$y - 3 = 2(x + 1)$$
$$y - 3 = 2x + 2$$
$$y = 2x + 5$$

41. First solve for y to find the slope:

$$2x - 5y = 10$$
$$-5y = -2x + 10$$
$$y = \frac{2}{5}x - 2$$

The parallel line will also have a slope of $\frac{2}{5}$. Now using the point-slope formula:

$$y - (-3) = \frac{2}{5}(x - 5)$$
$$y + 3 = \frac{2}{5}x - 2$$
$$y = \frac{2}{5}x - 5$$

43. The domain is $\{-3, -2\}$ and the range is $\{0, 1\}$. This is not a function.

45. Evaluating the function: $f(3) + g(2) = [3 - 2] + [3 \cdot 2 + 4] = 1 + 10 = 11$

47. Evaluating the function: $f(g(2)) = f(3 \cdot 2 + 4) = f(10) = 10 - 2 = 8$

49. The variation equation is $y = Kx^2$. Substituting $x = 5$ and $y = 50$:

$$50 = K(5)^2$$
$$50 = 25K$$
$$K = 2$$

The equation is $y = 2x^2$. Substituting $x = 3$: $y = 2(3)^2 = 2 \cdot 9 = 18$

Chapter 4 Test

1. Multiply the first equation by 2:

$$4x + 8y = 6$$
$$-4x - 8y = -6$$

Adding yields $0 = 0$, so the system is dependent. The solution is $\{(x, y) \mid 2x + 4y = 3\}$.

2. Multiply the first equation by 5 and the second equation by 4:

$$20x - 35y = -10$$
$$-20x + 24y = -12$$

Adding yields:

$$-11y = -22$$
$$y = 2$$

Substituting to find x:

$$4x - 14 = -2$$
$$4x = 12$$
$$x = 3$$

The solution is (3,2).

3. To clear each equation of fractions, multiply the first equation by 6 and the second equation by 20:

$$2x - y = 18$$
$$-4x + 5y = 0$$

Multiply the first equation by 2:

$$4x - 2y = 36$$
$$-4x + 5y = 0$$

Adding yields:

$$3y = 36$$
$$y = 12$$

Substituting to find x:

$$2x - 12 = 18$$
$$2x = 30$$
$$x = 15$$

The solution is $(15, 12)$.

4. Substituting into the first equation:

$$2x - 5(3x + 8) = 14$$
$$2x - 15x - 40 = 14$$
$$-13x = 54$$
$$x = -\frac{54}{13}$$

Substituting to find y: $y = 3\left(-\dfrac{54}{13}\right) + 8 = -\dfrac{162}{13} + \dfrac{104}{13} = -\dfrac{58}{13}$. The solution is $\left(-\dfrac{54}{13}, -\dfrac{58}{13}\right)$.

5. Multiply the second equation by 5:

$$2x - 5y = -8$$
$$15x + 5y = 25$$

Adding yields:

$$17x = 17$$
$$x = 1$$

Substituting to find y:

$$3 + y = 5$$
$$y = 2$$

The solution is $(1, 2)$.

6. The first equation is equivalent to $x = 2y$. Substituting into the second equation:

$$-4(2y) - 8y = -6$$
$$8y - 8y = -6$$
$$0 = -6$$

Since this statement is false, there is no solution. This is an inconsistent system.

7. Adding the first and third equations:
$$5x = 15$$
$$x = 3$$
Adding the first and second equations:
$$3x - 2z = 7$$
$$9 - 2z = 7$$
$$-2z = -2$$
$$z = 1$$
Substituting to find y:
$$3 + y - 3 = -2$$
$$y = -2$$
The solution is $(3, -2, 1)$.

8. Adding the second and third equations:
$$4x - 6y = 10$$
$$2x - 3y = 5$$
Multiplying the second equation by 3 and adding it to the first equation:
$$3x - 12y - 3z = 18$$
$$2x - y + 3z = 2$$
Adding yields $5x - 13y = 20$. This results in the system:
$$2x - 3y = 5$$
$$5x - 13y = 20$$
Multiplying the first equation by -5 and the second equation by 2:
$$-10x + 15y = -25$$
$$10x - 26y = 40$$
Adding yields:
$$-11y = 15$$
$$y = -\frac{15}{11}$$
Substituting into $2x - 3y = 5$:
$$2x - 3\left(-\frac{15}{11}\right) = 5$$
$$2x + \frac{45}{11} = 5$$
$$2x = \frac{10}{11}$$
$$x = \frac{5}{11}$$
Substituting into $3x - 2y + z = 4$:
$$3\left(\frac{5}{11}\right) - 2\left(-\frac{15}{11}\right) + z = 4$$
$$\frac{15}{11} + \frac{30}{11} + z = 4$$
$$\frac{45}{11} + z = 4$$
$$z = -\frac{1}{11}$$
The solution is $\left(\frac{5}{11}, -\frac{15}{11}, -\frac{1}{11}\right)$.

9. Multiplying the first equation by 2 and adding it to the second equation:
$$2x + 4y - 2z = 14$$
$$3x - 4y - 3z = -4$$
Adding yields:
$$5x - 5z = 10$$
$$x - z = 2$$
Multiplying the third equation by 4 and adding it to the second equation:
$$8x + 4y - 8z = 4$$
$$3x - 4y - 3z = -4$$
Adding yields:
$$11x - 11z = 0$$
$$x = z$$
Substituting into $x - z = 2$ results in $0 = 2$, which is false. There is no solution, and the system is inconsistent.

10. Let x and $2x - 1$ represent the two numbers. The equation is:
$$x + 2x - 1 = 14$$
$$3x = 15$$
$$x = 5$$
$$2x - 1 = 9$$
The two numbers are 5 and 9.

11. Let x and $2x$ represent the two investments. The equation is:
$$0.05(x) + 0.06(2x) = 680$$
$$0.17x = 680$$
$$x = 4,000$$
$$2x = 8,000$$
John invested \$4,000 at 5% and \$8,000 at 6%.

12. Let a represent the adult ticket sales and c represent the children's ticket sales. The system of equations is:
$$a + c = 750$$
$$2a + 1c = 1,090$$
Multiplying the first equation by -1:
$$-a - c = -750$$
$$2a + c = 1090$$
Adding yields $a = 340$ and $c = 410$. There were 340 adult tickets and 410 children's tickets sold.

13. Let x represent the amount of 30% alcohol and y represent the amount of 70% alcohol. The system of equations is:
$$x + y = 16$$
$$0.30x + 0.70y = 0.60(16)$$
Multiplying the first equation by -0.3:
$$-0.30x - 0.30y = -4.8$$
$$0.30x + 0.70y = 9.6$$
Adding yields:
$$0.40y = 4.8$$
$$y = 12$$
$$x = 4$$
The mixture contains 4 gallons of 30% alcohol and 12 gallons of 70% alcohol.

14. Let b and c represent the rate of the boat and current. The system of equations is:

$$2(b+c) = 20$$

$$3(b-c) = 18$$

Simplifying the system:

$$b+c = 10$$

$$b-c = 6$$

Adding yields:

$$2b = 16$$

$$b = 8$$

$$c = 2$$

The boat's rate is 8 mph and the current's rate is 2 mph.

15. Let $n, d,$ and q represent the number of nickels, dimes, and quarters. The system of equations is:

$$n+d+q = 15$$

$$0.05n + 0.10d + 0.25q = 1.10$$

$$n = 4d - 1$$

Substituting into the first equation:

$$4d - 1 + d + q = 15$$

$$5d + q = 16$$

Substituting into the second equation:

$$0.05(4d-1) + 0.10d + 0.25q = 1.10$$

$$0.3d + 0.25q = 1.15$$

The system of equations becomes:

$$5d + q = 16$$

$$0.3d + 0.25q = 1.15$$

Multiply the first equation by -0.25:

$$-1.25d - 0.25q = -4$$

$$0.3d + 0.25q = 1.15$$

Adding yields:

$$-0.95d = -2.85$$

$$d = 3$$

Substituting to find q:

$$15 + q = 16$$

$$q = 1$$

Substituting to find n:

$$n + 3 + 1 = 15$$

$$n = 11$$

The collection contains 11 nickels, 3 dimes, and 1 quarter.

16.   Graphing the solution set:

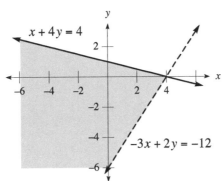

17.   The first inequality is $x + y \le -3$ and the second inequality is $x + y \ge 2$. Since these two inequalities cannot both be true, there is no solution.

18.   Graphing the solution set:

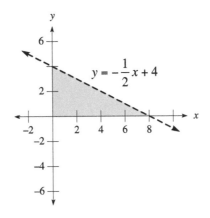

Chapter 5
Polynomials and Factoring

5.1 Sums and Differences of Polynomials

1. This is a trinomial. The degree is 2 and the leading coefficient is 5.
3. This is a binomial. The degree is 1 and the leading coefficient is 3.
5. This is a trinomial. The degree is 5 and the leading coefficient is 8.
7. This is a polynomial. The degree is 3 and the leading coefficient is 4.
9. This is a monomial. The degree is 0 and the leading coefficient is $-\dfrac{3}{4}$.
11. This is a trinomial. The degree is 3 and the leading coefficient is 6.
13. Simplifying: $2x^2 - 3x + 10x - 15 = 2x^2 + 7x - 15$
15. Simplifying: $12a^2 + 8ab - 15ab - 10b^2 = 12a^2 - 7ab - 10b^2$
17. Simplifying: $(4x + 2) + (3x - 1) = 7x + 1$
19. Simplifying: $(5x^2 - 6x + 1) - (4x^2 + 7x - 2) = 5x^2 - 6x + 1 - 4x^2 - 7x + 2 = x^2 - 13x + 3$
21. Simplifying: $\left(\dfrac{1}{2}x^2 - \dfrac{1}{3}x - \dfrac{1}{6}\right) - \left(\dfrac{1}{4}x^2 + \dfrac{7}{12}x\right) + \left(\dfrac{1}{3}x - \dfrac{1}{12}\right) = \dfrac{1}{2}x^2 - \dfrac{1}{3}x - \dfrac{1}{6} - \dfrac{1}{4}x^2 - \dfrac{7}{12}x + \dfrac{1}{3}x - \dfrac{1}{12} = \dfrac{1}{4}x^2 - \dfrac{7}{12}x - \dfrac{1}{4}$
23. Simplifying: $(y^3 - 2y^2 - 3y + 4) - (2y^3 - y^2 + y - 3) = y^3 - 2y^2 - 3y + 4 - 2y^3 + y^2 - y + 3 = -y^3 - y^2 - 4y + 7$
25. Simplifying: $(5x^3 - 4x^2) - (3x + 4) + (5x^2 - 7) - (3x^3 + 6) = 5x^3 - 4x^2 - 3x - 4 + 5x^2 - 7 - 3x^3 - 6 = 2x^3 + x^2 - 3x - 17$
27. Simplifying:

$$\left(\dfrac{4}{7}x^2 - \dfrac{1}{7}xy + \dfrac{1}{14}y^2\right) - \left(\dfrac{1}{2}x^2 - \dfrac{2}{7}xy - \dfrac{9}{14}y^2\right) = \dfrac{4}{7}x^2 - \dfrac{1}{7}xy + \dfrac{1}{14}y^2 - \dfrac{1}{2}x^2 + \dfrac{2}{7}xy + \dfrac{9}{14}y^2$$

$$= \dfrac{8}{14}x^2 - \dfrac{7}{14}x^2 - \dfrac{1}{7}xy + \dfrac{2}{7}xy + \dfrac{1}{14}y^2 + \dfrac{9}{14}y^2$$

$$= \dfrac{1}{14}x^2 + \dfrac{1}{7}xy + \dfrac{5}{7}y^2$$

29. Simplifying:

$$(3a^3 + 2a^2b + ab^2 - b^3) - (6a^3 - 4a^2b + 6ab^2 - b^3) = 3a^3 + 2a^2b + ab^2 - b^3 - 6a^3 + 4a^2b - 6ab^2 + b^3$$

$$= -3a^3 + 6a^2b - 5ab^2$$

31. Adding: $(x^2 - 6xy + y^2) + (2x^2 - 6xy - y^2) = x^2 - 6xy + y^2 + 2x^2 - 6xy - y^2 = 3x^2 - 12xy$
33. Adding:

$$(11a^2 + 3ab + 2b^2) + (9a^2 - 2ab + b^2) + (-6a^2 - 3ab + 5b^2) = 11a^2 + 3ab + 2b^2 + 9a^2 - 2ab + b^2 - 6a^2 - 3ab + 5b^2$$

$$= 14a^2 - 2ab + 8b^2$$

35. Subtracting: $(2x^2 - 7x) - (2x^2 - 4x) = 2x^2 - 7x - 2x^2 + 4x = -3x$
37. Subtracting: $q(x) - p(x) = (9x^5 - 4x^3 - 6) - (-8x^5 - 4x^3 + 6) = 9x^5 - 4x^3 - 6 + 8x^5 + 4x^3 - 6 = 17x^5 - 12$

39. Simplifying: $-[2-(4-x)]=-(2-4+x)=-(-2+x)=2-x$

41. Simplifying: $-5[-(x-3)-(x+2)]=-5(-x+3-x-2)=-5(-2x+1)=10x-5$

43. Simplifying: $4x-5[3-(x-4)]=4x-5(3-x+4)=4x-5(7-x)=4x-35+5x=9x-35$

45. Simplifying:
$$-(3x-4y)-[(4x+2y)-(3x+7y)]=-(3x-4y)-(4x+2y-3x-7y)$$
$$=-(3x-4y)-(x-5y)$$
$$=-3x+4y-x+5y$$
$$=9y-4x$$

47. Simplifying:
$$4a-\{3a+2[a-5(a+1)+4]\}=4a-[3a+2(a-5a-5+4)]$$
$$=4a-[3a+2(-4a-1)]$$
$$=4a-(3a-8a-2)$$
$$=4a-(-5a-2)$$
$$=4a+5a+2$$
$$=9a+2$$

49. Evaluating when $x=2$: $2(2)^2-3(2)-4=2(4)-3(2)-4=8-6-4=-2$

51. **a.** Evaluating when $x=12$: $P(12)=\frac{3}{2}(12)^2-\frac{3}{4}(12)+1=\frac{3}{2}(144)-\frac{3}{4}(12)+1=216-9+1=208$

   b. Evaluating when $x=-8$: $P(-8)=\frac{3}{2}(-8)^2-\frac{3}{4}(-8)+1=\frac{3}{2}(64)-\frac{3}{4}(-8)+1=96+6+1=103$

53. **a.** Evaluating when $x=4$: $Q(4)=(4)^3-(4)^2+(4)-1=64-16+4-1=51$

   b. Evaluating when $x=-2$: $Q(-2)=(-2)^3-(-2)^2+(-2)-1=-8-4-2-1=-15$

55. **a.** Evaluating when $x=10$: $R(10)=11.5(10)-0.05(10)^2=115-5=110$

   b. Evaluating when $x=-10$: $R(-10)=11.5(-10)-0.05(-10)^2=-115-5=-120$

57. **a.** Evaluating when $x=-4$: $P(-4)=600+1,000(-4)-100(-4)^2=600-4,000-1,600=-5,000$

   b. Evaluating when $x=4$: $P(4)=600+1,000(4)-100(4)^2=600+4,000-1,600=3,000$

59. The amount of caffeine Mary drinks is: $3(43)+54+2(23)=229$ milligrams

61. Substituting $t=3$: $h=-16(3)^2+128(3)=240$ feet   Substituting $t=5$: $h=-16(5)^2+128(5)=240$ feet

63. The weekly profit is given by:
$$P(x)=R(x)-C(x)=(100x-0.5x^2)-(60x+300)=100x-0.5x^2-60x-300=-0.5x^2+40x-300$$
Substituting $x=60$: $P(60)=-0.5(60)^2+40(60)-300=\$300$

65. The weekly profit is given by:
$$P(x)=R(x)-C(x)=(10x-0.002x^2)-(800+6.5x)=10x-0.002x^2-800-6.5x=-0.002x^2+3.5x-800$$
Substituting $x=1,000$: $P(1,000)=-0.002(1,000)^2+3.5(1,000)-800=\$700$

67. The expression is: $6+0.05(x-400)=6+0.05x-20=0.05x-14$

Substituting $x=592$: $0.05(592)-14=\$15.60$

69. The degree is 5. The correct answer is a.

71. Evaluating when $x=-2$: $5(-2)^2-3(-2)-1=5(4)-3(-2)-1=20+6-1=25$. The correct answer is a.

73. Simplifying: $12a^2 + 8ab - 15ab - 10b^2 = 12a^2 - 7ab - 10b^2$

75. Simplifying: $(3x^3 - 15x^2 + 18x) + (2x^2 - 10x + 12) = 3x^3 - 13x^2 + 8x + 12$

77. Simplifying: $5x^2(-4x) = -20x^{2+1} = -20x^3$

79. Simplifying: $5x^2(3x^2) = 15x^{2+2} = 15x^4$

81. Simplifying: $(a^4)^2 = a^{4 \cdot 2} = a^8$

83. Simplifying: $-0.05(130)^2 + 9.5(130) - 200 = -845 + 1,235 - 200 = 190$

5.2 Multiplication of Polynomials

1. Multiplying: $2x(6x^2 - 5x + 4) = 2x \cdot 6x^2 - 2x \cdot 5x + 2x \cdot 4 = 12x^3 - 10x^2 + 8x$

3. Multiplying: $-3a^2(a^3 - 6a^2 + 7) = -3a^2 \cdot a^3 - (-3a^2) \cdot 6a^2 + (-3a^2) \cdot 7 = -3a^5 + 18a^4 - 21a^2$

5. Multiplying: $2a^2b(a^3 - ab + b^3) = 2a^2b \cdot a^3 - 2a^2b \cdot ab + 2a^2b \cdot b^3 = 2a^5b - 2a^3b^2 + 2a^2b^4$

7. Multiplying using the vertical format:

x	-5
x	$+3$
x^2	$-5x$
$+3x$	-15
$x^2 \quad -2x$	-15

The product is $x^2 - 2x - 15$.

9. Multiplying using the vertical format:

$2x^2$	-3
$3x^2$	-5
$6x^4$	$-9x^2$
$-10x^2$	$+15$
$6x^4 \quad -19x^2$	$+15$

The product is $6x^4 - 19x^2 + 15$.

11. Multiplying using the vertical format:

x^2	$+6x$	$+5$
	x	$+3$
x^3	$+6x^2$	$+5x$
	$+3x^2$	$+18x \quad +15$
x^3	$+9x^2$	$+23x \quad +15$

The product is $x^3 + 9x^2 + 23x + 15$.

13. Multiplying using the vertical format:

a^2	$+ab$	$+b^2$
	a	$-b$
a^3	$+a^2b$	$+ab^2$
	$-a^2b$	$-ab^2 \quad -b^3$
a^3		$-b^3$

The product is $a^3 - b^3$.

15. Multiplying using the vertical format:

$4x^2$	$-2xy$	$+y^2$
	$2x$	$+y$
$8x^3$	$-4x^2y$	$+2xy^2$
	$+4x^2y$	$-2xy^2 \quad +y^3$
$8x^3$		$+y^3$

The product is $8x^3 + y^3$.

17. Multiplying using the vertical format:

a^2	$+ab$	$+b^2$
	$2a$	$-3b$
$2a^3$	$+2a^2b$	$+2ab^2$
	$-3a^2b$	$-3ab^2 \quad -3b^3$
$2a^3$	$-a^2b$	$-ab^2 \quad -3b^3$

The product is $2a^3 - a^2b - ab^2 - 3b^3$.

19. Multiplying using FOIL: $(x - 2)(x + 3) = x^2 + 3x - 2x - 6 = x^2 + x - 6$

21. Multiplying using FOIL: $(2a + 3)(3a + 2) = 6a^2 + 4a + 9a + 6 = 6a^2 + 13a + 6$

23. Multiplying using FOIL: $(5 - 3t)(4 + 2t) = 20 + 10t - 12t - 6t^2 = 20 - 2t - 6t^2$

25. Multiplying using FOIL: $(x^3 + 3)(x^3 - 5) = x^6 - 5x^3 + 3x^3 - 15 = x^6 - 2x^3 - 15$

27. Multiplying using FOIL: $(5x - 6y)(4x + 3y) = 20x^2 + 15xy - 24xy - 18y^2 = 20x^2 - 9xy - 18y^2$

29. Multiplying using FOIL: $\left(3t + \dfrac{1}{3}\right)\left(6t - \dfrac{2}{3}\right) = 18t^2 - 2t + 2t - \dfrac{2}{9} = 18t^2 - \dfrac{2}{9}$

31.   **a.**   Simplifying: $p(x) - q(x) = (4x - 3) - (2x + 1) = 4x - 3 - 2x - 1 = 2x - 4$

       b.   Simplifying: $p(x) + q(x) = (4x - 3) + (2x + 1) = 6x - 2$

       c.   Simplifying: $p(x) \cdot q(x) = (4x - 3)(2x + 1) = 8x^2 - 2x - 3$

33.   Finding the product: $(5x + 2y)^2 = (5x)^2 + 2(5x)(2y) + (2y)^2 = 25x^2 + 20xy + 4y^2$

35.   Finding the product: $(5 - 3t^3)^2 = (5)^2 - 2(5)(3t^3) + (3t^3)^2 = 25 - 30t^3 + 9t^6$

37.   Finding the product: $(2a + 3b)(2a - 3b) = (2a)^2 - (3b)^2 = 4a^2 - 9b^2$

39.   Finding the product: $(3r^2 + 7s)(3r^2 - 7s) = (3r^2)^2 - (7s)^2 = 9r^4 - 49s^2$

41.   Finding the product: $\left(y + \dfrac{3}{2}\right)^2 = (y)^2 + 2(y)\left(\dfrac{3}{2}\right) + \left(\dfrac{3}{2}\right)^2 = y^2 + 3y + \dfrac{9}{4}$

43.   Finding the product: $\left(a - \dfrac{1}{2}\right)^2 = (a)^2 - 2(a)\left(\dfrac{1}{2}\right) + \left(\dfrac{1}{2}\right)^2 = a^2 - a + \dfrac{1}{4}$

45.   Finding the product: $\left(x + \dfrac{1}{4}\right)^2 = (x)^2 + 2(x)\left(\dfrac{1}{4}\right) + \left(\dfrac{1}{4}\right)^2 = x^2 + \dfrac{1}{2}x + \dfrac{1}{16}$

47.   Finding the product: $\left(t + \dfrac{1}{3}\right)^2 = (t)^2 + 2(t)\left(\dfrac{1}{3}\right) + \left(\dfrac{1}{3}\right)^2 = t^2 + \dfrac{2}{3}t + \dfrac{1}{9}$

49.   Finding the product: $\left(\dfrac{1}{3}x - \dfrac{2}{5}\right)\left(\dfrac{1}{3}x + \dfrac{2}{5}\right) = \left(\dfrac{1}{3}x\right)^2 - \left(\dfrac{2}{5}\right)^2 = \dfrac{1}{9}x^2 - \dfrac{4}{25}$

51.   Expanding and simplifying:

$$\begin{aligned}
(x - 2)^3 &= (x - 2)(x - 2)^2 \\
&= (x - 2)(x^2 - 4x + 4) \\
&= x^3 - 4x^2 + 4x - 2x^2 + 8x - 8 \\
&= x^3 - 6x^2 + 12x - 8
\end{aligned}$$

53.   Expanding and simplifying:

$$\begin{aligned}
\left(x - \dfrac{1}{2}\right)^3 &= \left(x - \dfrac{1}{2}\right)\left(x - \dfrac{1}{2}\right)^2 \\
&= \left(x - \dfrac{1}{2}\right)\left(x^2 - x + \dfrac{1}{4}\right) \\
&= x^3 - x^2 + \dfrac{1}{4}x - \dfrac{1}{2}x^2 + \dfrac{1}{2}x - \dfrac{1}{8} \\
&= x^3 - \dfrac{3}{2}x^2 + \dfrac{3}{4}x - \dfrac{1}{8}
\end{aligned}$$

55.   Expanding and simplifying:

$$\begin{aligned}
3(x - 1)(x - 2)(x - 3) &= 3(x - 1)(x^2 - 5x + 6) \\
&= 3(x^3 - 5x^2 + 6x - x^2 + 5x - 6) \\
&= 3(x^3 - 6x^2 + 11x - 6) \\
&= 3x^3 - 18x^2 + 33x - 18
\end{aligned}$$

57.   Expanding and simplifying: $(b^2 + 8)(a^2 + 1) = a^2b^2 + b^2 + 8a^2 + 8$

59.   Expanding and simplifying: $(x + 1)^2 + (x + 2)^2 + (x + 3)^2 = x^2 + 2x + 1 + x^2 + 4x + 4 + x^2 + 6x + 9 = 3x^2 + 12x + 14$

61.   Expanding and simplifying: $(2x + 3)^2 - (2x - 3)^2 = (4x^2 + 12x + 9) - (4x^2 - 12x + 9) = 4x^2 + 12x + 9 - 4x^2 + 12x - 9 = 24x$

63.   Simplifying: $(x + 3)^2 - 2(x + 3) - 8 = x^2 + 6x + 9 - 2x - 6 - 8 = x^2 + 4x - 5$

65.   Simplifying: $(2a - 3)^2 - 9(2a - 3) + 20 = 4a^2 - 12a + 9 - 18a + 27 + 20 = 4a^2 - 30a + 56$

67. Simplifying:
$$2(4a+2)^2 - 3(4a+2) - 20 = 2(16a^2+16a+4) - 3(4a+2) - 20$$
$$= 32a^2 + 32a + 8 - 12a - 6 - 20$$
$$= 32a^2 + 20a - 18$$

69. Evaluating when $a = 2$ and $b = 3$:
   a. $a^4 - b^4 = 2^4 - 3^4 = 16 - 81 = -65$
   b. $(a-b)^4 = (2-3)^4 = (-1)^4 = 1$
   c. $(a^2+b^2)(a+b)(a-b) = (2^2+3^2)(2+3)(2-3) = (13)(5)(-1) = -65$

71. Since $R = xp$, substitute $x = 900 - 300p$ to obtain: $R(p) = (900 - 300p)p = 900p - 300p^2$

   To find $R(x)$, we first solve for p:
$$x = 900 - 300p$$
$$300p = 900 - x$$
$$p = 3 - \frac{x}{300}$$

   Now substitute to obtain: $R(x) = x\left(3 - \frac{x}{300}\right) = 3x - \frac{x^2}{300}$

   Substituting $p = \$1.60$: $R(1.60) = 900(1.60) - 300(1.60)^2 = \$672$. The revenue is $672.

73. Since $R = xp$, substitute $x = 350 - 10p$ to obtain: $R(p) = (350 - 10p)p = 350p - 10p^2$

   To find $R(x)$, we first solve for p:
$$x = 350 - 10p$$
$$10p = 350 - x$$
$$p = 35 - \frac{x}{10}$$

   Now substitute to obtain: $R(x) = x\left(35 - \frac{x}{10}\right) = 35x - \frac{x^2}{10}$

   Substituting $x = 65$: $R(65) = 35(65) - \frac{(65)^2}{10} = \$1{,}852.50$. The revenue is $1,852.50.

75. Since $R(x) = 35x - \frac{x^2}{10}$ and $C(x) = 5x + 500$, then:
$$P(x) = R(x) - C(x) = 35x - \frac{x^2}{10} - (5x + 500) = -\frac{x^2}{10} + 30x - 500$$
$$P(60) = -\frac{(60)^2}{10} + 30(60) - 500 = \$940$$

77. An expression for the area of the pathway is: $A = (10+2x)(40+2x) - 400 = 400 + 80x + 20x + 4x^2 - 400 = 4x^2 + 100x$

   Substituting $x = 5$: $A = 4(5)^2 + 100(5) = 100 + 500 = 600$ ft^2

   Substituting $x = 8$: $A = 4(8)^2 + 100(8) = 256 + 800 = 1{,}056$ ft^2

79. The volume of the box is given by: $V = (9-2x)(12-2x)(x)$ in^2

   Substituting $x = 2$: $V = (9 - 2 \cdot 2)(12 - 2 \cdot 2)(2) = (5)(8)(2) = 80$ in^2

81. Expanding the formula:

$$A = 100(1+r)^4$$

$$= 100(1+r)^2(1+r)^2$$

$$= 100(1+2r+r^2)(1+2r+r^2)$$

$$= 100(1+2r+r^2+2r+4r^2+2r^3+r^2+2r^3+r^4)$$

$$= 100(1+4r+6r^2+4r^3+r^4)$$

$$= 100+400r+600r^2+400r^3+100r^4$$

83. Finding the cost in 10 years: $F = 4.00(1+0.08)^{10} = 4(1.08)^{10} \approx \$8.64$

85. Finding the tuition 20 years ago: $F = 5,131(1+0.08)^{-20} = 5,131(1.08)^{-20} \approx \$1,100.85$

Finding the tuition 30 years ago: $F = 5,131(1+0.08)^{-30} = 5,131(1.08)^{-30} \approx \$509.91$

87. Multiplying: $(x+2)(3x^2-4x+5) = 3x^3-4x^2+5x+6x^2-8x+10 = 3x^3+2x^2-3x+10$

The correct answer is b.

89. Finding the product: $(2a-3b)^2 = (2a)^2-2(2a)(3b)+(3b)^2 = 4a^2-12ab+9b^2$. The correct answer is c.

91. Dividing: $\dfrac{4x^4y^3}{-2x^2y} = -2x^{4-2}y^{3-1} = -2x^2y^2$

93. Dividing: $4,628 \div 25 = 185.12$

95. Dividing: $\dfrac{(x-3)^2}{x-3} = x-3$

97. Multiplying: $2x^2(2x-4) = 4x^3-8x^2$

99. Multiplying:

$$(2x-4)(2x^2+4x+5) = 2x(2x^2+4x+5)-4(2x^2+4x+5)$$

$$= 4x^3+8x^2+10x-8x^2-16x-20$$

$$= 4x^3-6x-20$$

101. Subtracting: $(2x^2-7x+9)-(2x^2-4x) = 2x^2-7x+9-2x^2+4x = -3x+9$

5.3 Division of Polynomials

1. Dividing: $\dfrac{4x^3-8x^2+6x}{2x} = \dfrac{4x^3}{2x}-\dfrac{8x^2}{2x}+\dfrac{6x}{2x} = 2x^2-4x+3$

3. Dividing: $\dfrac{10x^4+15x^3-20x^2}{-5x^2} = \dfrac{10x^4}{-5x^2}+\dfrac{15x^3}{-5x^2}-\dfrac{20x^2}{-5x^2} = -2x^2-3x+4$

5. Dividing: $\dfrac{8y^5+10y^3-6y}{4y^3} = \dfrac{8y^5}{4y^3}+\dfrac{10y^3}{4y^3}-\dfrac{6y}{4y^3} = 2y^2+\dfrac{5}{2}-\dfrac{3}{2y^2}$

7. Dividing: $\dfrac{5x^3-8x^2-6x}{-2x^2} = \dfrac{5x^3}{-2x^2}-\dfrac{8x^2}{-2x^2}-\dfrac{6x}{-2x^2} = -\dfrac{5}{2}x+4+\dfrac{3}{x}$

9. Dividing: $\dfrac{28a^3b^5+42a^4b^3}{7a^2b^2} = \dfrac{28a^3b^5}{7a^2b^2}+\dfrac{42a^4b^3}{7a^2b^2} = 4ab^3+6a^2b$

11. Dividing: $\dfrac{10x^3y^2-20x^2y^3-30x^3y^3}{-10x^2y} = \dfrac{10x^3y^2}{-10x^2y}-\dfrac{20x^2y^3}{-10x^2y}-\dfrac{30x^3y^3}{-10x^2y} = -xy+2y^2+3xy^2$

13. Dividing using long division:

$$\begin{array}{r} x-7 \\ x+2\overline{)x^2-5x-7} \\ \underline{x^2+2x} \\ -7x-7 \\ \underline{-7x-14} \\ 7 \end{array}$$

The quotient is $x-7+\dfrac{7}{x+2}$.

15. Dividing using long division:

$$\begin{array}{r} 2x+5 \\ 3x-4\overline{)6x^2+7x-18} \\ \underline{6x^2-8x} \\ 15x-18 \\ \underline{15x-20} \\ 2 \end{array}$$

The quotient is $2x+5+\dfrac{2}{3x-4}$.

17. Finding the quotient using long division:

$$\begin{array}{r} 2x^2-5x+1 \\ x+1\overline{)2x^3-3x^2-4x+5} \\ \underline{2x^3+2x^2} \\ -5x^2-4x \\ \underline{-5x^2-5x} \\ x+5 \\ \underline{x+1} \\ 4 \end{array}$$

The quotient is $2x^2-5x+1+\dfrac{4}{x+1}$.

19. Finding the quotient using long division:

$$\begin{array}{r} y^2-3y-13 \\ 2y-3\overline{)2y^3-9y^2-17y+39} \\ \underline{2y^3-3y^2} \\ -6y^2-17y \\ \underline{-6y^2+9y} \\ -26y+39 \\ \underline{-26y+39} \\ 0 \end{array}$$

The quotient is $y^2-3y-13$.

21. Dividing using long division:

$$\begin{array}{r} x-3 \\ 2x^2-3x+2\overline{)2x^3-9x^2+11x-6} \\ \underline{2x^3-3x^2+\,2x} \\ -6x^2+9x-6 \\ \underline{-6x^2+9x-6} \\ 0 \end{array}$$

The quotient is $x-3$.

23. Dividing using long division:

$$\begin{array}{r} 3y^2+6y+8 \\ 2y-4\overline{)6y^3+0y^2-8y+5} \\ \underline{6y^3-12y^2} \\ 12y^2-8y \\ \underline{12y^2-24y} \\ 16y+5 \\ \underline{16y-32} \\ 37 \end{array}$$

The quotient is $3y^2+6y+8+\dfrac{37}{2y-4}$.

25. Dividing using long division:

$$a-2\overline{\smash{)}a^4+0a^3+0a^2-2a+5}$$ with quotient a^3+2a^2+4a+6

$$
\begin{array}{r}
a^3+2a^2+4a+6 \\
a-2\overline{\smash{)}a^4+0a^3+0a^2-2a+5} \\
\underline{a^4-2a^3} \\
2a^3+0a^2 \\
\underline{2a^3-4a^2} \\
4a^2-2a \\
\underline{4a^2-8a} \\
6a+5 \\
\underline{6a-12} \\
17
\end{array}
$$

The quotient is $a^3+2a^2+4a+6+\dfrac{17}{a-2}$.

27. Dividing using long division:

$$
\begin{array}{r}
y^3+2y^2+4y+8 \\
y-2\overline{\smash{)}y^4+0y^3+0y^2+0y-16} \\
\underline{y^4-2y^3} \\
2y^3+0y^2 \\
\underline{2y^3-4y^2} \\
4y^2+0y \\
\underline{4y^2-8y} \\
8y-16 \\
\underline{8y-16} \\
0
\end{array}
$$

The quotient is y^3+2y^2+4y+8.

29. Finding the quotient using long division:

$$
\begin{array}{r}
x^2-2x+1 \\
x^2+3x+2\overline{\smash{)}x^4+\ x^3-3x^2-\ x+2} \\
\underline{x^4+3x^3+2x^2} \\
-2x^3-5x^2-\ x \\
\underline{-2x^3-6x^2-4x} \\
x^2+3x+2 \\
\underline{x^2+3x+2} \\
0
\end{array}
$$

The quotient is x^2-2x+1.

31. Using synthetic division:

$$
\begin{array}{r|rrr}
-2 & 1 & -5 & 6 \\
   &   & -2 & 14 \\
\hline
   & 1 & -7 & 20
\end{array}
$$

The quotient is $x-7+\dfrac{20}{x+2}$.

33. Using synthetic division:

$$
\begin{array}{r|rrr}
1 & 3 & -4 & 1 \\
  &   & 3 & -1 \\
\hline
  & 3 & -1 & 0
\end{array}
$$

The quotient is $3x-1$.

35. Using synthetic division:

$$
\begin{array}{r|rrrr}
2 & 1 & 2 & 3 & 4 \\
  &   & 2 & 8 & 22 \\
\hline
  & 1 & 4 & 11 & 26
\end{array}
$$

The quotient is $x^2+4x+11+\dfrac{26}{x-2}$.

37. Using synthetic division:

$$
\begin{array}{r|rrrr}
3 & 3 & -1 & 2 & 5 \\
  &   & 9 & 24 & 78 \\
\hline
  & 3 & 8 & 26 & 83
\end{array}
$$

The quotient is $3x^2+8x+26+\dfrac{83}{x-3}$.

39. Using synthetic division:

$$
\begin{array}{r|rrrr}
1 & 2 & 0 & 1 & -3 \\
  &   & 2 & 2 & 3 \\
\hline
  & 2 & 2 & 3 & 0
\end{array}
$$

The quotient is $2x^2+2x+3$.

41. Using synthetic division:

$$
\begin{array}{r|rrrrr}
-4 & 1 & 0 & 2 & 0 & 1 \\
   &   & -4 & 16 & -72 & 288 \\
\hline
   & 1 & -4 & 18 & -72 & 289
\end{array}
$$

The quotient is $x^3-4x^2+18x-72+\dfrac{289}{x+4}$.

43. Using synthetic division:

$$\begin{array}{r|rrrrr} 2 & 1 & -2 & 1 & -3 & -1 & 1 \\ & & 2 & 0 & 2 & -2 & -6 \\ \hline & 1 & 0 & 1 & -1 & -3 & -5 \end{array}$$

The quotient is $x^4 + x^2 - x - 3 - \dfrac{5}{x-2}$.

45. Using synthetic division:

$$\begin{array}{r|rrr} 1 & 1 & 1 & 1 \\ & & 1 & 2 \\ \hline & 1 & 2 & 3 \end{array}$$

The quotient is $x + 2 + \dfrac{3}{x-1}$.

47. Using synthetic division:

$$\begin{array}{r|rrrrr} -1 & 1 & 0 & 0 & 0 & -1 \\ & & -1 & 1 & -1 & 1 \\ \hline & 1 & -1 & 1 & -1 & 0 \end{array}$$

The quotient is $x^3 - x^2 + x - 1$.

49. Using synthetic division:

$$\begin{array}{r|rrrr} 1 & 1 & 0 & 0 & -1 \\ & & 1 & 1 & 1 \\ \hline & 1 & 1 & 1 & 0 \end{array}$$

The quotient is $x^2 + x + 1$.

51. Evaluating the function: $P(-2) = (-2)^2 - 5(-2) - 7 = 4 + 10 - 7 = 7$

The remainder is the same (7).

53. **a.** Completing the table:

x	1	5	10	15	20
$C(x)$	2.15	2.75	3.50	4.25	5.00

b. The average cost function is $\overline{C}(x) = \dfrac{2 + 0.15x}{x} = \dfrac{2}{x} + 0.15$.

c. Completing the table:

x	1	5	10	15	20
$\overline{C}(x)$	2.15	0.55	0.35	0.28	0.25

d. The average cost function decreases.

e. For $C(x)$, the domain is $\{x \mid 1 \le x \le 20\}$ and the range is $\{y \mid 2.15 \le y \le 5.00\}$.

For $\overline{C}(x)$, the domain is $\{x \mid 1 \le x \le 20\}$ and the range is $\{y \mid 0.25 \le y \le 2.15\}$.

55. **a.** Evaluating the total cost:

$$T(100) = 4.95 + 0.07(100) = \$11.95$$
$$T(400) = 4.95 + 0.07(400) = \$32.95$$
$$T(500) = 4.95 + 0.07(500) = \$39.95$$

b. The average cost function is given by: $\overline{T}(m) = \dfrac{4.95 + 0.07m}{m} = \dfrac{4.95}{m} + 0.07$

c. Evaluating the average cost:

$$\overline{T}(100) = \dfrac{4.95}{100} + 0.07 = \$0.1195$$
$$\overline{T}(400) = \dfrac{4.95}{400} + 0.07 \approx \$0.0824$$
$$\overline{T}(500) = \dfrac{4.95}{500} + 0.07 = \$0.0799$$

57. Dividing: $\dfrac{12x^5 - 4x^3 + 10x^2}{2x^2} = \dfrac{12x^5}{2x^2} - \dfrac{4x^3}{2x^2} + \dfrac{10x^2}{2x^2} = 6x^3 - 2x + 5$. The correct answer is c.

59. Using synthetic division:

$$-2\overline{)\begin{array}{ccc} 1 & -1 & 6 \\ & -2 & 6 \\ \hline 1 & -3 & 12 \end{array}}$$

The quotient is $x - 3 + \dfrac{12}{x+2}$. The correct answer is b.

61. Simplifying: $\dfrac{8a^3}{a} = 8a^{3-1} = 8a^2$

63. Simplifying: $\dfrac{-48a}{a} = -48$

65. Simplifying: $\dfrac{16a^5b^4}{8a^2b^3} = 2a^{5-2}b^{4-3} = 2a^3b$

67. Simplifying: $\dfrac{-24a^5b^5}{8a^5b^3} = -3a^{5-5}b^{5-3} = -3b^2$

69. Multiplying: $8a\left(a^2 - a - 6\right) = 8a^3 - 8a^2 - 48a$

71. Multiplying: $(x+y)(5+x) = 5x + x^2 + 5y + xy$

5.4 Greatest Common Factor and Factoring by Grouping

1. Factoring the expression: $10x^3 - 15x^2 = 5x^2\left(2x - 3\right)$

3. Factoring the expression: $9y^6 + 18y^3 = 9y^3\left(y^3 + 2\right)$

5. Factoring the expression: $9a^2b - 6ab^2 = 3ab\left(3a - 2b\right)$

7. Factoring the expression: $21xy^4 + 7x^2y^2 = 7xy^2\left(3y^2 + x\right)$

9. Factoring the expression: $3a^2 - 21a + 33 = 3\left(a^2 - 7a + 11\right)$

11. Factoring the expression: $4x^3 - 16x^2 + 20x = 4x\left(x^2 - 4x + 5\right)$

13. Factoring the expression: $10x^4y^2 + 20x^3y^3 + 30x^2y^4 = 10x^2y^2\left(x^2 + 2xy + 3y^2\right)$

15. Factoring the expression: $-x^2y + xy^2 - x^2y^2 = xy\left(-x + y - xy\right)$

17. Factoring the expression: $4x^3y^2z - 8x^2y^2z^2 + 6xy^2z^3 = 2xy^2z\left(2x^2 - 4xz + 3z^2\right)$

19. Factoring the expression: $20a^2b^2c^2 - 30ab^2c + 25a^2bc^2 = 5abc\left(4abc - 6b + 5ac\right)$

21. Factoring the expression: $5x\left(a - 2b\right) - 3y\left(a - 2b\right) = \left(a - 2b\right)\left(5x - 3y\right)$

23. Factoring the expression: $3x^2\left(x+y\right)^2 - 6y^2\left(x+y\right)^2 = 3\left(x+y\right)^2\left(x^2 - 2y^2\right)$

25. Factoring the expression: $2x^2\left(x+5\right) + 7x\left(x+5\right) + 8\left(x+5\right) = \left(x+5\right)\left(2x^2 + 7x + 8\right)$

27. Factoring by grouping: $3xy + 3y + 2ax + 2a = 3y\left(x+1\right) + 2a\left(x+1\right) = \left(x+1\right)\left(3y + 2a\right)$

29. Factoring by grouping: $x^2y + x + 3xy + 3 = x\left(xy + 1\right) + 3\left(xy + 1\right) = \left(xy + 1\right)\left(x + 3\right)$

31. Factoring by grouping: $3xy^2 - 6y^2 + 4x - 8 = 3y^2\left(x - 2\right) + 4\left(x - 2\right) = \left(x - 2\right)\left(3y^2 + 4\right)$

33. Factoring by grouping: $x^2 - ax - bx + ab = x\left(x - a\right) - b\left(x - a\right) = \left(x - a\right)\left(x - b\right)$

35. Factoring by grouping: $ab + 5a - b - 5 = a\left(b + 5\right) - 1\left(b + 5\right) = \left(b + 5\right)\left(a - 1\right)$

37. Factoring by grouping: $a^4b^2 + a^4 - 5b^2 - 5 = a^4\left(b^2 + 1\right) - 5\left(b^2 + 1\right) = \left(b^2 + 1\right)\left(a^4 - 5\right)$

39. Factoring by grouping: $x^3 + 3x^2 + 4x + 12 = x^2\left(x + 3\right) + 4\left(x + 3\right) = \left(x + 3\right)\left(x^2 + 4\right)$

41. Factoring by grouping: $x^3 + 2x^2 + 25x + 50 = x^2\left(x + 2\right) + 25\left(x + 2\right) = \left(x + 2\right)\left(x^2 + 25\right)$

43. Factoring by grouping: $2x^3 + 3x^2 + 8x + 12 = x^2\left(2x + 3\right) + 4\left(2x + 3\right) = \left(2x + 3\right)\left(x^2 + 4\right)$

45. Factoring by grouping: $4x^3 + 12x^2 + 9x + 27 = 4x^2\left(x + 3\right) + 9\left(x + 3\right) = \left(x + 3\right)\left(4x^2 + 9\right)$

47. It will be $3 \cdot 2 = 6$.

49. Using factoring by grouping: $P + Pr + (P + Pr)r = (P + Pr) + (P + Pr)r = (P + Pr)(1 + r) = P(1 + r)(1 + r) = P(1 + r)^2$

51. Factoring the revenue: $R(x) = 35x - 0.1x^2 = x(35 - 0.1x)$. So the price is $p = 35 - 0.1x$.

Substituting $x = 65$: $p = 35 - 0.1(65) = \$28.50$. The price is \$28.50.

53. Factoring out the greatest common factor: $12x^6y^3 - 18x^4y + 4x^2y^2 = 2x^2y(6x^4y^2 - 9x^2 + 2y)$

The correct answer is b.

55. Factoring out the greatest common factor: $3x^4 - 9x^3y - 18x^2y^2 = 3x^2(x^2 - 3xy - 6y^2)$

57. Factoring out the greatest common factor: $2x^2(x - 3) - 4x(x - 3) - 3(x - 3) = (x - 3)(2x^2 - 4x - 3)$

59. Multiplying using FOIL: $(x + 2)(3x - 1) = 3x^2 - x + 6x - 2 = 3x^2 + 5x - 2$

61. Multiplying using FOIL: $(x - 1)(3x - 2) = 3x^2 - 2x - 3x + 2 = 3x^2 - 5x + 2$

63. Multiplying using FOIL: $(x + 2)(x + 3) = x^2 + 3x + 2x + 6 = x^2 + 5x + 6$

65. Multiplying using FOIL: $(2y + 5)(3y - 7) = 6y^2 - 14y + 15y - 35 = 6y^2 + y - 35$

67. Multiplying using FOIL: $(4 - 3a)(5 - a) = 20 - 4a - 15a + 3a^2 = 20 - 19a + 3a^2$

69. Multiplying using FOIL: $(5 + 2x)(5 - 2x) = 25 - 10x + 10x - 4x^2 = 25 - 4x^2$

71. Completing the table:

Two Numbers	Their Product	Their Sum
a and b	ab	$a + b$
1,–24	–24	–23
–1,24	–24	23
2,–12	–24	–10
–2,12	–24	10
3,–8	–24	–5
–3,8	–24	5
4,–6	–24	–2
–4,6	–24	2

73. The two numbers are 9 and 4.   **75.** The two numbers are 8 and –5.

77. The two numbers are –12 and 4.

5.5 Factoring Trinomials

1. Factoring the trinomial: $x^2 + 7x + 12 = (x + 3)(x + 4)$ **3.** Factoring the trinomial: $x^2 - x - 12 = (x + 3)(x - 4)$

5. Factoring the trinomial: $y^2 + y - 6 = (y + 3)(y - 2)$ **7.** Factoring the trinomial: $16 - 6x - x^2 = (2 - x)(8 + x)$

9. Factoring the trinomial: $12 + 8x + x^2 = (2 + x)(6 + x)$ **11.** Factoring the trinomial: $16 - x^2 = (4 + x)(4 - x)$

13. Factoring the trinomial: $x^2 + 3xy + 2y^2 = (x + 2y)(x + y)$

15. Factoring the trinomial: $a^2 + 3ab - 18b^2 = (a + 6b)(a - 3b)$

17. Factoring the trinomial: $x^2 - 2xa - 48a^2 = (x - 8a)(x + 6a)$

19. Factoring the trinomial: $x^2 - 12xb + 36b^2 = (x - 6b)^2$

21. Factoring the trinomial: $3a^2 - 21a + 30 = 3(a^2 - 7a + 10) = 3(a - 5)(a - 2)$

23. Factoring the trinomial: $4x^3 - 16x^2 - 20x = 4x(x^2 - 4x - 5) = 4x(x - 5)(x + 1)$

25. Factoring the trinomial: $3x^2 - 6xy - 9y^2 = 3(x^2 - 2xy - 3y^2) = 3(x - 3y)(x + y)$

27. Factoring the trinomial: $2a^5 + 4a^4b + 4a^3b^2 = 2a^3\left(a^2 + 2ab + 2b^2\right)$

29. Factoring the trinomial: $10x^4y^2 + 20x^3y^3 - 30x^2y^4 = 10x^2y^2\left(x^2 + 2xy - 3y^2\right) = 10x^2y^2(x+3y)(x-y)$

31. Factoring completely: $2x^2 + 7x - 15 = (2x-3)(x+5)$

33. Factoring completely: $2x^2 + x - 15 = (2x-5)(x+3)$

35. Factoring completely: $2x^2 - 13x + 15 = (2x-3)(x-5)$

37. Factoring completely: $2x^2 - 11x + 15 = (2x-5)(x-3)$

39. The trinomial $2x^2 + 7x + 15$ does not factor (prime).

41. Factoring completely: $2 + 7a + 6a^2 = (2+3a)(1+2a)$

43. Factoring completely: $60y^2 - 15y - 45 = 15\left(4y^2 - y - 3\right) = 15(4y+3)(y-1)$

45. Factoring completely: $6x^4 - x^3 - 2x^2 = x^2\left(6x^2 - x - 2\right) = x^2(3x-2)(2x+1)$

47. Factoring completely: $40r^3 - 120r^2 + 90r = 10r\left(4r^2 - 12r + 9\right) = 10r(2r-3)^2$

49. Factoring completely: $4x^2 - 11xy - 3y^2 = (4x+y)(x-3y)$

51. Factoring completely: $10x^2 - 3xa - 18a^2 = (2x-3a)(5x+6a)$

53. Factoring completely: $18a^2 + 3ab - 28b^2 = (3a+4b)(6a-7b)$

55. Factoring completely: $600 + 800t - 800t^2 = 200\left(3 + 4t - 4t^2\right) = 200(1+2t)(3-2t)$

57. Factoring completely: $9y^4 + 9y^3 - 10y^2 = y^2\left(9y^2 + 9y - 10\right) = y^2(3y-2)(3y+5)$

59. Factoring completely: $24a^2 - 2a^3 - 12a^4 = 2a^2\left(12 - a - 6a^2\right) = 2a^2(3+2a)(4-3a)$

61. Factoring completely: $8x^4y^2 - 47x^3y^3 - 6x^2y^4 = x^2y^2\left(8x^2 - 47xy - 6y^2\right) = x^2y^2(8x+y)(x-6y)$

63. Factoring completely: $20a^4 + 37a^2 + 15 = \left(5a^2+3\right)\left(4a^2+5\right)$

65. Factoring completely: $2 - 4r^2 - 30r^4 = 2\left(1 - 2r^2 - 15r^4\right) = 2\left(1+3r^2\right)\left(1-5r^2\right)$

67. Factoring completely: $2x^2(x+2) + 13x(x+2) + 15(x+2) = (x+2)\left(2x^2+13x+15\right) = (x+2)(2x+3)(x+5)$

69. Factoring completely: $2x^2(x+1) + 7x(x+1) + 6(x+1) = (x+1)\left(2x^2+7x+6\right) = (x+1)(2x+3)(x+2)$

71. Factoring completely: $4x^2(x+6) + 23x(x+6) + 15(x+6) = (x+6)\left(4x^2+23x+15\right) = (x+6)(4x+3)(x+5)$

73. Factoring completely: $10x^2(x+4) - 33x(x+4) - 7(x+4) = (x+4)\left(10x^2-33x-7\right) = (x+4)(5x+1)(2x-7)$

75. Factoring completely: $24x^2(x-6) + 38x(x-6) + 15(x-6) = (x-6)\left(24x^2+38x+15\right) = (x-6)(4x+3)(6x+5)$

77. Factoring completely: $14x^2(3x+4) - 39x(3x+4) + 10(3x+4) = (3x+4)\left(14x^2-39x+10\right) = (3x+4)(2x-5)(7x-2)$

79. Factoring completely: $15x^2(4x-5) - 2x(4x-5) - 24(4x-5) = (4x-5)\left(15x^2-2x-24\right) = (4x-5)(3x-4)(5x+6)$

81. Multiplying out, the polynomial is: $(7x+2y)(7x-2y) = 49x^2 - 4y^2$

83. The polynomial factors as $a^2 - 75a - 2500 = (a+25)(a-100)$, so the other factor is $a-100$.

85. The polynomial factors as $36x^2 + 134x - 40 = (2x+8)(18x-5)$, so the other factor is $18x-5$.

87. The polynomial factors as $63x^2 + 110x + 48 = (7x+6)(9x+8)$, so the other factor is $9x+8$.

89. The polynomial factors as $36x^2 + 43x - 35 = (4x+7)(9x-5)$, so the other factor is $9x-5$.

91. Factoring the right side: $y = 9x^2 + 33x - 12 = 3(3x^2 + 11x - 4) = 3(x + 4)(3x - 1)$

Evaluating when $x = \frac{1}{3}$: $y = 3\left(\frac{1}{3} + 4\right)\left(3 \cdot \frac{1}{3} - 1\right) = 3\left(\frac{13}{3}\right)(0) = 0$

Evaluating when $x = -4$: $y = 3(-4 + 4)(3 \cdot (-4) - 1) = 3(0)(-13) = 0$

Evaluating when $x = 3$: $y = 3(3 + 4)(3 \cdot 3 - 1) = 3(7)(8) = 168$

93. Factoring the trinomial: $12x^2 - x - 6 = (4x - 3)(3x + 2)$. The correct answer is b.

95. Writing as a square: $\frac{4}{9} = \left(\frac{2}{3}\right)^2$

97. Writing as a square: $x^8 = \left(x^4\right)^2$

99. Writing as a square: $81y^4 = \left(9y^2\right)^2$

101. Writing as a cube: $\frac{1}{27} = \left(\frac{1}{3}\right)^3$

103. Writing as a cube: $x^{12} = \left(x^4\right)^3$

105. Writing as a cube: $125y^3 = \left(5y\right)^3$

107. Writing as a cube: $1000x^3 = \left(10x\right)^3$

5.6 Factoring Special Products

1. Factoring the trinomial: $x^2 - 6x + 9 = (x - 3)^2$

3. Factoring the trinomial: $a^2 - 12a + 36 = (a - 6)^2$

5. Factoring the trinomial: $25 - 10t + t^2 = (5 - t)^2$

7. Factoring the trinomial: $\frac{1}{9}x^2 + 2x + 9 = \left(\frac{1}{3}x + 3\right)^2$

9. Factoring the trinomial: $4y^4 - 12y^2 + 9 = \left(2y^2 - 3\right)^2$

11. Factoring the trinomial: $16a^2 + 40ab + 25b^2 = (4a + 5b)^2$

13. Factoring the trinomial: $\frac{1}{25} + \frac{1}{10}t^2 + \frac{1}{16}t^4 = \left(\frac{1}{5} + \frac{1}{4}t^2\right)^2$

15. Factoring the trinomial: $y^2 + 3y + \frac{9}{4} = \left(y + \frac{3}{2}\right)^2$

17. Factoring the trinomial: $a^2 - a + \frac{1}{4} = \left(a - \frac{1}{2}\right)^2$

19. Factoring the trinomial: $x^2 - \frac{1}{2}x + \frac{1}{16} = \left(x - \frac{1}{4}\right)^2$

21. Factoring the trinomial: $t^2 + \frac{2}{3}t + \frac{1}{9} = \left(t + \frac{1}{3}\right)^2$

23. Factoring the trinomial: $16x^2 - 48x + 36 = 4\left(4x^2 - 12x + 9\right) = 4(2x - 3)^2$

25. Factoring the trinomial: $75a^3 + 30a^2 + 3a = 3a\left(25a^2 + 10a + 1\right) = 3a(5a + 1)^2$

27. Factoring the trinomial: $(x + 2)^2 + 6(x + 2) + 9 = (x + 2 + 3)^2 = (x + 5)^2$

29. Factoring: $x^2 - 9 = (x + 3)(x - 3)$

31. Factoring: $49x^2 - 64y^2 = (7x + 8y)(7x - 8y)$

33. Factoring: $4a^2 - \frac{1}{4} = \left(2a + \frac{1}{2}\right)\left(2a - \frac{1}{2}\right)$

35. Factoring: $x^2 - \frac{9}{25} = \left(x + \frac{3}{5}\right)\left(x - \frac{3}{5}\right)$

37. Factoring: $9x^2 - 16y^2 = (3x + 4y)(3x - 4y)$

39. Factoring: $250 - 10t^2 = 10\left(25 - t^2\right) = 10(5 + t)(5 - t)$

41. Factoring: $x^4 - 81 = \left(x^2 + 9\right)\left(x^2 - 9\right) = \left(x^2 + 9\right)(x + 3)(x - 3)$

43. Factoring: $9x^6 - 1 = \left(3x^3 + 1\right)\left(3x^3 - 1\right)$

45. Factoring: $16a^4 - 81 = \left(4a^2 + 9\right)\left(4a^2 - 9\right) = \left(4a^2 + 9\right)(2a + 3)(2a - 3)$

47. Factoring: $\frac{1}{81} - \frac{y^4}{16} = \left(\frac{1}{9} + \frac{y^2}{4}\right)\left(\frac{1}{9} - \frac{y^2}{4}\right) = \left(\frac{1}{9} + \frac{y^2}{4}\right)\left(\frac{1}{3} + \frac{y}{2}\right)\left(\frac{1}{3} - \frac{y}{2}\right)$

49. Factoring: $\dfrac{x^4}{16} - \dfrac{16}{81} = \left(\dfrac{x^2}{4} + \dfrac{4}{9}\right)\left(\dfrac{x^2}{4} - \dfrac{4}{9}\right) = \left(\dfrac{x^2}{4} + \dfrac{4}{9}\right)\left(\dfrac{x}{2} + \dfrac{2}{3}\right)\left(\dfrac{x}{2} - \dfrac{2}{3}\right)$

51. Factoring: $a^4 - \dfrac{81}{256} = \left(a^2 + \dfrac{9}{16}\right)\left(a^2 - \dfrac{9}{16}\right) = \left(a^2 + \dfrac{9}{16}\right)\left(a + \dfrac{3}{4}\right)\left(a - \dfrac{3}{4}\right)$

53. Factoring: $x^6 - y^6 = \left(x^3 + y^3\right)\left(x^3 - y^3\right) = (x+y)(x-y)\left(x^2 - xy + y^2\right)\left(x^2 + xy + y^2\right)$

55. Factoring: $2a^7 - 128a = 2a\left(a^6 - 64\right) = 2a\left(a^3 + 8\right)\left(a^3 - 8\right) = 2a(a+2)(a-2)\left(a^2 - 2a + 4\right)\left(a^2 + 2a + 4\right)$

57. Factoring: $(x-2)^2 - 9 = (x - 2 + 3)(x - 2 - 3) = (x+1)(x-5)$

59. Factoring: $(y+4)^2 - 16 = (y + 4 + 4)(y + 4 - 4) = y(y+8)$

61. Factoring: $x^2 - 10x + 25 - y^2 = (x-5)^2 - y^2 = (x - 5 + y)(x - 5 - y)$

63. Factoring: $a^2 + 8a + 16 - b^2 = (a+4)^2 - b^2 = (a + 4 + b)(a + 4 - b)$

65. Factoring: $x^2 + 2xy + y^2 - a^2 = (x+y)^2 - a^2 = (x + y + a)(x + y - a)$

67. Factoring: $x^3 + 3x^2 - 4x - 12 = x^2(x+3) - 4(x+3) = (x+3)\left(x^2 - 4\right) = (x+3)(x+2)(x-2)$

69. Factoring: $x^3 + 2x^2 - 25x - 50 = x^2(x+2) - 25(x+2) = (x+2)\left(x^2 - 25\right) = (x+2)(x+5)(x-5)$

71. Factoring: $2x^3 + 3x^2 - 8x - 12 = x^2(2x+3) - 4(2x+3) = (2x+3)\left(x^2 - 4\right) = (2x+3)(x+2)(x-2)$

73. Factoring: $4x^3 + 12x^2 - 9x - 27 = 4x^2(x+3) - 9(x+3) = (x+3)\left(4x^2 - 9\right) = (x+3)(2x+3)(2x-3)$

75. Factoring: $(2x-5)^2 - 100 = (2x - 5 - 10)(2x - 5 + 10) = (2x - 15)(2x + 5)$

77. Factoring: $(a-3)^2 - (4b)^2 = (a - 3 - 4b)(a - 3 + 4b)$

79. Factoring: $a^2 - 6a + 9 - 16b^2 = (a-3)^2 - (4b)^2 = (a - 3 - 4b)(a - 3 + 4b)$

81. Factoring: $x^2(x+4) - 6x(x+4) + 9(x+4) = (x+4)\left(x^2 - 6x + 9\right) = (x+4)(x-3)^2$

83. Factoring: $x^3 - y^3 = (x-y)\left(x^2 + xy + y^2\right)$ **85.** Factoring: $a^3 + 8 = (a+2)\left(a^2 - 2a + 4\right)$

87. Factoring: $27 + x^3 = (3+x)\left(9 - 3x + x^2\right)$ **89.** Factoring: $y^3 - 1 = (y-1)\left(y^2 + y + 1\right)$

91. Factoring: $10r^3 - 1{,}250 = 10\left(r^3 - 125\right) = 10(r-5)\left(r^2 + 5r + 25\right)$

93. Factoring: $64 + 27a^3 = (4 + 3a)\left(16 - 12a + 9a^2\right)$ **95.** Factoring: $8x^3 - 27y^3 = (2x - 3y)\left(4x^2 + 6xy + 9y^2\right)$

97. Factoring: $t^3 + \dfrac{1}{27} = \left(t + \dfrac{1}{3}\right)\left(t^2 - \dfrac{1}{3}t + \dfrac{1}{9}\right)$ **99.** Factoring: $27x^3 - \dfrac{1}{27} = \left(3x - \dfrac{1}{3}\right)\left(9x^2 + x + \dfrac{1}{9}\right)$

101. Factoring: $64a^3 + 125b^3 = (4a + 5b)\left(16a^2 - 20ab + 25b^2\right)$

103. Since $9x^2 + 30x + 25 = (3x + 5)^2$ and $9x^2 - 30x + 25 = (3x - 5)^2$, two values of b are $b = 30$ and $b = -30$.

105. Since $25x^2 - 90x + 81 = (5x - 9)^2$, a value of c is $c = 81$.

107. Factoring: $16x^2 - 40x + 25 = (4x - 5)(4x - 5) = (4x - 5)^2$. The correct answer is a.

109. Factoring: $8x^3 - 27 = (2x - 3)\left(4x^2 + 6x + 9\right)$. The correct answer is d.

111. Factoring the greatest common factor: $2ab^5 + 8ab^4 + 2ab^3 = 2ab^3\left(b^2 + 4b + 1\right)$

113. Factoring by grouping: $4x^2 - 6x + 2ax - 3a = 2x(2x - 3) + a(2x - 3) = (2x - 3)(2x + a)$

115. Factoring by grouping: $15ax - 10a + 12x - 8 = 5a(3x - 2) + 4(3x - 2) = (3x - 2)(5a + 4)$

117. Factoring the difference of squares: $x^2 - 4 = (x + 2)(x - 2)$

119. Factoring the difference of squares: $A^2 - 25 = (A+5)(A-5)$

121. Factoring the perfect square trinomial: $x^2 - 6x + 9 = (x-3)^2$

123. Factoring the perfect square trinomial: $x^2 + 8xy + 16y^2 = (x+4y)^2$

125. Factoring: $6a^2 - 11a + 4 = (3a-4)(2a-1)$

127. Factoring: $12x^2 - 32x - 35 = (6x+5)(2x-7)$

129. Factoring the sum of cubes: $x^3 + 8 = (x+2)(x^2 - 2x + 4)$

131. Factoring the difference of cubes: $8x^3 - 27 = (2x-3)(4x^2 + 6x + 9)$

5.7 Factoring: A General Review

1. Factoring: $x^2 - 81 = (x+9)(x-9)$ 　　**3.** Factoring: $x^2 + 2x - 15 = (x-3)(x+5)$

5. Factoring: $x^2(x+2) + 6x(x+2) + 9(x+2) = (x+2)(x^2 + 6x + 9) = (x+2)(x+3)^2$

7. Factoring: $x^2y^2 + 2y^2 + x^2 + 2 = y^2(x^2 + 2) + 1(x^2 + 2) = (x^2 + 2)(y^2 + 1)$

9. Factoring: $2a^3b + 6a^2b + 2ab = 2ab(a^2 + 3a + 1)$ 　　**11.** The polynomial $x^2 + x + 1$ does not factor (prime).

13. Factoring: $12a^2 - 75 = 3(4a^2 - 25) = 3(2a+5)(2a-5)$ 　**15.** Factoring: $9x^2 - 12xy + 4y^2 = (3x-2y)^2$

17. Factoring: $25 - 10t + t^2 = (5-t)^2$ 　　　　　**19.** Factoring: $4x^3 + 16xy^2 = 4x(x^2 + 4y^2)$

21. Factoring: $2y^3 + 20y^2 + 50y = 2y(y^2 + 10y + 25) = 2y(y+5)^2$

23. Factoring: $a^7 + 8a^4b^3 = a^4(a^3 + 8b^3) = a^4(a+2b)(a^2 - 2ab + 4b^2)$

25. Factoring: $t^2 + 6t + 9 - x^2 = (t+3)^2 - x^2 = (t+3+x)(t+3-x)$

27. Factoring: $x^3 + 5x^2 - 9x - 45 = x^2(x+5) - 9(x+5) = (x+5)(x^2 - 9) = (x+5)(x+3)(x-3)$

29. Factoring: $5a^2 + 10ab + 5b^2 = 5(a^2 + 2ab + b^2) = 5(a+b)^2$

31. The polynomial $x^2 + 49$ does not factor (prime).

33. Factoring: $3x^2 + 15xy + 18y^2 = 3(x^2 + 5xy + 6y^2) = 3(x+2y)(x+3y)$

35. Factoring: $9a^2 + 2a + \dfrac{1}{9} = \left(3a + \dfrac{1}{3}\right)^2$

37. Factoring: $x^2(x-3) - 14x(x-3) + 49(x-3) = (x-3)(x^2 - 14x + 49) = (x-3)(x-7)^2$

39. Factoring: $x^2 - 64 = (x+8)(x-8)$

41. Factoring: $8 - 14x - 15x^2 = (2-5x)(4+3x)$

43. Factoring: $49a^7 - 9a^5 = a^5(49a^2 - 9) = a^5(7a+3)(7a-3)$

45. Factoring: $r^2 - \dfrac{1}{25} = \left(r + \dfrac{1}{5}\right)\left(r - \dfrac{1}{5}\right)$

47. The polynomial $49x^2 + 9y^2$ does not factor (prime).

49. Factoring: $100x^2 - 100x - 600 = 100(x^2 - x - 6) = 100(x-3)(x+2)$

51. Factoring: $25a^3 + 20a^2 + 3a = a(25a^2 + 20a + 3) = a(5a+3)(5a+1)$

53. Factoring: $3x^4 - 14x^2 - 5 = (3x^2 + 1)(x^2 - 5)$

55. Factoring: $24a^5b - 3a^2b = 3a^2b(8a^3 - 1) = 3a^2b(2a-1)(4a^2 + 2a + 1)$

57. Factoring: $64 - r^3 = (4 - r)(16 + 4r + r^2)$

59. Factoring: $20x^4 - 45x^2 = 5x^2(4x^2 - 9) = 5x^2(2x + 3)(2x - 3)$

61. Factoring: $400t^2 - 900 = 100(4t^2 - 9) = 100(2t + 3)(2t - 3)$

63. Factoring: $16x^5 - 44x^4 + 30x^3 = 2x^3(8x^2 - 22x + 15) = 2x^3(4x - 5)(2x - 3)$

65. Factoring: $y^6 - 1 = (y^3 + 1)(y^3 - 1) = (y + 1)(y - 1)(y^2 - y + 1)(y^2 + y + 1)$

67. Factoring: $50 - 2a^2 = 2(25 - a^2) = 2(5 + a)(5 - a)$

69. Factoring: $12x^4 y^2 + 36x^3 y^3 + 27x^2 y^4 = 3x^2 y^2(4x^2 + 12xy + 9y^2) = 3x^2 y^2(2x + 3y)^2$

71. Factoring: $x^2 - 4x + 4 - y^2 = (x - 2)^2 - y^2 = (x - 2 + y)(x - 2 - y)$

73. Factoring: $a^2 - \dfrac{4}{3}ab + \dfrac{4}{9}b^2 = \left(a - \dfrac{2}{3}b\right)^2$

75. Factoring: $x^2 - \dfrac{4}{5}xy + \dfrac{4}{25}y^2 = \left(x - \dfrac{2}{5}y\right)^2$

77. Factoring: $a^2 - \dfrac{5}{3}ab + \dfrac{25}{36}b^2 = \left(a - \dfrac{5}{6}b\right)^2$

79. Factoring: $x^2 - \dfrac{8}{5}xy + \dfrac{16}{25}y^2 = \left(x - \dfrac{4}{5}y\right)^2$

81. Factoring: $2x^2(x + 2) - 13x(x + 2) + 15(x + 2) = (x + 2)(2x^2 - 13x + 15) = (x + 2)(2x - 3)(x - 5)$

83. Factoring: $(x - 4)^3 + (x - 4)^4 = (x - 4)^3(1 + x - 4) = (x - 4)^3(x - 3)$

85. Factoring: $2y^3 - 54 = 2(y^3 - 27) = 2(y - 3)(y^2 + 3y + 9)$

87. Factoring: $2a^3 - 128b^3 = 2(a^3 - 64b^3) = 2(a - 4b)(a^2 + 4ab + 16b^2)$

89. Factoring: $2x^3 + 432y^3 = 2(x^3 + 216y^3) = 2(x + 6y)(x^2 - 6xy + 36y^2)$

91. We should always try greatest common factor first. The correct answer is b.

93. Simplifying: $x^2 + (x + 1)^2 = x^2 + x^2 + 2x + 1 = 2x^2 + 2x + 1$

95. Simplifying: $\dfrac{16t^2 - 64t + 48}{16} = \dfrac{16(t^2 - 4t + 3)}{16} = t^2 - 4t + 3$

97. Factoring: $x^2 - 2x - 24 = (x - 6)(x + 4)$

99. Factoring: $2x^3 - 5x^2 - 3x = x(2x^2 - 5x - 3) = x(2x + 1)(x - 3)$

101. Factoring: $x^3 + 2x^2 - 9x - 18 = x^2(x + 2) - 9(x + 2) = (x + 2)(x^2 - 9) = (x + 2)(x + 3)(x - 3)$

103. Factoring: $x^3 + 2x^2 - 5x - 10 = x^2(x + 2) - 5(x + 2) = (x + 2)(x^2 - 5)$

105. Solving the equation:

$$x - 6 = 0$$
$$x = 6$$

107. Solving the equation:

$$2x + 1 = 0$$
$$2x = -1$$
$$x = -\dfrac{1}{2}$$

5.8 Solving Equations by Factoring

1. Solving the equation:
$$x^2 - 5x - 6 = 0$$
$$(x+1)(x-6) = 0$$
$$x = -1, 6$$

3. Solving the equation:
$$3y^2 + 11y - 4 = 0$$
$$(3y-1)(y+4) = 0$$
$$y = -4, \frac{1}{3}$$

5. Solving the equation:
$$60x^2 - 130x + 60 = 0$$
$$10(6x^2 - 13x + 6) = 0$$
$$10(3x-2)(2x-3) = 0$$
$$x = \frac{2}{3}, \frac{3}{2}$$

7. Solving the equation:
$$\frac{1}{10}t^2 - \frac{5}{2} = 0$$
$$10\left(\frac{1}{10}t^2 - \frac{5}{2}\right) = 10(0)$$
$$t^2 - 25 = 0$$
$$(t+5)(t-5) = 0$$
$$t = -5, 5$$

9. Solving the equation:
$$\frac{1}{5}y^2 - 2 = -\frac{3}{10}y$$
$$10\left(\frac{1}{5}y^2 - 2\right) = 10\left(-\frac{3}{10}y\right)$$
$$2y^2 - 20 = -3y$$
$$2y^2 + 3y - 20 = 0$$
$$(y+4)(2y-5) = 0$$
$$y = -4, \frac{5}{2}$$

11. Solving the equation:
$$9x^2 - 12x = 0$$
$$3x(3x-4) = 0$$
$$x = 0, \frac{4}{3}$$

13. Solving the equation:
$$0.02r + 0.01 = 0.15r^2$$
$$2r + 1 = 15r^2$$
$$15r^2 - 2r - 1 = 0$$
$$(5r+1)(3r-1) = 0$$
$$r = -\frac{1}{5}, \frac{1}{3}$$

15. Solving the equation:
$$-100x = 10x^2$$
$$0 = 10x^2 + 100x$$
$$0 = 10x(x+10)$$
$$x = -10, 0$$

17. Solving the equation:
$$(x+6)(x-2) = -7$$
$$x^2 + 4x - 12 = -7$$
$$x^2 + 4x - 5 = 0$$
$$(x+5)(x-1) = 0$$
$$x = -5, 1$$

19. Solving the equation:
$$(y-4)(y+1) = -6$$
$$y^2 - 3y - 4 = -6$$
$$y^2 - 3y + 2 = 0$$
$$(y-2)(y-1) = 0$$
$$y = 1, 2$$

21. Solving the equation:

$$(x+1)^2 = 3x+7$$
$$x^2 + 2x + 1 = 3x + 7$$
$$x^2 - x - 6 = 0$$
$$(x+2)(x-3) = 0$$
$$x = -2, 3$$

23. Solving the equation:

$$(2r+3)(2r-1) = -(3r+1)$$
$$4r^2 + 4r - 3 = -3r - 1$$
$$4r^2 + 7r - 2 = 0$$
$$(r+2)(4r-1) = 0$$
$$r = -2, \frac{1}{4}$$

25. Solving the equation:

$$3x^2 + x = 10$$
$$3x^2 + x - 10 = 0$$
$$(3x-5)(x+2) = 0$$
$$x = -2, \frac{5}{3}$$

27. Solving the equation:

$$12(x+3) + 12(x-3) = 3(x^2 - 9)$$
$$12x + 36 + 12x - 36 = 3x^2 - 27$$
$$24x = 3x^2 - 27$$
$$3x^2 - 24x - 27 = 0$$
$$3(x^2 - 8x - 9) = 0$$
$$3(x-9)(x+1) = 0$$
$$x = -1, 9$$

29. Solving the equation:

$$(y+3)^2 + y^2 = 9$$
$$y^2 + 6y + 9 + y^2 = 9$$
$$2y^2 + 6y = 0$$
$$2y(y+3) = 0$$
$$y = -3, 0$$

31. Solving the equation:

$$(x+3)^2 + 1^2 = 2$$
$$x^2 + 6x + 9 + 1 = 2$$
$$x^2 + 6x + 8 = 0$$
$$(x+4)(x+2) = 0$$
$$x = -4, -2$$

33. Solving the equation:

$$(3x+1)(x-4) = (x-3)(x+3)$$
$$3x^2 - 11x - 4 = x^2 - 9$$
$$2x^2 - 11x + 5 = 0$$
$$(2x-1)(x-5) = 0$$
$$x = \frac{1}{2}, 5$$

35. Solving the equation:

$$(3x-2)(x+1) = (x-4)^2$$
$$3x^2 + x - 2 = x^2 - 8x + 16$$
$$2x^2 + 9x - 18 = 0$$
$$(2x-3)(x+6) = 0$$
$$x = -6, \frac{3}{2}$$

37. Solving the equation:

$$(2x-3)(x-5) = (x+1)(x-3)$$
$$2x^2 - 13x + 15 = x^2 - 2x - 3$$
$$x^2 - 11x + 18 = 0$$
$$(x-2)(x-9) = 0$$
$$x = 2, 9$$

39. Solving the equation:

$$x^3 - 5x^2 + 6x = 0$$
$$x(x^2 - 5x + 6) = 0$$
$$x(x-2)(x-3) = 0$$
$$x = 0, 2, 3$$

41. Solving the equation:

$$100x^4 = 400x^3 + 2100x^2$$
$$100x^4 - 400x^3 - 2100x^2 = 0$$
$$100x^2(x^2 - 4x - 21) = 0$$
$$100x^2(x-7)(x+3) = 0$$
$$x = -3, 0, 7$$

43. Solving the equation:

$$x^3 + 3x^2 - 4x - 12 = 0$$
$$x^2(x+3) - 4(x+3) = 0$$
$$(x+3)(x^2 - 4) = 0$$
$$(x+3)(x+2)(x-2) = 0$$
$$x = -3, -2, 2$$

45. Solving the equation:
$$x^3 + 2x^2 - 25x - 50 = 0$$
$$x^2(x+2) - 25(x+2) = 0$$
$$(x+2)(x^2 - 25) = 0$$
$$(x+2)(x+5)(x-5) = 0$$
$$x = -5, -2, 5$$

47. Solving the equation:
$$9a^3 = 16a$$
$$9a^3 - 16a = 0$$
$$a(9a^2 - 16) = 0$$
$$a(3a+4)(3a-4) = 0$$
$$a = -\frac{4}{3}, 0, \frac{4}{3}$$

49. Solving the equation:
$$2x^3 + 3x^2 - 8x - 12 = 0$$
$$x^2(2x+3) - 4(2x+3) = 0$$
$$(2x+3)(x^2-4) = 0$$
$$(2x+3)(x+2)(x-2) = 0$$
$$x = -2, -\frac{3}{2}, 2$$

51. Solving the equation:
$$4x^3 + 12x^2 - 9x - 27 = 0$$
$$4x^2(x+3) - 9(x+3) = 0$$
$$(x+3)(4x^2-9) = 0$$
$$(x+3)(2x+3)(2x-3) = 0$$
$$x = -3, -\frac{3}{2}, \frac{3}{2}$$

53. a. Solving the equation:
$$8x - 5 = 0$$
$$8x = 5$$
$$x = \frac{5}{8}$$

b. Adding: $(8x-5) + (2x-3) = 10x - 8$

c. Multiplying: $(8x-5)(2x-3) = 16x^2 - 24x - 10x + 15 = 16x^2 - 34x + 15$

d. Solving the equation:
$$16x^2 - 34x + 15 = 0$$
$$(8x-5)(2x-3) = 0$$
$$x = \frac{5}{8}, \frac{3}{2}$$

55. a. Solving the equation:
$$9x - 25 = 0$$
$$9x = 25$$
$$x = \frac{25}{9}$$

b. Solving the equation:
$$9x^2 - 25 = 0$$
$$(3x+5)(3x-5) = 0$$
$$x = -\frac{5}{3}, \frac{5}{3}$$

c. Solving the equation:
$$9x^2 - 25 = 56$$
$$9x^2 - 81 = 0$$
$$9(x+3)(x-3) = 0$$
$$x = -3, 3$$

d. Solving the equation:
$$9x^2 - 25 = 30x - 50$$
$$9x^2 - 30x + 25 = 0$$
$$(3x-5)^2 = 0$$
$$3x - 5 = 0$$
$$3x = 5$$
$$x = \frac{5}{3}$$

57. Solving $f(x) = 0$:

$$\left(x + \frac{3}{2}\right)^2 = 0$$

$$x + \frac{3}{2} = 0$$

$$x = -\frac{3}{2}$$

59. Solving $f(x) = 0$:

$$(x-3)^2 - 25 = 0$$

$$x^2 - 6x + 9 - 25 = 0$$

$$x^2 - 6x - 16 = 0$$

$$(x+2)(x-8) = 0$$

$$x = -2, 8$$

61. Solving $f(x) = g(x)$:

$$x^2 + 6x + 3 = -6$$

$$x^2 + 6x + 9 = 0$$

$$(x+3)^2 = 0$$

$$x + 3 = 0$$

$$x = -3$$

63. Solving $f(x) = g(x)$:

$$x^2 + 6x + 3 = 10$$

$$x^2 + 6x - 7 = 0$$

$$(x+7)(x-1) = 0$$

$$x = -7, 1$$

65. Solving $h(x) = f(x)$:

$$x^2 - 5x = 0$$

$$x(x-5) = 0$$

$$x = 0, 5$$

67. Solving $h(x) = f(x)$:

$$x^2 - 5x = 2x + 8$$

$$x^2 - 7x - 8 = 0$$

$$(x-8)(x+1) = 0$$

$$x = -1, 8$$

69. Solving $f(x) = x$:

$$x^2 = x$$

$$x^2 - x = 0$$

$$x(x-1) = 0$$

$$x = 0, 1$$

71. Solving $f(x) = x$:

$$\frac{1}{3}x + 1 = x$$

$$x + 3 = 3x$$

$$2x = 3$$

$$x = \frac{3}{2}$$

73. Let x and $x + 2$ represent the two integers. The equation is:

$$x(x+2) = 99$$

$$x^2 + 2x = 99$$

$$x^2 + 2x - 99 = 0$$

$$(x+11)(x-9) = 0$$

$$x = -11, 9$$

$$x + 2 = -9, 11$$

The two integers are either –11 and –9, or 9 and 11.

75. Let x and $14 - x$ represent the two numbers. The equation is:

$$x(14-x) = 48$$

$$14x - x^2 = 48$$

$$0 = x^2 - 14x + 48$$

$$0 = (x-8)(x-6)$$

$$x = 8, 6$$

$$14 - x = 6, 8$$

The two numbers are 6 and 8.

77. Let x and $x + 2$ represent the two integers. The equation is:

$$x(x+2) = 5(x+x+2)-10$$
$$x(x+2) = 5(2x+2)-10$$
$$x^2 + 2x = 10x + 10 - 10$$
$$x^2 - 8x = 0$$
$$x(x-8) = 0$$
$$x = 8 \quad (x = 0 \text{ is impossible})$$
$$x + 2 = 10$$

The dimensions are 8 and 10.

79. Let x and $x + 2$ represent the two integers. The equation is:

$$x(x+2) = 4(x+x+2)-1$$
$$x(x+2) = 4(2x+2)-1$$
$$x^2 + 2x = 8x + 8 - 1$$
$$x^2 + 2x = 8x + 7$$
$$x^2 - 6x - 7 = 0$$
$$(x+1)(x-7) = 0$$
$$x = 7 \quad (x = -1 \text{ is impossible})$$
$$x + 2 = 9$$

The two integers are 7 and 9.

81. Solving the equation:

$$(2x+1)(4x-2) = 126$$
$$8x^2 - 2 = 126$$
$$8x^2 - 128 = 0$$
$$x^2 - 16 = 0$$
$$(x+4)(x-4) = 0$$
$$x = 4 \quad (x = -4 \text{ is impossible})$$
$$l = 4(4)-2 = 14$$
$$w = 2(4)+1 = 9$$

The length is 14 cm and the width is 9 cm.

83. Solving the equation:

$$\frac{1}{2}(2x)(3x+1) = 80$$
$$3x^2 + x = 80$$
$$3x^2 + x - 80 = 0$$
$$(3x+16)(x-5) = 0$$
$$x = 5 \quad \left(x = -\frac{16}{3} \text{ is impossible}\right)$$
$$b = 3(5)+1 = 16$$
$$h = 2(5) = 10$$

The base is 16 m and the height is 10 m.

85. Solving the equation:

$$\frac{1}{2}(2x+4)(x+4)=63$$
$$x^2+6x+8=63$$
$$x^2+6x-55=0$$
$$(x+11)(x-5)=0$$
$$x=5 \quad (x=-11 \text{ is impossible})$$
$$b=5+4=9$$
$$h=2(5)+4=14$$

The base is 9 in. and the height is 14 in.

87. Using the Pythagorean theorem:

$$(2x+2)^2+x^2=(3x-2)^2$$
$$4x^2+8x+4+x^2=9x^2-12x+4$$
$$5x^2+8x+4=9x^2-12x+4$$
$$4x^2-20x=0$$
$$4x(x-5)=0$$
$$x=5 \quad (x=0 \text{ is impossible})$$

89. Let $x, x+2$, and $x+4$ represent the three sides. Using the Pythagorean theorem:

$$x^2+(x+2)^2=(x+4)^2$$
$$x^2+x^2+4x+4=x^2+8x+16$$
$$2x^2+4x+4=x^2+8x+16$$
$$x^2-4x-12=0$$
$$(x-6)(x+2)=0$$
$$x=6 \quad (x=-2 \text{ is impossible})$$

The lengths of the three sides are $6, 8$, and 10.

91. Let w represent the width and $3w + 2$ represent the length. Using the area formula:

$$w(3w+2)=16$$
$$3w^2+2w=16$$
$$3w^2+2w-16=0$$
$$(3w+8)(w-2)=0$$
$$w=2 \quad (w=-\frac{8}{3} \text{ is impossible})$$
$$3w+2=8$$

The dimensions are 2 meters by 8 meters.

93. Let h represent the height and $4h + 2$ represent the base. Using the area formula:

$$\frac{1}{2}(4h+2)(h) = 36$$

$$4h^2 + 2h = 72$$

$$4h^2 + 2h - 72 = 0$$

$$2(2h^2 + h - 36) = 0$$

$$2(2h+9)(h-4) = 0$$

$$h = 4 \quad (h = -\frac{9}{2} \text{ is impossible})$$

$$4h + 2 = 18$$

The base is 18 cm and the height is 4 cm.

95. Let w represent the width of the lawn. The dimensions of the large rectangle (garden plus lawn) are $40 + 2w$ by $35 + 2w$. Solving the equation:

$$(40+2w)(35+2w) - (40)(35) = 316$$

$$1,400 + 150w + 4w^2 - 1,400 = 316$$

$$4w^2 + 150w - 316 = 0$$

$$2w^2 + 75w - 158 = 0$$

$$(2w+79)(w-2) = 0$$

$$w = 2 \quad \left(w = -\frac{79}{2} \text{ is impossible}\right)$$

The width of the lawn is 2 yards.

97. The area of the path is the difference in the two areas: $2,975 - (75)(35) = 2,975 - 2,625 = 350 \text{ ft}^2$

99. Let x and $2x$ represent the widths of the path. The dimensions of the large rectangle (tennis court plus path) are $78 + 4x$ by $36 + 2x$. Solving the equation:

$$(78+4x)(36+2x) = 7,560$$

$$2,808 + 300x + 8x^2 = 7,560$$

$$8x^2 + 300x - 4,752 = 0$$

$$2x^2 + 75x - 1,188 = 0$$

$$(2x+99)(x-12) = 0$$

$$x = 12 \quad \left(x = -\frac{99}{2} \text{ is impossible}\right)$$

The width of the path is 12 feet.

101. Let x and $2x$ represent the widths of the margin. The dimensions of the small rectangle (page minus margins) are $10 - 3x$ by $7 - 3x$. Solving the equation:

$$70 - (10-3x)(7-3x) = 23.25$$

$$70 - (70 - 51x + 9x^2) = 23.25$$

$$51x - 9x^2 = 23.25$$

$$9x^2 - 51x + 23.25 = 0$$

$$900x^2 - 5,100x + 2,325 = 0$$

$$12x^2 - 68x + 31 = 0$$

$$(6x-31)(2x-1) = 0$$

$$x = \frac{1}{2} \quad \left(x = \frac{31}{6} \approx 5.2 \text{ is too large}\right)$$

The width of the left margin is 0.5 inches.

103. Substituting $v = 48$ and $h = 32$:
$$h = vt - 16t^2$$
$$32 = 48t - 16t^2$$
$$0 = -16t^2 + 48t - 32$$
$$0 = -16\left(t^2 - 3t + 2\right)$$
$$0 = -16(t - 1)(t - 2)$$
$$t = 1, 2$$

It will reach a height of 32 feet after 1 sec and 2 sec.

105. Substituting $v = 24$ and $h = 0$:
$$h = vt - 16t^2$$
$$0 = 24t - 16t^2$$
$$0 = -16t^2 + 24t$$
$$0 = -8t(2t - 3)$$
$$t = 0, \frac{3}{2}$$

It will be on the ground after 0 sec and $\frac{3}{2}$ sec.

107. Substituting $h = 192$:
$$192 = 96 + 80t - 16t^2$$
$$0 = -16t^2 + 80t - 96$$
$$0 = -16\left(t^2 - 5t + 6\right)$$
$$0 = -16(t - 2)(t - 3)$$
$$t = 2, 3$$

The bullet will be 192 feet in the air after 2 sec and 3 sec.

109. Solving the equation:
$$x^2 - x - 12 = 0$$
$$(x + 3)(x - 4) = 0$$
$$x = -3, 4$$

The correct answer is a.

111. Solving the equation:
$$2x^3 + x^2 - 18x - 9 = 0$$
$$x^2(2x + 1) - 9(2x + 1) = 0$$
$$(2x + 1)\left(x^2 - 9\right) = 0$$
$$(2x + 1)(x + 3)(x - 3) = 0$$
$$x = -3, -\frac{1}{2}, 3$$

The correct answer is c.

113. Multiply the second equation by 5:
$$2x - 5y = -8$$
$$15x + 5y = 25$$
Adding yields:
$$17x = 17$$
$$x = 1$$
Substituting to find y:
$$3 + y = 5$$
$$y = 2$$
The solution is $(1, 2)$.

115. To clear each equation of fractions, multiply the first equation by 6 and the second equation by 20:
$$2x - y = 18$$
$$-4x + 5y = 0$$
Multiply the first equation by 2:
$$4x - 2y = 36$$
$$-4x + 5y = 0$$
Adding yields:
$$3y = 36$$
$$y = 12$$
Substituting to find x:
$$2x - 12 = 18$$
$$2x = 30$$
$$x = 15$$
The solution is $(15, 12)$.

117. Graphing the solution set:

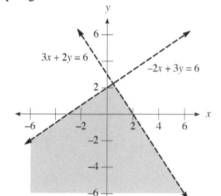

119. Graphing the solution set:

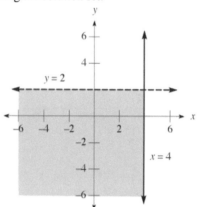

Chapter 5 Test

1. Simplifying: $\left(\dfrac{6}{5}x^3 - 2x - \dfrac{3}{5}\right) - \left(\dfrac{6}{5}x^2 - \dfrac{2}{5}x + \dfrac{3}{5}\right) = \dfrac{6}{5}x^3 - 2x - \dfrac{3}{5} - \dfrac{6}{5}x^2 + \dfrac{2}{5}x - \dfrac{3}{5} = \dfrac{6}{5}x^3 - \dfrac{6}{5}x^2 - \dfrac{8}{5}x - \dfrac{6}{5}$

2. Simplifying: $5 - 7\big[9(2x+1) - 16x\big] = 5 - 7(18x + 9 - 16x) = 5 - 7(2x + 9) = 5 - 14x - 63 = -14x - 58$

3. The revenue is given by: $R(x) = xp = x(36 - 0.3x) = 36x - 0.3x^2$

4. The profit is given by: $P(x) = R(x) - C(x) = (36x - 0.3x^2) - (4x + 50) = 36x - 0.3x^2 - 4x - 50 = -0.3x^2 + 32x - 50$

5. Substituting $x = 100$ into the revenue equation: $R(100) = 36(100) - 0.3(100)^2 = 3{,}600 - 3{,}000 = \$600$.
The revenue is $600.

6. Substituting $x = 100$ into the cost equation: $C(100) = 4(100) + 50 = 400 + 50 = \$450$. The cost is $450.

7. Substituting $x = 100$ into the profit equation: $P(100) = -0.3(100)^2 + 32(100) - 50 = -3{,}000 + 3{,}200 - 50 = \$150$
The profit is $150. Note that this also could have been found by subtracting the answers from problems 5 and 6.

8. Multiplying: $(x + 7)(-5x + 4) = -5x^2 + 4x - 35x + 28 = -5x^2 - 31x + 28$

9. Multiplying: $(3x - 2)(2x^2 + 6x - 5) = 6x^3 + 18x^2 - 15x - 4x^2 - 12x + 10 = 6x^3 + 14x^2 - 27x + 10$

10. Multiplying: $(3a^4 - 7)^2 = (3a^4)^2 - 2(3a^4)(7) + (7)^2 = 9a^8 - 42a^4 + 49$

11. Multiplying: $(2x + 3)(2x - 3) = (2x)^2 - (3)^2 = 4x^2 - 9$

12. Multiplying: $x(x-7)(3x+4) = x(3x^2 - 17x - 28) = 3x^3 - 17x^2 - 28x$

13. Multiplying: $\left(2x - \dfrac{1}{7}\right)\left(7x + \dfrac{1}{2}\right) = 14x^2 + x - x - \dfrac{1}{14} = 14x^2 - \dfrac{1}{14}$

14. Dividing: $\dfrac{24x^3y + 12x^2y^2 - 16xy^3}{4xy} = \dfrac{24x^3y}{4xy} + \dfrac{12x^2y^2}{4xy} - \dfrac{16xy^3}{4xy} = 6x^2 + 3xy - 4y^2$

15. Dividing using long division:

$$
\begin{array}{r}
x^2 - 4x - 2 \\
2x-1\overline{\smash{\big)}\,2x^3 - 9x^2 + 0x + 10} \\
\underline{2x^3 - x^2} \\
-8x^2 + 0x \\
\underline{-8x^2 + 4x} \\
-4x + 10 \\
\underline{-4x + 2} \\
8
\end{array}
$$

The quotient is $x^2 - 4x - 2 + \dfrac{8}{2x-1}$.

16. Using synthetic division:

$$
\begin{array}{r|rrrr}
-5 & 1 & 2 & -25 & -50 \\
   &   & -5 & 15 & 50 \\
\hline
   & 1 & -3 & -10 & 0
\end{array}
$$

The quotient is $x^2 - 3x - 10$.

17. Using synthetic division:

$$
\begin{array}{r|rrrr}
1 & 1 & 0 & 0 & 16 \\
  &   & 1 & 1 & 1 \\
\hline
  & 1 & 1 & 1 & 17
\end{array}
$$

The quotient is $y^2 + y + 1 + \dfrac{17}{y-1}$.

18. Factoring: $x^2 - 6x + 5 = (x-5)(x-1)$

19. Factoring: $15x^4 + 33x^2 - 36 = 3(5x^4 + 11x^2 - 12) = 3(5x^2 - 4)(x^2 + 3)$

20. Factoring: $81x^4 - 16y^4 = (9x^2 + 4y^2)(9x^2 - 4y^2) = (9x^2 + 4y^2)(3x + 2y)(3x - 2y)$

21. Factoring: $6ax - ay + 18b^2x - 3b^2y = a(6x - y) + 3b^2(6x - y) = (6x - y)(a + 3b^2)$

22. Factoring: $y^3 - \dfrac{1}{27} = y^3 - \left(\dfrac{1}{3}\right)^3 = \left(y - \dfrac{1}{3}\right)\left(y^2 + \dfrac{1}{3}y + \dfrac{1}{9}\right)$

23. Factoring: $3x^4y^4 + 15x^3y^5 - 72x^2y^6 = 3x^2y^4(x^2 + 5xy - 24y^2) = 3x^2y^4(x + 8y)(x - 3y)$

24. Factoring: $a^2 - 2ab - 36 + b^2 = a^2 - 2ab + b^2 - 36 = (a-b)^2 - 6^2 = (a - b + 6)(a - b - 6)$

25. Factoring: $16 - x^4 = (4 + x^2)(4 - x^2) = (4 + x^2)(2 + x)(2 - x)$

26. Solving the equation:

$$\frac{1}{4}x^2 = -\frac{21}{8}x - \frac{5}{4}$$
$$8\left(\frac{1}{4}x^2\right) = 8\left(-\frac{21}{8}x - \frac{5}{4}\right)$$
$$2x^2 = -21x - 10$$
$$2x^2 + 21x + 10 = 0$$
$$(2x + 1)(x + 10) = 0$$
$$x = -10, -\frac{1}{2}$$

27. Solving the equation:

$$243x^3 = 81x^4$$
$$243x^3 - 81x^4 = 0$$
$$81x^3(3 - x) = 0$$
$$x = 0, 3$$

28. Solving the equation:
$$(x+5)(x-2) = 8$$
$$x^2 + 3x - 10 = 8$$
$$x^2 + 3x - 18 = 0$$
$$(x+6)(x-3) = 0$$
$$x = -6, 3$$

29. Solving the equation:
$$x^3 + 5x^2 - 9x - 45 = 0$$
$$x^2(x+5) - 9(x+5) = 0$$
$$(x+5)(x^2 - 9) = 0$$
$$(x+5)(x+3)(x-3) = 0$$
$$x = -5, -3, 3$$

30. Setting $f(x) = g(x)$:
$$x^2 - 2x - 15 = 0$$
$$(x-5)(x+3) = 0$$
$$x = -3, 5$$

31. Setting $f(x) = g(x)$:
$$x^2 - 2x - 15 = 5 - 3x$$
$$x^2 + x - 20 = 0$$
$$(x+5)(x-4) = 0$$
$$x = -5, 4$$

32. Using the Pythagorean theorem:
$$(2x)^2 + 8^2 = (3x+1)^2$$
$$4x^2 + 64 = 9x^2 + 6x + 1$$
$$5x^2 + 6x - 63 = 0$$
$$(5x+21)(x-3) = 0$$
$$x = 3 \qquad \left(x = -\frac{21}{5} \text{ is impossible}\right)$$

33. Using the area formula:
$$\frac{1}{2}(2x+6)\left(\frac{x}{2}-1\right) = 12$$
$$(x+3)\left(\frac{x}{2}-1\right) = 12$$
$$\frac{1}{2}x^2 + \frac{1}{2}x - 3 = 12$$
$$\frac{1}{2}x^2 + \frac{1}{2}x - 15 = 0$$
$$x^2 + x - 30 = 0$$
$$(x+6)(x-5) = 0$$
$$x = 5 \text{ in.} \qquad (x = -6 \text{ is impossible})$$

34. Using the area formula:
$$x(x-4) = 12$$
$$x^2 - 4x = 12$$
$$x^2 - 4x - 12 = 0$$
$$(x-6)(x+2) = 0$$
$$x = 6 \text{ cm} \qquad (x = -2 \text{ is impossible})$$

35. Setting $h = 0$ in the equation:
$$64t - 16t^2 = 0$$
$$16t(4-t) = 0$$
$$t = 0, 4$$
The object is on the ground at 0 and 4 seconds.

Chapter 6
Rational Expressions and Rational Functions

6.1 Evaluating and Reducing Rational Expressions

1. Evaluating if $x = -2$: $\dfrac{-2-3}{-2+1} = \dfrac{-5}{-1} = 5$ Evaluating if $x = 3$: $\dfrac{3-3}{3+1} = \dfrac{0}{4} = 0$

3. Evaluating if $x = -2$: $\dfrac{-2}{(-2)^2 - 5} = \dfrac{-2}{4-5} = \dfrac{-2}{-1} = 2$ Evaluating if $x = 3$: $\dfrac{3}{(3)^2 - 5} = \dfrac{3}{9-5} = \dfrac{3}{4}$

5. Evaluating if $x = 2$ and $y = -1$: $\dfrac{(2)^2 - (2)(-1)}{-1 - 2(2)} = \dfrac{4+2}{-1-4} = -\dfrac{6}{5}$

7. The expression is undefined if $x = -2$.

9. The expression is undefined if $x = 0$.

11. The denominator factors as $(x+2)(x-2)$, so the expression is undefined if $x = -2, 2$.

13. The denominator factors as $(x+2)(x-5)$, so the expression is undefined if $x = -2, 5$.

15. The denominator factors as $(x-1)(x-2)$, so the expression is undefined if $x = 1, 2$.

17. Since the denominator is never equal to 0, the expression is defined for all real numbers.

19. Reducing to lowest terms: $\dfrac{x^2 - 16}{6x + 24} = \dfrac{(x+4)(x-4)}{6(x+4)} = \dfrac{x-4}{6}$

21. Reducing to lowest terms: $\dfrac{a^4 - 81}{a-3} = \dfrac{(a^2 + 9)(a^2 - 9)}{a-3} = \dfrac{(a^2 + 9)(a+3)(a-3)}{a-3} = (a^2 + 9)(a+3)$

23. Reducing to lowest terms: $\dfrac{20y^2 - 45}{10y^2 - 5y - 15} = \dfrac{5(4y^2 - 9)}{5(2y^2 - y - 3)} = \dfrac{5(2y+3)(2y-3)}{5(2y-3)(y+1)} = \dfrac{2y+3}{y+1}$

25. Reducing to lowest terms: $\dfrac{12y - 2xy - 2x^2 y}{6y - 4xy - 2x^2 y} = \dfrac{2y(6 - x - x^2)}{2y(3 - 2x - x^2)} = \dfrac{2y(3+x)(2-x)}{2y(3+x)(1-x)} = \dfrac{2-x}{1-x} = \dfrac{x-2}{x-1}$

27. Reducing to lowest terms: $\dfrac{(x-3)^2 (x+2)}{(x+2)^2 (x-3)} = \dfrac{x-3}{x+2}$

29. Reducing to lowest terms: $\dfrac{x^3 + 1}{x^2 - 1} = \dfrac{(x+1)(x^2 - x + 1)}{(x+1)(x-1)} = \dfrac{x^2 - x + 1}{x-1}$

31. Reducing to lowest terms: $\dfrac{4am - 4an}{3n - 3m} = \dfrac{4a(m-n)}{3(n-m)} = \dfrac{-4a}{3}$

33. Reducing to lowest terms: $\dfrac{ab - a + b - 1}{ab + a + b + 1} = \dfrac{a(b-1) + 1(b-1)}{a(b+1) + 1(b+1)} = \dfrac{(b-1)(a+1)}{(b+1)(a+1)} = \dfrac{b-1}{b+1}$

35. Reducing to lowest terms: $\dfrac{21x^2-23x+6}{21x^2+x-10}=\dfrac{(7x-3)(3x-2)}{(7x+5)(3x-2)}=\dfrac{7x-3}{7x+5}$

37. Reducing to lowest terms: $\dfrac{8x^2-6x-9}{8x^2-18x+9}=\dfrac{(4x+3)(2x-3)}{(4x-3)(2x-3)}=\dfrac{4x+3}{4x-3}$

39. Reducing to lowest terms: $\dfrac{4x^2+29x+45}{8x^2-10x-63}=\dfrac{(x+5)(4x+9)}{(2x-7)(4x+9)}=\dfrac{x+5}{2x-7}$

41. Reducing to lowest terms: $\dfrac{a^3+b^3}{a^2-b^2}=\dfrac{(a+b)(a^2-ab+b^2)}{(a+b)(a-b)}=\dfrac{a^2-ab+b^2}{a-b}$

43. Reducing to lowest terms: $\dfrac{8x^4-8x}{4x^4+4x^3+4x^2}=\dfrac{8x(x^3-1)}{4x^2(x^2+x+1)}=\dfrac{8x(x-1)(x^2+x+1)}{4x^2(x^2+x+1)}=\dfrac{2(x-1)}{x}=\dfrac{2x-2}{x}$

45. Reducing to lowest terms: $\dfrac{ax+2x+3a+6}{ay+2y-4a-8}=\dfrac{x(a+2)+3(a+2)}{y(a+2)-4(a+2)}=\dfrac{(a+2)(x+3)}{(a+2)(y-4)}=\dfrac{x+3}{y-4}$

47. Reducing to lowest terms: $\dfrac{x^3+3x^2-4x-12}{x^2+x-6}=\dfrac{x^2(x+3)-4(x+3)}{(x+3)(x-2)}=\dfrac{(x+3)(x^2-4)}{(x+3)(x-2)}=\dfrac{(x+3)(x+2)(x-2)}{(x+3)(x-2)}=x+2$

49. Reducing to lowest terms: $\dfrac{x^3-8}{x^2-4}=\dfrac{(x-2)(x^2+2x+4)}{(x-2)(x+2)}=\dfrac{x^2+2x+4}{x+2}$

51. Reducing to lowest terms: $\dfrac{8x^3-27}{4x^2-9}=\dfrac{(2x-3)(4x^2+6x+9)}{(2x-3)(2x+3)}=\dfrac{4x^2+6x+9}{2x+3}$

53. Reducing to lowest terms: $\dfrac{x+7}{7+x}=\dfrac{x+7}{x+7}=1$

55. This expression does not reduce.

57. Reducing to lowest terms: $\dfrac{x-4}{4-x}=\dfrac{x-4}{-1(x-4)}=-1$

59. Reducing to lowest terms: $\dfrac{y^2-36}{6-y}=\dfrac{(y+6)(y-6)}{-1(y-6)}=-(y+6)=-y-6$

61. Reducing to lowest terms: $\dfrac{1-9a^2}{9a^2-6a+1}=\dfrac{-1(9a^2-1)}{(3a-1)^2}=\dfrac{-1(3a+1)(3a-1)}{(3a-1)^2}=-\dfrac{3a+1}{3a-1}$

63. Reducing to lowest terms: $\dfrac{x^2-7x+12}{6+x-x^2}=\dfrac{x^2-7x+12}{-1(x^2-x-6)}=\dfrac{(x-3)(x-4)}{-(x-3)(x+2)}=-\dfrac{x-4}{x+2}$

Note: Your version of the problem may have the wrong numerator printed, in which case the fraction does not simplify.

65. Reducing to lowest terms: $\dfrac{(3x-5)-(3a-5)}{x-a}=\dfrac{3x-3a}{x-a}=\dfrac{3(x-a)}{x-a}=3$

67. Reducing to lowest terms: $\dfrac{(x^2-4)-(a^2-4)}{x-a}=\dfrac{x^2-a^2}{x-a}=\dfrac{(x+a)(x-a)}{x-a}=x+a$

69. Reducing to lowest terms: $\dfrac{x^2-x-6}{x-3}=\dfrac{(x+2)(x-3)}{x-3}=x+2$

71. Reducing to lowest terms: $\dfrac{2a^2-3a-9}{2a+3}=\dfrac{(2a+3)(a-3)}{2a+3}=a-3$

73. Reducing to lowest terms: $\dfrac{x^3+8}{x+2}=\dfrac{(x+2)(x^2-2x+4)}{x+2}=x^2-2x+4$

75. **a.** Evaluating if $x = 3$: $\dfrac{2(3)-2}{(3)^2-3} = \dfrac{6-2}{9-3} = \dfrac{4}{6} = \dfrac{2}{3}$

   b. Reducing to lowest terms: $\dfrac{2x-2}{x^2-x} = \dfrac{2(x-1)}{x(x-1)} = \dfrac{2}{x}$

   c. The denominator factors as $x(x-1)$, so the expression is undefined if $x = 0, 1$.

   d. Evaluating if $x = -1$: $\dfrac{2(-1)-2}{(-1)^2-(-1)} = \dfrac{-2-2}{1+1} = \dfrac{-4}{2} = -2$

77. Evaluating if $x = 1$: $\dfrac{(1)^2-4}{(1)^2-2(1)} = \dfrac{1-4}{1-2} = \dfrac{-3}{-1} = 3$. The correct answer is c.

79. Reducing to lowest terms: $\dfrac{x^2-4}{x^2-2x} = \dfrac{(x+2)(x-2)}{x(x-2)} = \dfrac{x+2}{x}$. The correct answer is d.

81. Multiplying: $\dfrac{6}{7} \cdot \dfrac{14}{18} = \dfrac{6}{7} \cdot \dfrac{2 \cdot 7}{3 \cdot 6} = \dfrac{2}{3}$

83. Multiplying: $5y^2 \cdot 4x^2 = 20x^2y^2$

85. Multiplying: $9x^4 \cdot 8y^5 = 72x^4y^5$

87. Factoring: $x^2 - 4 = (x+2)(x-2)$

89. Factoring: $x^3 - x^2y = x^2(x-y)$

91. Factoring: $2y^2 - 2 = 2(y^2-1) = 2(y+1)(y-1)$

6.2 Multiplication and Division of Rational Expressions

1. Performing the operations: $\dfrac{2}{9} \cdot \dfrac{3}{4} = \dfrac{2}{3 \cdot 3} \cdot \dfrac{3}{2 \cdot 2} = \dfrac{1}{2 \cdot 3} = \dfrac{1}{6}$

3. Performing the operations: $\dfrac{3}{4} \div \dfrac{1}{3} = \dfrac{3}{4} \cdot \dfrac{3}{1} = \dfrac{9}{4}$

5. Performing the operations: $\dfrac{3}{7} \cdot \dfrac{14}{24} \div \dfrac{1}{2} = \dfrac{1}{4} \div \dfrac{1}{2} = \dfrac{1}{4} \cdot \dfrac{2}{1} = \dfrac{2}{4} = \dfrac{1}{2}$

7. Performing the operations: $\dfrac{10x^2}{5y^2} \cdot \dfrac{15y^3}{2x^4} = \dfrac{150x^2y^3}{10x^4y^2} = \dfrac{15y}{x^2}$

9. Performing the operations: $\dfrac{11a^2b}{5ab^2} \div \dfrac{22a^3b^2}{10ab^4} = \dfrac{11a^2b}{5ab^2} \cdot \dfrac{10ab^4}{22a^3b^2} = \dfrac{110a^3b^5}{110a^4b^4} = \dfrac{b}{a}$

11. Performing the operations: $\dfrac{6x^2}{5y^3} \cdot \dfrac{11z^2}{2x^2} \div \dfrac{33z^5}{10y^8} = \dfrac{33z^2}{5y^3} \cdot \dfrac{10y^8}{33z^5} = \dfrac{2y^8z^2}{y^3z^5} = \dfrac{2y^5}{z^3}$

13. Performing the operations: $\dfrac{x^2-9}{x^2-4} \cdot \dfrac{x-2}{x-3} = \dfrac{(x+3)(x-3)}{(x+2)(x-2)} \cdot \dfrac{x-2}{x-3} = \dfrac{x+3}{x+2}$

15. Performing the operations: $\dfrac{y^2-1}{y+2} \cdot \dfrac{y^2+5y+6}{y^2+2y-3} = \dfrac{(y+1)(y-1)}{y+2} \cdot \dfrac{(y+2)(y+3)}{(y+3)(y-1)} = y+1$

17. Performing the operations: $\dfrac{3x-12}{x^2-4} \cdot \dfrac{x^2+6x+8}{x-4} = \dfrac{3(x-4)}{(x+2)(x-2)} \cdot \dfrac{(x+4)(x+2)}{x-4} = \dfrac{3(x+4)}{x-2}$

19. Performing the operations: $\dfrac{xy}{xy+1} \div \dfrac{x}{y} = \dfrac{xy}{xy+1} \cdot \dfrac{y}{x} = \dfrac{y^2}{xy+1}$

21. Performing the operations: $\dfrac{1}{x^2-9} \div \dfrac{1}{x^2+9} = \dfrac{1}{x^2-9} \cdot \dfrac{x^2+9}{1} = \dfrac{x^2+9}{x^2-9}$

23. Performing the operations: $\dfrac{y-3}{y^2-6y+9}\cdot\dfrac{y-3}{4}=\dfrac{y-3}{(y-3)^2}\cdot\dfrac{y-3}{4}=\dfrac{1}{4}$

25. Performing the operations: $\dfrac{5x+2y}{25x^2-5xy-6y^2}\cdot\dfrac{20x^2-7xy-3y^2}{4x+y}=\dfrac{5x+2y}{(5x+2y)(5x-3y)}\cdot\dfrac{(5x-3y)(4x+y)}{4x+y}=1$

27. Performing the operations:

$$\dfrac{a^2-5a+6}{a^2-2a-3}\div\dfrac{5-a}{a^2+3a+2}=\dfrac{a^2-5a+6}{a^2-2a-3}\cdot\dfrac{a^2+3a+2}{5-a}=\dfrac{(a-3)(a-2)}{(a-3)(a+1)}\cdot\dfrac{(a+2)(a+1)}{-1(a-5)}=-\dfrac{(a-2)(a+2)}{a-5}$$

29. Performing the operations:

$$\dfrac{4t^2-1}{6t^2+t-2}\div\dfrac{8t^3+1}{27t^3+8}=\dfrac{4t^2-1}{6t^2+t-2}\cdot\dfrac{27t^3+8}{8t^3+1}=\dfrac{(2t+1)(2t-1)}{(3t+2)(2t-1)}\cdot\dfrac{(3t+2)(9t^2-6t+4)}{(2t+1)(4t^2-2t+1)}=\dfrac{9t^2-6t+4}{4t^2-2t+1}$$

31. Performing the operations:

$$\dfrac{2x^2-5x-12}{4x^2+8x+3}\div\dfrac{x^2-16}{2x^2+7x+3}=\dfrac{2x^2-5x-12}{4x^2+8x+3}\cdot\dfrac{2x^2+7x+3}{x^2-16}=\dfrac{(2x+3)(x-4)}{(2x+1)(2x+3)}\cdot\dfrac{(2x+1)(x+3)}{(x+4)(x-4)}=\dfrac{x+3}{x+4}$$

33. Performing the operations:

$$\dfrac{2a^2-21ab-36b^2}{a^2-11ab-12b^2}\div\dfrac{10a+15b}{b^2-a^2}=\dfrac{2a^2-21ab-36b^2}{a^2-11ab-12b^2}\cdot\dfrac{b^2-a^2}{10a+15b}=\dfrac{(2a+3b)(a-12b)}{(a-12b)(a+b)}\cdot\dfrac{-1(a+b)(a-b)}{5(2a+3b)}=-\dfrac{a-b}{5}$$

35. Performing the operations: $\dfrac{6c^2-c-15}{9c^2-25}\cdot\dfrac{15c^2+22c-5}{6c^2+5c-6}=\dfrac{(3c-5)(2c+3)}{(3c+5)(3c-5)}\cdot\dfrac{(3c+5)(5c-1)}{(3c-2)(2c+3)}=\dfrac{5c-1}{3c-2}$

37. Performing the operations:

$$\dfrac{6a^2b+2ab^2-20b^3}{4a^2b-16b^3}\cdot\dfrac{10a^2-22ab+4b^2}{27a^3-125b^3}=\dfrac{2b(3a^2+ab-10b^2)}{4b(a^2-4b^2)}\cdot\dfrac{2(5a^2-11ab+2b^2)}{27a^3-125b^3}$$

$$=\dfrac{2b(3a-5b)(a+2b)}{4b(a+2b)(a-2b)}\cdot\dfrac{2(5a-b)(a-2b)}{(3a-5b)(9a^2+15ab+25b^2)}$$

$$=\dfrac{5a-b}{9a^2+15ab+25b^2}$$

39. Performing the operations:

$$\dfrac{360x^3-490x}{36x^2+84x+49}\cdot\dfrac{30x^2+83x+56}{150x^3+65x^2-280x}=\dfrac{10x(36x^2-49)}{(6x+7)^2}\cdot\dfrac{(6x+7)(5x+8)}{5x(30x^2+13x-56)}$$

$$=\dfrac{10x(6x+7)(6x-7)}{(6x+7)^2}\cdot\dfrac{(6x+7)(5x+8)}{5x(6x-7)(5x+8)}$$

$$=2$$

41. Performing the operations:

$$\dfrac{x^5-x^2}{5x^2-5x}\cdot\dfrac{10x^4-10x^2}{2x^4+2x^3+2x^2}=\dfrac{x^2(x^3-1)}{5x(x-1)}\cdot\dfrac{10x^2(x^2-1)}{2x^2(x^2+x+1)}$$

$$=\dfrac{x^2(x-1)(x^2+x+1)}{5x(x-1)}\cdot\dfrac{10x^2(x+1)(x-1)}{2x^2(x^2+x+1)}$$

$$=x(x+1)(x-1)$$

43. Performing the operations:

$$\frac{a^2-16b^2}{a^2-8ab+16b^2}\cdot\frac{a^2-9ab+20b^2}{a^2-7ab+12b^2}\div\frac{a^2-25b^2}{a^2-6ab+9b^2}$$

$$=\frac{a^2-16b^2}{a^2-8ab+16b^2}\cdot\frac{a^2-9ab+20b^2}{a^2-7ab+12b^2}\cdot\frac{a^2-6ab+9b^2}{a^2-25b^2}$$

$$=\frac{(a+4b)(a-4b)}{(a-4b)^2}\cdot\frac{(a-5b)(a-4b)}{(a-3b)(a-4b)}\cdot\frac{(a-3b)^2}{(a+5b)(a-5b)}$$

$$=\frac{(a+4b)(a-3b)}{(a-4b)(a+5b)}$$

45. Performing the operations:

$$\frac{2y^2-7y-15}{42y^2-29y-5}\cdot\frac{12y^2-16y+5}{7y^2-36y+5}\div\frac{9-4y^2}{49y^2-1}=\frac{2y^2-7y-15}{42y^2-29y-5}\cdot\frac{12y^2-16y+5}{7y^2-36y+5}\cdot\frac{49y^2-1}{-1(4y^2-9)}$$

$$=-\frac{(2y+3)(y-5)}{(6y-5)(7y+1)}\cdot\frac{(6y-5)(2y-1)}{(7y-1)(y-5)}\cdot\frac{(7y+1)(7y-1)}{(2y+3)(2y-3)}$$

$$=-\frac{2y-1}{2y-3}$$

47. Performing the operations:

$$\frac{xy-2x+3y-6}{xy+2x-4y-8}\cdot\frac{xy+x-4y-4}{xy-x+3y-3}=\frac{x(y-2)+3(y-2)}{x(y+2)-4(y+2)}\cdot\frac{x(y+1)-4(y+1)}{x(y-1)+3(y-1)}$$

$$=\frac{(y-2)(x+3)}{(y+2)(x-4)}\cdot\frac{(y+1)(x-4)}{(y-1)(x+3)}$$

$$=\frac{(y-2)(y+1)}{(y+2)(y-1)}$$

49. Performing the operations:

$$\frac{xy^2-y^2+4xy-4y}{xy-3y+4x-12}\div\frac{xy^3+2xy^2+y^3+2y^2}{xy^2-3y^2+2xy-6y}=\frac{xy^2-y^2+4xy-4y}{xy-3y+4x-12}\cdot\frac{xy^2-3y^2+2xy-6y}{xy^3+2xy^2+y^3+2y^2}$$

$$=\frac{y^2(x-1)+4y(x-1)}{y(x-3)+4(x-3)}\cdot\frac{y^2(x-3)+2y(x-3)}{xy^2(y+2)+y^2(y+2)}$$

$$=\frac{y(x-1)(y+4)}{(x-3)(y+4)}\cdot\frac{y(x-3)(y+2)}{y^2(y+2)(x+1)}$$

$$=\frac{x-1}{x+1}$$

51. Performing the operations:

$$\frac{2x^3+10x^2-8x-40}{x^3+4x^2-9x-36}\cdot\frac{x^2+x-12}{2x^2+14x+20}=\frac{2x^2(x+5)-8(x+5)}{x^2(x+4)-9(x+4)}\cdot\frac{(x+4)(x-3)}{2(x^2+7x+10)}$$

$$=\frac{2(x+5)(x^2-4)}{(x+4)(x^2-9)}\cdot\frac{(x+4)(x-3)}{2(x+5)(x+2)}$$

$$=\frac{2(x+5)(x+2)(x-2)}{(x+4)(x+3)(x-3)}\cdot\frac{(x+4)(x-3)}{2(x+5)(x+2)}$$

$$=\frac{x-2}{x+3}$$

53. Performing the operations: $\dfrac{w^3-w^2x}{wy-w}\div\left(\dfrac{x-w}{y-1}\right)^2=\dfrac{w^3-w^2x}{wy-w}\cdot\left(\dfrac{y-1}{x-w}\right)^2=\dfrac{-w^2(x-w)}{w(y-1)}\cdot\dfrac{(y-1)^2}{(x-w)^2}=-\dfrac{w(y-1)}{x-w}=\dfrac{w(y-1)}{w-x}$

55. Performing the operations:

$$\dfrac{mx+my+2x+2y}{6x^2-5xy-4y^2}\div\dfrac{2mx-4x+my-2y}{3mx-6x-4my+8y}=\dfrac{mx+my+2x+2y}{6x^2-5xy-4y^2}\cdot\dfrac{3mx-6x-4my+8y}{2mx-4x+my-2y}$$

$$=\dfrac{m(x+y)+2(x+y)}{(3x-4y)(2x+y)}\cdot\dfrac{3x(m-2)-4y(m-2)}{2x(m-2)+y(m-2)}$$

$$=\dfrac{(x+y)(m+2)}{(3x-4y)(2x+y)}\cdot\dfrac{(m-2)(3x-4y)}{(m-2)(2x+y)}$$

$$=\dfrac{(x+y)(m+2)}{(2x+y)^2}$$

57. Finding the product: $(3x-6)\cdot\dfrac{x}{x-2}=\dfrac{3(x-2)}{1}\cdot\dfrac{x}{x-2}=3x$

59. Finding the product: $\left(x^2-25\right)\cdot\dfrac{2}{x-5}=\dfrac{(x+5)(x-5)}{1}\cdot\dfrac{2}{x-5}=2(x+5)$

61. Finding the product: $\left(x^2-3x+2\right)\cdot\dfrac{3}{3x-3}=\dfrac{(x-2)(x-1)}{1}\cdot\dfrac{3}{3(x-1)}=x-2$

63. Finding the product: $(y-3)(y-4)(y+3)\cdot\dfrac{-1}{y^2-9}=\dfrac{(y-3)(y-4)(y+3)}{1}\cdot\dfrac{-1}{(y+3)(y-3)}=-(y-4)=4-y$

65. Finding the product: $a(a+5)(a-5)\cdot\dfrac{a+1}{a^2+5a}=\dfrac{a(a+5)(a-5)}{1}\cdot\dfrac{a+1}{a(a+5)}=(a-5)(a+1)$

67. **a.** Simplifying: $\dfrac{16-1}{64-1}=\dfrac{15}{63}=\dfrac{5}{21}$

  b. Reducing: $\dfrac{25x^2-9}{125x^3-27}=\dfrac{(5x-3)(5x+3)}{(5x-3)\left(25x^2+15x+9\right)}=\dfrac{5x+3}{25x^2+15x+9}$

  c. Multiplying: $\dfrac{25x^2-9}{125x^3-27}\cdot\dfrac{5x-3}{5x+3}=\dfrac{(5x-3)(5x+3)}{(5x-3)\left(25x^2+15x+9\right)}\cdot\dfrac{5x-3}{5x+3}=\dfrac{5x-3}{25x^2+15x+9}$

  d. Dividing: $\dfrac{25x^2-9}{125x^3-27}\div\dfrac{5x-3}{25x^2+15x+9}=\dfrac{(5x-3)(5x+3)}{(5x-3)\left(25x^2+15x+9\right)}\cdot\dfrac{25x^2+15x+9}{5x-3}=\dfrac{5x+3}{5x-3}$

69. Multiplying: $\dfrac{x^2-1}{x^2+x-6}\cdot\dfrac{x+3}{1-x}=\dfrac{(x+1)(x-1)}{(x+3)(x-2)}\cdot\dfrac{x+3}{-1(x-1)}=-\dfrac{x+1}{x-2}$. The correct answer is d.

71. Combining: $\dfrac{4}{9}+\dfrac{2}{9}=\dfrac{6}{9}=\dfrac{2\cdot3}{3\cdot3}=\dfrac{2}{3}$

73. Combining: $\dfrac{3}{14}+\dfrac{7}{30}=\dfrac{3}{14}\cdot\dfrac{15}{15}+\dfrac{7}{30}\cdot\dfrac{7}{7}=\dfrac{45}{210}+\dfrac{49}{210}=\dfrac{94}{210}=\dfrac{47}{105}$

75. Multiplying: $-1(7-x)=-7+x=x-7$ **77.** Factoring: $x^2-1=(x+1)(x-1)$

79. Factoring: $2x+10=2(x+5)$ **81.** Factoring: $a^3-b^3=(a-b)\left(a^2+ab+b^2\right)$

6.3 Addition and Subtraction of Rational Expressions

1. Combining the fractions: $\dfrac{3}{4}+\dfrac{1}{2}=\dfrac{3}{4}+\dfrac{1}{2}\cdot\dfrac{2}{2}=\dfrac{3}{4}+\dfrac{2}{4}=\dfrac{5}{4}$

3. Combining the fractions: $\dfrac{2}{5}-\dfrac{1}{15}=\dfrac{2}{5}\cdot\dfrac{3}{3}-\dfrac{1}{15}=\dfrac{6}{15}-\dfrac{1}{15}=\dfrac{5}{15}=\dfrac{1}{3}$

5. Combining the fractions: $\dfrac{5}{6}+\dfrac{7}{8}=\dfrac{5}{6}\cdot\dfrac{4}{4}+\dfrac{7}{8}\cdot\dfrac{3}{3}=\dfrac{20}{24}+\dfrac{21}{24}=\dfrac{41}{24}$

7. Combining the fractions: $\dfrac{9}{48}-\dfrac{3}{54}=\dfrac{9}{48}\cdot\dfrac{9}{9}-\dfrac{3}{54}\cdot\dfrac{8}{8}=\dfrac{81}{432}-\dfrac{24}{432}=\dfrac{57}{432}=\dfrac{19}{144}$

9. Combining the fractions: $\dfrac{3}{4}-\dfrac{1}{8}+\dfrac{2}{3}=\dfrac{3}{4}\cdot\dfrac{6}{6}-\dfrac{1}{8}\cdot\dfrac{3}{3}+\dfrac{2}{3}\cdot\dfrac{8}{8}=\dfrac{18}{24}-\dfrac{3}{24}+\dfrac{16}{24}=\dfrac{31}{24}$

11. Combining the rational expressions: $\dfrac{x}{x+3}+\dfrac{3}{x+3}=\dfrac{x+3}{x+3}=1$

13. Combining the rational expressions: $\dfrac{4}{y-4}-\dfrac{y}{y-4}=\dfrac{4-y}{y-4}=\dfrac{-1(y-4)}{y-4}=-1$

15. Combining the rational expressions: $\dfrac{x}{x^2-y^2}-\dfrac{y}{x^2-y^2}=\dfrac{x-y}{x^2-y^2}=\dfrac{x-y}{(x+y)(x-y)}=\dfrac{1}{x+y}$

17. Combining the rational expressions: $\dfrac{2x-3}{x-2}-\dfrac{x+1}{x-2}=\dfrac{2x-3-x-1}{x-2}=\dfrac{x-4}{x-2}$

19. Combining the rational expressions: $\dfrac{7x-2}{2x+1}-\dfrac{5x-3}{2x+1}=\dfrac{7x-2-5x+3}{2x+1}=\dfrac{2x+1}{2x+1}=1$

21. Combining the rational expressions: $\dfrac{3x-11}{x^2+x-6}+\dfrac{2x+1}{x^2+x-6}=\dfrac{3x-11+2x+1}{x^2+x-6}=\dfrac{5x-10}{x^2+x-6}=\dfrac{5(x-2)}{(x+3)(x-2)}=\dfrac{5}{x+3}$

23. Combining the rational expressions:

    $\dfrac{2x^2-x+6}{x^2-3x-4}-\dfrac{x^2-5x+3}{x^2-3x-4}=\dfrac{2x^2-x+6-x^2+5x-3}{x^2-3x-4}=\dfrac{x^2+4x+3}{x^2-3x-4}=\dfrac{(x+3)(x+1)}{(x+1)(x-4)}=\dfrac{x+3}{x-4}$

25. The LCD is $x(x-3)$.

27. The LCD is $(x+4)(x-4)$.

29. Factoring each denominator:

    $x^2+6x+9=(x+3)^2$

    $x^2-x-12=(x+3)(x-4)$

    The LCD is $(x+3)^2(x-4)$.

31. Combining the rational expressions: $\dfrac{1}{a}+\dfrac{2}{a^2}-\dfrac{3}{a^3}=\dfrac{1}{a}\cdot\dfrac{a^2}{a^2}+\dfrac{2}{a^2}\cdot\dfrac{a}{a}-\dfrac{3}{a^3}=\dfrac{a^2+2a-3}{a^3}$

33. Combining the rational expressions:

    $\dfrac{3x+1}{2x-6}-\dfrac{x+2}{x-3}=\dfrac{3x+1}{2(x-3)}-\dfrac{x+2}{x-3}\cdot\dfrac{2}{2}=\dfrac{3x+1}{2(x-3)}-\dfrac{2x+4}{2(x-3)}=\dfrac{3x+1-2x-4}{2(x-3)}=\dfrac{x-3}{2(x-3)}=\dfrac{1}{2}$

35. Combining the rational expressions:

    $\dfrac{6x+5}{5x-25}-\dfrac{x+2}{x-5}=\dfrac{6x+5}{5(x-5)}-\dfrac{x+2}{x-5}\cdot\dfrac{5}{5}=\dfrac{6x+5}{5(x-5)}-\dfrac{5x+10}{5(x-5)}=\dfrac{6x+5-5x-10}{5(x-5)}=\dfrac{x-5}{5(x-5)}=\dfrac{1}{5}$

37. Combining the rational expressions:

    $\dfrac{2}{x}+\dfrac{5}{x-3}=\dfrac{2}{x}\cdot\dfrac{x-3}{x-3}+\dfrac{5}{x-3}\cdot\dfrac{x}{x}=\dfrac{2x-6}{x(x-3)}+\dfrac{5x}{x(x-3)}=\dfrac{2x-6+5x}{x(x-3)}=\dfrac{7x-6}{x(x-3)}$

39. Combining the rational expressions:

$$\frac{3}{x+2}+\frac{2}{x+3}=\frac{3}{x+2}\cdot\frac{x+3}{x+3}+\frac{2}{x+3}\cdot\frac{x+2}{x+2}=\frac{3x+9}{(x+2)(x+3)}+\frac{2x+4}{(x+2)(x+3)}=\frac{3x+9+2x+4}{(x+2)(x+3)}=\frac{5x+13}{(x+2)(x+3)}$$

41. Combining the rational expressions:

$$\frac{x+1}{2x-2}-\frac{2}{x^2-1}=\frac{x+1}{2(x-1)}\cdot\frac{x+1}{x+1}-\frac{2}{(x+1)(x-1)}\cdot\frac{2}{2}$$

$$=\frac{x^2+2x+1}{2(x+1)(x-1)}-\frac{4}{2(x+1)(x-1)}$$

$$=\frac{x^2+2x-3}{2(x+1)(x-1)}$$

$$=\frac{(x+3)(x-1)}{2(x+1)(x-1)}$$

$$=\frac{x+3}{2(x+1)}$$

43. Combining the rational expressions:

$$\frac{1}{a-b}-\frac{3ab}{a^3-b^3}=\frac{1}{a-b}\cdot\frac{a^2+ab+b^2}{a^2+ab+b^2}-\frac{3ab}{a^3-b^3}$$

$$=\frac{a^2+ab+b^2}{a^3-b^3}-\frac{3ab}{a^3-b^3}$$

$$=\frac{a^2-2ab+b^2}{a^3-b^3}$$

$$=\frac{(a-b)^2}{(a-b)(a^2+ab+b^2)}$$

$$=\frac{a-b}{a^2+ab+b^2}$$

45. Combining the rational expressions:

$$\frac{1}{2y-3}-\frac{18y}{8y^3-27}=\frac{1}{2y-3}\cdot\frac{4y^2+6y+9}{4y^2+6y+9}-\frac{18y}{8y^3-27}$$

$$=\frac{4y^2+6y+9}{8y^3-27}-\frac{18y}{8y^3-27}$$

$$=\frac{4y^2-12y+9}{8y^3-27}$$

$$=\frac{(2y-3)^2}{(2y-3)(4y^2+6y+9)}$$

$$=\frac{2y-3}{4y^2+6y+9}$$

47. Combining the rational expressions:

$$\frac{x}{x^2-5x+6} - \frac{3}{3-x} = \frac{x}{(x-2)(x-3)} + \frac{3}{x-3} \cdot \frac{x-2}{x-2}$$

$$= \frac{x}{(x-2)(x-3)} + \frac{3x-6}{(x-2)(x-3)}$$

$$= \frac{4x-6}{(x-2)(x-3)}$$

$$= \frac{2(2x-3)}{(x-3)(x-2)}$$

49. Combining the rational expressions:

$$\frac{2}{4t-5} + \frac{9}{8t^2-38t+35} = \frac{2}{4t-5} \cdot \frac{2t-7}{2t-7} + \frac{9}{(4t-5)(2t-7)}$$

$$= \frac{4t-14}{(4t-5)(2t-7)} + \frac{9}{(4t-5)(2t-7)}$$

$$= \frac{4t-5}{(4t-5)(2t-7)}$$

$$= \frac{1}{2t-7}$$

51. Combining the rational expressions:

$$\frac{1}{a^2-5a+6} + \frac{3}{a^2-a-2} = \frac{1}{(a-2)(a-3)} \cdot \frac{a+1}{a+1} + \frac{3}{(a-2)(a+1)} \cdot \frac{a-3}{a-3}$$

$$= \frac{a+1}{(a-2)(a-3)(a+1)} + \frac{3a-9}{(a-2)(a-3)(a+1)}$$

$$= \frac{4a-8}{(a-2)(a-3)(a+1)}$$

$$= \frac{4(a-2)}{(a-2)(a-3)(a+1)}$$

$$= \frac{4}{(a-3)(a+1)}$$

53. Combining the rational expressions:

$$\frac{1}{8x^3-1} - \frac{1}{4x^2-1} = \frac{1}{(2x-1)(4x^2+2x+1)} \cdot \frac{2x+1}{2x+1} - \frac{1}{(2x+1)(2x-1)} \cdot \frac{4x^2+2x+1}{4x^2+2x+1}$$

$$= \frac{2x+1}{(2x+1)(2x-1)(4x^2+2x+1)} - \frac{4x^2+2x+1}{(2x+1)(2x-1)(4x^2+2x+1)}$$

$$= \frac{2x+1-4x^2-2x-1}{(2x+1)(2x-1)(4x^2+2x+1)}$$

$$= \frac{-4x^2}{(2x+1)(2x-1)(4x^2+2x+1)}$$

55. Combining the rational expressions:

$$\frac{4}{4x^2-9} - \frac{6}{8x^2-6x-9} = \frac{4}{(2x+3)(2x-3)} \cdot \frac{4x+3}{4x+3} - \frac{6}{(2x-3)(4x+3)} \cdot \frac{2x+3}{2x+3}$$

$$= \frac{16x+12}{(2x+3)(2x-3)(4x+3)} - \frac{12x+18}{(2x+3)(2x-3)(4x+3)}$$

$$= \frac{16x+12-12x-18}{(2x+3)(2x-3)(4x+3)}$$

$$= \frac{4x-6}{(2x+3)(2x-3)(4x+3)}$$

$$= \frac{2(2x-3)}{(2x+3)(2x-3)(4x+3)}$$

$$= \frac{2}{(2x+3)(4x+3)}$$

57. Combining the rational expressions:

$$\frac{4a}{a^2+6a+5} - \frac{3a}{a^2+5a+4} = \frac{4a}{(a+5)(a+1)} \cdot \frac{a+4}{a+4} - \frac{3a}{(a+4)(a+1)} \cdot \frac{a+5}{a+5}$$

$$= \frac{4a^2+16a}{(a+4)(a+5)(a+1)} - \frac{3a^2+15a}{(a+4)(a+5)(a+1)}$$

$$= \frac{4a^2+16a-3a^2-15a}{(a+4)(a+5)(a+1)}$$

$$= \frac{a^2+a}{(a+4)(a+5)(a+1)}$$

$$= \frac{a(a+1)}{(a+4)(a+5)(a+1)}$$

$$= \frac{a}{(a+4)(a+5)}$$

59. Combining the rational expressions:

$$\frac{2x-1}{x^2+x-6} - \frac{x+2}{x^2+5x+6} = \frac{2x-1}{(x+3)(x-2)} \cdot \frac{x+2}{x+2} - \frac{x+2}{(x+3)(x+2)} \cdot \frac{x-2}{x-2}$$

$$= \frac{2x^2+3x-2}{(x+3)(x+2)(x-2)} - \frac{x^2-4}{(x+3)(x+2)(x-2)}$$

$$= \frac{2x^2+3x-2-x^2+4}{(x+3)(x+2)(x-2)}$$

$$= \frac{x^2+3x+2}{(x+3)(x+2)(x-2)}$$

$$= \frac{(x+2)(x+1)}{(x+3)(x+2)(x-2)}$$

$$= \frac{x+1}{(x-2)(x+3)}$$

61. Combining the rational expressions:

$$\frac{2x-8}{3x^2+8x+4}+\frac{x+3}{3x^2+5x+2}=\frac{2x-8}{(3x+2)(x+2)}+\frac{x+3}{(3x+2)(x+1)}$$

$$=\frac{2x-8}{(3x+2)(x+2)}\cdot\frac{x+1}{x+1}+\frac{x+3}{(3x+2)(x+1)}\cdot\frac{x+2}{x+2}$$

$$=\frac{2x^2-6x-8}{(3x+2)(x+2)(x+1)}+\frac{x^2+5x+6}{(3x+2)(x+2)(x+1)}$$

$$=\frac{3x^2-x-2}{(3x+2)(x+2)(x+1)}$$

$$=\frac{(3x+2)(x-1)}{(3x+2)(x+2)(x+1)}$$

$$=\frac{x-1}{(x+1)(x+2)}$$

63. Combining the rational expressions:

$$\frac{2}{x^2+5x+6}-\frac{4}{x^2+4x+3}+\frac{3}{x^2+3x+2}=\frac{2}{(x+3)(x+2)}-\frac{4}{(x+3)(x+1)}+\frac{3}{(x+2)(x+1)}$$

$$=\frac{2}{(x+3)(x+2)}\cdot\frac{x+1}{x+1}-\frac{4}{(x+3)(x+1)}\cdot\frac{x+2}{x+2}+\frac{3}{(x+2)(x+1)}\cdot\frac{x+3}{x+3}$$

$$=\frac{2x+2}{(x+3)(x+2)(x+1)}-\frac{4x+8}{(x+3)(x+2)(x+1)}+\frac{3x+9}{(x+3)(x+2)(x+1)}$$

$$=\frac{2x+2-4x-8+3x+9}{(x+3)(x+2)(x+1)}$$

$$=\frac{x+3}{(x+3)(x+2)(x+1)}$$

$$=\frac{1}{(x+2)(x+1)}$$

65. Combining the rational expressions:

$$\frac{2x+8}{x^2+5x+6}-\frac{x+5}{x^2+4x+3}-\frac{x-1}{x^2+3x+2}=\frac{2x+8}{(x+3)(x+2)}-\frac{x+5}{(x+3)(x+1)}-\frac{x-1}{(x+2)(x+1)}$$

$$=\frac{2x+8}{(x+3)(x+2)}\cdot\frac{x+1}{x+1}-\frac{x+5}{(x+3)(x+1)}\cdot\frac{x+2}{x+2}-\frac{x-1}{(x+2)(x+1)}\cdot\frac{x+3}{x+3}$$

$$=\frac{2x^2+10x+8}{(x+3)(x+2)(x+1)}-\frac{x^2+7x+10}{(x+3)(x+2)(x+1)}-\frac{x^2+2x-3}{(x+3)(x+2)(x+1)}$$

$$=\frac{2x^2+10x+8-x^2-7x-10-x^2-2x+3}{(x+3)(x+2)(x+1)}$$

$$=\frac{x+1}{(x+3)(x+2)(x+1)}$$

$$=\frac{1}{(x+2)(x+3)}$$

67. Combining the rational expressions: $2+\dfrac{3}{2x+1}=\dfrac{2}{1}\cdot\dfrac{2x+1}{2x+1}+\dfrac{3}{2x+1}=\dfrac{4x+2}{2x+1}+\dfrac{3}{2x+1}=\dfrac{4x+5}{2x+1}$

69. Combining the rational expressions: $5+\dfrac{2}{4-t}=\dfrac{5}{1}\cdot\dfrac{4-t}{4-t}+\dfrac{2}{4-t}=\dfrac{20-5t}{4-t}+\dfrac{2}{4-t}=\dfrac{22-5t}{4-t}$

71. Combining the rational expressions: $x - \dfrac{4}{2x+3} = \dfrac{x}{1} \cdot \dfrac{2x+3}{2x+3} - \dfrac{4}{2x+3} = \dfrac{2x^2+3x}{2x+3} - \dfrac{4}{2x+3} = \dfrac{2x^2+3x-4}{2x+3}$

73. Combining the rational expressions:

$$\dfrac{x}{x+2} + \dfrac{1}{2x+4} - \dfrac{3}{x^2+2x} = \dfrac{x}{x+2} \cdot \dfrac{2x}{2x} + \dfrac{1}{2(x+2)} \cdot \dfrac{x}{x} - \dfrac{3}{x(x+2)} \cdot \dfrac{2}{2}$$

$$= \dfrac{2x^2}{2x(x+2)} + \dfrac{x}{2x(x+2)} - \dfrac{6}{2x(x+2)}$$

$$= \dfrac{2x^2+x-6}{2x(x+2)}$$

$$= \dfrac{(2x-3)(x+2)}{2x(x+2)}$$

$$= \dfrac{2x-3}{2x}$$

75. Combining the rational expressions:

$$\dfrac{1}{x} + \dfrac{x}{2x+4} - \dfrac{2}{x^2+2x} = \dfrac{1}{x} \cdot \dfrac{2(x+2)}{2(x+2)} + \dfrac{x}{2(x+2)} \cdot \dfrac{x}{x} - \dfrac{2}{x(x+2)} \cdot \dfrac{2}{2}$$

$$= \dfrac{2x+4}{2x(x+2)} + \dfrac{x^2}{2x(x+2)} - \dfrac{4}{2x(x+2)}$$

$$= \dfrac{x^2+2x}{2x(x+2)}$$

$$= \dfrac{x(x+2)}{2x(x+2)}$$

$$= \dfrac{1}{2}$$

77. Finding the sum:

$$f(x) + g(x) = \dfrac{2}{x+4} + \dfrac{x-1}{x^2+3x-4}$$

$$= \dfrac{2}{x+4} \cdot \dfrac{x-1}{x-1} + \dfrac{x-1}{(x+4)(x-1)}$$

$$= \dfrac{2x-2}{(x+4)(x-1)} + \dfrac{x-1}{(x+4)(x-1)}$$

$$= \dfrac{3x-3}{(x+4)(x-1)}$$

$$= \dfrac{3(x-1)}{(x+4)(x-1)}$$

$$= \dfrac{3}{x+4}$$

79. Finding the difference:

$$f(x) - g(x) = \frac{7}{x^2 - x - 12} - \frac{5}{x^2 + x - 6}$$

$$= \frac{7}{(x-4)(x+3)} \cdot \frac{x-2}{x-2} - \frac{5}{(x+3)(x-2)} \cdot \frac{x-4}{x-4}$$

$$= \frac{7x-14}{(x-4)(x+3)(x-2)} - \frac{5x-20}{(x-4)(x+3)(x-2)}$$

$$= \frac{2x+6}{(x-4)(x+3)(x-2)}$$

$$= \frac{2(x+3)}{(x-4)(x+3)(x-2)}$$

$$= \frac{2}{(x-4)(x-2)}$$

81. **a.** Multiplying: $\dfrac{3}{8} \cdot \dfrac{1}{6} = \dfrac{3}{8} \cdot \dfrac{1}{2 \cdot 3} = \dfrac{1}{16}$

b. Dividing: $\dfrac{3}{8} \div \dfrac{1}{6} = \dfrac{3}{8} \cdot \dfrac{6}{1} = \dfrac{3}{2 \cdot 4} \cdot \dfrac{2 \cdot 3}{1} = \dfrac{9}{4}$

c. Adding: $\dfrac{3}{8} + \dfrac{1}{6} = \dfrac{3}{8} \cdot \dfrac{3}{3} + \dfrac{1}{6} \cdot \dfrac{4}{4} = \dfrac{9}{24} + \dfrac{4}{24} = \dfrac{13}{24}$

d. Multiplying: $\dfrac{x+3}{x-3} \cdot \dfrac{5x+15}{x^2-9} = \dfrac{x+3}{x-3} \cdot \dfrac{5(x+3)}{(x+3)(x-3)} = \dfrac{5(x+3)}{(x-3)^2}$

e. Dividing: $\dfrac{x+3}{x-3} \div \dfrac{5x+15}{x^2-9} = \dfrac{x+3}{x-3} \cdot \dfrac{(x+3)(x-3)}{5(x+3)} = \dfrac{x+3}{5}$

f. Subtracting:

$$\frac{x+3}{x-3} - \frac{5x+15}{x^2-9} = \frac{x+3}{x-3} \cdot \frac{x+3}{x+3} - \frac{5x+15}{(x+3)(x-3)}$$

$$= \frac{x^2+6x+9}{(x+3)(x-3)} - \frac{5x+15}{(x+3)(x-3)}$$

$$= \frac{x^2+x-6}{(x+3)(x-3)}$$

$$= \frac{(x+3)(x-2)}{(x+3)(x-3)}$$

$$= \frac{x-2}{x-3}$$

83. Substituting the values: $P = \dfrac{1}{10} + \dfrac{1}{0.2} = 0.1 + 5 = 5.1 = \dfrac{51}{10}$

85. Writing the expression and simplifying: $x + \dfrac{4}{x} = \dfrac{x^2+4}{x}$

87. Writing the expression and simplifying: $\dfrac{1}{x} + \dfrac{1}{x+1} = \dfrac{1}{x} \cdot \dfrac{x+1}{x+1} + \dfrac{1}{x+1} \cdot \dfrac{x}{x} = \dfrac{x+1}{x(x+1)} + \dfrac{x}{x(x+1)} = \dfrac{2x+1}{x(x+1)}$

89. Combining the rational expressions: $\dfrac{2x+1}{x^2-4} + \dfrac{3}{x^2-4} = \dfrac{2x+4}{x^2-4} = \dfrac{2(x+2)}{(x+2)(x-2)} = \dfrac{2}{x-2}$

The correct answer is a.

91. Factoring each denominator:

$$x^2 + 2x + 1 = (x+1)^2$$

$$x^2 + 4x + 3 = (x+3)(x+1)$$

The LCD is $(x+1)^2(x+3)$. The correct answer is a.

93. Dividing: $\dfrac{3}{4} \div \dfrac{5}{8} = \dfrac{3}{4} \cdot \dfrac{8}{5} = \dfrac{24}{20} = \dfrac{4 \cdot 6}{4 \cdot 5} = \dfrac{6}{5}$

95. Multiplying: $x\left(1 + \dfrac{2}{x}\right) = x \cdot 1 + x \cdot \dfrac{2}{x} = x + 2$

97. Multiplying: $3x\left(\dfrac{1}{x} - \dfrac{1}{3}\right) = 3x \cdot \dfrac{1}{x} - 3x \cdot \dfrac{1}{3} = 3 - x$

99. Factoring: $x^2 - 4 = (x+2)(x-2)$

6.4 Complex Fractions

1. Simplifying the complex fraction: $\dfrac{\frac{3}{4}}{\frac{2}{3}} = \dfrac{\frac{3}{4} \cdot 12}{\frac{2}{3} \cdot 12} = \dfrac{9}{8}$

3. Simplifying the complex fraction: $\dfrac{\frac{1}{3} - \frac{1}{4}}{\frac{1}{2} + \frac{1}{8}} = \dfrac{\left(\frac{1}{3} - \frac{1}{4}\right) \cdot 24}{\left(\frac{1}{2} + \frac{1}{8}\right) \cdot 24} = \dfrac{8-6}{12+3} = \dfrac{2}{15}$

5. Simplifying the complex fraction: $\dfrac{3 + \frac{2}{5}}{1 - \frac{3}{7}} = \dfrac{\left(3 + \frac{2}{5}\right) \cdot 35}{\left(1 - \frac{3}{7}\right) \cdot 35} = \dfrac{105 + 14}{35 - 15} = \dfrac{119}{20}$

7. Simplifying the complex fraction: $\dfrac{\frac{1}{x}}{1 + \frac{1}{x}} = \dfrac{\left(\frac{1}{x}\right) \cdot x}{\left(1 + \frac{1}{x}\right) \cdot x} = \dfrac{1}{x+1}$

9. Simplifying the complex fraction: $\dfrac{1 + \frac{1}{a}}{1 - \frac{1}{a}} = \dfrac{\left(1 + \frac{1}{a}\right) \cdot a}{\left(1 - \frac{1}{a}\right) \cdot a} = \dfrac{a+1}{a-1}$

11. Simplifying the complex fraction: $\dfrac{\frac{1}{x} - \frac{1}{y}}{\frac{1}{x} + \frac{1}{y}} = \dfrac{\left(\frac{1}{x} - \frac{1}{y}\right) \cdot xy}{\left(\frac{1}{x} + \frac{1}{y}\right) \cdot xy} = \dfrac{y-x}{y+x}$

13. Simplifying the complex fraction: $\dfrac{\frac{x-5}{x^2-4}}{\frac{x^2-25}{x+2}} = \dfrac{\frac{x-5}{(x+2)(x-2)} \cdot (x+2)(x-2)}{\frac{(x+5)(x-5)}{x+2} \cdot (x+2)(x-2)} = \dfrac{x-5}{(x+5)(x-5)(x-2)} = \dfrac{1}{(x+5)(x-2)}$

15. Simplifying the complex fraction: $\dfrac{\frac{4a}{2a^3+2}}{\frac{8a}{4a+4}} = \dfrac{\frac{4a}{2(a+1)(a^2-a+1)} \cdot 2(a+1)(a^2-a+1)}{\frac{8a}{4(a+1)} \cdot 2(a+1)(a^2-a+1)} = \dfrac{4a}{4a(a^2-a+1)} = \dfrac{1}{a^2-a+1}$

17. Simplifying the complex fraction: $\dfrac{1-\dfrac{9}{x^2}}{1-\dfrac{1}{x}-\dfrac{6}{x^2}}=\dfrac{\left(1-\dfrac{9}{x^2}\right)\cdot x^2}{\left(1-\dfrac{1}{x}-\dfrac{6}{x^2}\right)\cdot x^2}=\dfrac{x^2-9}{x^2-x-6}=\dfrac{(x+3)(x-3)}{(x+2)(x-3)}=\dfrac{x+3}{x+2}$

19. Simplifying the complex fraction: $\dfrac{2+\dfrac{5}{a}-\dfrac{3}{a^2}}{2-\dfrac{5}{a}+\dfrac{2}{a^2}}=\dfrac{\left(2+\dfrac{5}{a}-\dfrac{3}{a^2}\right)\cdot a^2}{\left(2-\dfrac{5}{a}+\dfrac{2}{a^2}\right)\cdot a^2}=\dfrac{2a^2+5a-3}{2a^2-5a+2}=\dfrac{(2a-1)(a+3)}{(2a-1)(a-2)}=\dfrac{a+3}{a-2}$

21. Simplifying the complex fraction:

$$\dfrac{2+\dfrac{3}{x}-\dfrac{18}{x^2}-\dfrac{27}{x^3}}{2+\dfrac{9}{x}+\dfrac{9}{x^2}}=\dfrac{\left(2+\dfrac{3}{x}-\dfrac{18}{x^2}-\dfrac{27}{x^3}\right)\cdot x^3}{\left(2+\dfrac{9}{x}+\dfrac{9}{x^2}\right)\cdot x^3}$$

$$=\dfrac{2x^3+3x^2-18x-27}{2x^3+9x^2+9x}$$

$$=\dfrac{x^2(2x+3)-9(2x+3)}{x(2x^2+9x+9)}$$

$$=\dfrac{(2x+3)(x^2-9)}{x(2x+3)(x+3)}$$

$$=\dfrac{(2x+3)(x+3)(x-3)}{x(2x+3)(x+3)}$$

$$=\dfrac{x-3}{x}$$

23. Simplifying the complex fraction: $\dfrac{1+\dfrac{1}{x+3}}{1-\dfrac{1}{x+3}}=\dfrac{\left(1+\dfrac{1}{x+3}\right)\cdot(x+3)}{\left(1-\dfrac{1}{x+3}\right)\cdot(x+3)}=\dfrac{x+3+1}{x+3-1}=\dfrac{x+4}{x+2}$

25. Simplifying the complex fraction:

$$\dfrac{1+\dfrac{1}{x+3}}{1+\dfrac{7}{x-3}}=\dfrac{\left(1+\dfrac{1}{x+3}\right)\cdot(x+3)(x-3)}{\left(1+\dfrac{7}{x-3}\right)\cdot(x+3)(x-3)}$$

$$=\dfrac{(x+3)(x-3)+x-3}{(x+3)(x-3)+7(x+3)}$$

$$=\dfrac{x^2-9+x-3}{x^2-9+7x+21}$$

$$=\dfrac{x^2+x-12}{x^2+7x+12}$$

$$=\dfrac{(x+4)(x-3)}{(x+4)(x+3)}$$

$$=\dfrac{x-3}{x+3}$$

27. Simplifying the complex fraction:

$$\dfrac{1-\dfrac{1}{a+1}}{1+\dfrac{1}{a-1}}=\dfrac{\left(1-\dfrac{1}{a+1}\right)\cdot(a+1)(a-1)}{\left(1+\dfrac{1}{a-1}\right)\cdot(a+1)(a-1)}$$

$$=\dfrac{(a+1)(a-1)-(a-1)}{(a+1)(a-1)+(a+1)}$$

$$=\dfrac{(a-1)(a+1-1)}{(a+1)(a-1+1)}$$

$$=\dfrac{a(a-1)}{a(a+1)}$$

$$=\dfrac{a-1}{a+1}$$

29. Simplifying the complex fraction:

$$\frac{\dfrac{1}{x+3}+\dfrac{1}{x-3}}{\dfrac{1}{x+3}-\dfrac{1}{x-3}}=\frac{\left(\dfrac{1}{x+3}+\dfrac{1}{x-3}\right)\bullet(x+3)(x-3)}{\left(\dfrac{1}{x+3}-\dfrac{1}{x-3}\right)\bullet(x+3)(x-3)}$$

$$=\frac{(x-3)+(x+3)}{(x-3)-(x+3)}$$

$$=\frac{2x}{-6}$$

$$=-\frac{x}{3}$$

31. Simplifying the complex fraction:

$$\frac{\dfrac{y+1}{y-1}+\dfrac{y-1}{y+1}}{\dfrac{y+1}{y-1}-\dfrac{y-1}{y+1}}=\frac{\left(\dfrac{y+1}{y-1}+\dfrac{y-1}{y+1}\right)\bullet(y+1)(y-1)}{\left(\dfrac{y+1}{y-1}-\dfrac{y-1}{y+1}\right)\bullet(y+1)(y-1)}$$

$$=\frac{(y+1)^2+(y-1)^2}{(y+1)^2-(y-1)^2}$$

$$=\frac{y^2+2y+1+y^2-2y+1}{y^2+2y+1-y^2+2y-1}$$

$$=\frac{2y^2+2}{4y}$$

$$=\frac{2(y^2+1)}{4y}$$

$$=\frac{y^2+1}{2y}$$

33. Simplifying the complex fraction: $1-\dfrac{x}{1-\dfrac{1}{x}}=1-\dfrac{x\bullet x}{\left(1-\dfrac{1}{x}\right)\bullet x}=1-\dfrac{x^2}{x-1}=\dfrac{x-1-x^2}{x-1}=\dfrac{-x^2+x-1}{x-1}$

35. Simplifying the complex fraction: $1+\dfrac{1}{1+\dfrac{1}{1+1}}=1+\dfrac{1}{1+\dfrac{1}{2}}=1+\dfrac{1}{\dfrac{3}{2}}=1+\dfrac{2}{3}=\dfrac{5}{3}$

37. Simplifying the complex fraction:

$$\frac{1-\dfrac{1}{x+\dfrac{1}{2}}}{1+\dfrac{1}{x+\dfrac{1}{2}}}=\frac{1-\dfrac{1\bullet2}{\left(x+\dfrac{1}{2}\right)\bullet2}}{1+\dfrac{1\bullet2}{\left(x+\dfrac{1}{2}\right)\bullet2}}=\frac{1-\dfrac{2}{2x+1}}{1+\dfrac{2}{2x+1}}=\frac{\left(1-\dfrac{2}{2x+1}\right)(2x+1)}{\left(1+\dfrac{2}{2x+1}\right)(2x+1)}=\frac{2x+1-2}{2x+1+2}=\frac{2x-1}{2x+3}$$

39. Simplifying the complex fraction: $\dfrac{\dfrac{1}{x+h}-\dfrac{1}{x}}{h}=\dfrac{\left(\dfrac{1}{x+h}-\dfrac{1}{x}\right)\bullet x(x+h)}{h\bullet x(x+h)}=\dfrac{x-(x+h)}{hx(x+h)}=\dfrac{x-x-h}{hx(x+h)}=\dfrac{-h}{hx(x+h)}=-\dfrac{1}{x(x+h)}$

41. Simplifying the complex fraction: $\dfrac{\dfrac{3}{ab}+\dfrac{4}{bc}-\dfrac{2}{ac}}{\dfrac{5}{abc}}=\dfrac{\left(\dfrac{3}{ab}+\dfrac{4}{bc}-\dfrac{2}{ac}\right)\bullet abc}{\left(\dfrac{5}{abc}\right)\bullet abc}=\dfrac{3c+4a-2b}{5}$

43. Simplifying the complex fraction: $\dfrac{\dfrac{t^2-2t-8}{t^2+7t+6}}{\dfrac{t^2-t-6}{t^2+2t+1}}=\dfrac{\dfrac{(t-4)(t+2)}{(t+6)(t+1)}\bullet(t+6)(t+1)^2}{\dfrac{(t-3)(t+2)}{(t+1)^2}\bullet(t+6)(t+1)^2}=\dfrac{(t-4)(t+2)(t+1)}{(t-3)(t+2)(t+6)}=\dfrac{(t-4)(t+1)}{(t+6)(t-3)}$

45. Simplifying the complex fraction:

$$\frac{5+\dfrac{4}{b-1}}{\dfrac{7}{b+5}-\dfrac{3}{b-1}}=\frac{\left(5+\dfrac{4}{b-1}\right)\cdot(b+5)(b-1)}{\left(\dfrac{7}{b+5}-\dfrac{3}{b-1}\right)\cdot(b+5)(b-1)}$$

$$=\frac{5(b+5)(b-1)+4(b+5)}{7(b-1)-3(b+5)}$$

$$=\frac{(b+5)(5b-5+4)}{7b-7-3b-15}$$

$$=\frac{(b+5)(5b-1)}{4b-22}$$

$$=\frac{(5b-1)(b+5)}{2(2b-11)}$$

47. Simplifying the complex fraction:

$$\frac{\dfrac{3}{x^2-x-6}}{\dfrac{2}{x+2}-\dfrac{4}{x-3}}=\frac{\dfrac{3}{(x-3)(x+2)}\cdot(x-3)(x+2)}{\left(\dfrac{2}{x+2}-\dfrac{4}{x-3}\right)\cdot(x-3)(x+2)}$$

$$=\frac{3}{2(x-3)-4(x+2)}$$

$$=\frac{3}{2x-6-4x-8}$$

$$=\frac{3}{-2x-14}$$

$$=-\frac{3}{2x+14}$$

49. Simplifying the complex fraction: $\dfrac{\dfrac{1}{m-4}+\dfrac{1}{m-5}}{\dfrac{1}{m^2-9m+20}}=\dfrac{\left(\dfrac{1}{m-4}+\dfrac{1}{m-5}\right)\cdot(m-4)(m-5)}{\dfrac{1}{(m-4)(m-5)}\cdot(m-4)(m-5)}=\dfrac{(m-5)+(m-4)}{1}=2m-9$

51. **a.** As v approaches 0, the denominator approaches 1.

   b. Solving for v:

$$h = \frac{f}{1 + \dfrac{v}{s}}$$

$$h = \frac{f \cdot s}{\left(1 + \dfrac{v}{s}\right)s}$$

$$h = \frac{fs}{s + v}$$

$$h(s + v) = fs$$

$$s + v = \frac{fs}{h}$$

$$v = \frac{fs}{h} - s$$

$$v = \frac{fs - sh}{h} = \frac{fs}{h} - s$$

53. Simplifying as a division: $\dfrac{\dfrac{x-1}{x^2+2x}}{\dfrac{2x^2-2x}{x^2-4}} = \dfrac{x-1}{x^2+2x} \div \dfrac{2x^2-2x}{x^2-4} = \dfrac{x-1}{x^2+2x} \cdot \dfrac{x^2-4}{2x^2-2x} = \dfrac{x-1}{x(x+2)} \cdot \dfrac{(x+2)(x-2)}{2x(x-1)} = \dfrac{x-2}{2x^2}$

   The correct answer is a.

55. Multiplying: $x(y-2) = xy - 2x$

57. Multiplying: $6\left(\dfrac{x}{2} - 3\right) = 6 \cdot \dfrac{x}{2} - 6 \cdot 3 = 3x - 18$

59. Multiplying: $xab \cdot \dfrac{1}{x} = ab$

61. Factoring: $y^2 - 25 = (y+5)(y-5)$

63. Factoring: $xa + xb = x(a+b)$

65. Solving the equation:

$$5x - 4 = 6$$

$$5x = 10$$

$$x = 2$$

6.5 Equations Involving Rational Expressions

1. Solving the equation:

$$\frac{x}{5} + 4 = \frac{5}{3}$$

$$15\left(\frac{x}{5} + 4\right) = 15\left(\frac{5}{3}\right)$$

$$3x + 60 = 25$$

$$3x = -35$$

$$x = -\frac{35}{3}$$

3. Solving the equation:

$$\frac{a}{3} + 2 = \frac{4}{5}$$

$$15\left(\frac{a}{3} + 2\right) = 15\left(\frac{4}{5}\right)$$

$$5a + 30 = 12$$

$$5a = -18$$

$$a = -\frac{18}{5}$$

5. Solving the equation:

$$\frac{y}{2} + \frac{y}{4} + \frac{y}{6} = 3$$

$$12\left(\frac{y}{2} + \frac{y}{4} + \frac{y}{6}\right) = 12(3)$$

$$6y + 3y + 2y = 36$$

$$11y = 36$$

$$y = \frac{36}{11}$$

7. Solving the equation:

$$\frac{5}{2x} = \frac{1}{x} + \frac{3}{4}$$

$$4x\left(\frac{5}{2x}\right) = 4x\left(\frac{1}{x} + \frac{3}{4}\right)$$

$$10 = 4 + 3x$$

$$3x = 6$$

$$x = 2$$

9. Solving the equation:

$$\frac{1}{x} = \frac{1}{3} - \frac{2}{3x}$$

$$3x\left(\frac{1}{x}\right) = 3x\left(\frac{1}{3} - \frac{2}{3x}\right)$$

$$3 = x - 2$$

$$x = 5$$

11. Solving the equation:

$$\frac{2x}{x-3} + 2 = \frac{2}{x-3}$$

$$(x-3)\left(\frac{2x}{x-3} + 2\right) = (x-3)\left(\frac{2}{x-3}\right)$$

$$2x + 2(x-3) = 2$$

$$2x + 2x - 6 = 2$$

$$4x = 8$$

$$x = 2$$

13. Solving the equation:

$$1 - \frac{1}{x} = \frac{12}{x^2}$$

$$x^2\left(1 - \frac{1}{x}\right) = x^2\left(\frac{12}{x^2}\right)$$

$$x^2 - x = 12$$

$$x^2 - x - 12 = 0$$

$$(x+3)(x-4) = 0$$

$$x = -3, 4$$

15. Solving the equation:

$$y - \frac{4}{3y} = -\frac{1}{3}$$

$$3y\left(y - \frac{4}{3y}\right) = 3y\left(-\frac{1}{3}\right)$$

$$3y^2 - 4 = -y$$

$$3y^2 + y - 4 = 0$$

$$(3y+4)(y-1) = 0$$

$$x = -\frac{4}{3}, 1$$

17. Solving the equation:

$$\frac{x+2}{x+1} = \frac{1}{x+1} + 2$$

$$(x+1)\left(\frac{x+2}{x+1}\right) = (x+1)\left(\frac{1}{x+1} + 2\right)$$

$$x+2 = 1 + 2(x+1)$$

$$x+2 = 1 + 2x + 2$$

$$x+2 = 2x + 3$$

$$x = -1 \quad (\text{does not check})$$

There is no solution (–1 does not check).

19. Solving the equation:

$$\frac{3}{a-2} = \frac{2}{a-3}$$

$$(a-2)(a-3)\left(\frac{3}{a-2}\right) = (a-2)(a-3)\left(\frac{2}{a-3}\right)$$

$$3(a-3) = 2(a-2)$$

$$3a - 9 = 2a - 4$$

$$a = 5$$

21. Solving the equation:

$$6 - \frac{5}{x^2} = \frac{7}{x}$$

$$x^2\left(6 - \frac{5}{x^2}\right) = x^2\left(\frac{7}{x}\right)$$

$$6x^2 - 5 = 7x$$

$$6x^2 - 7x - 5 = 0$$

$$(2x+1)(3x-5) = 0$$

$$x = -\frac{1}{2}, \frac{5}{3}$$

23. Solving the equation:

$$\frac{1}{x-1} - \frac{1}{x+1} = \frac{3x}{x^2-1}$$

$$(x+1)(x-1)\left(\frac{1}{x-1} - \frac{1}{x+1}\right) = (x+1)(x-1)\left(\frac{3x}{(x+1)(x-1)}\right)$$

$$(x+1) - (x-1) = 3x$$

$$x + 1 - x + 1 = 3x$$

$$3x = 2$$

$$x = \frac{2}{3}$$

25. Solving the equation:

$$\frac{2}{x-3} + \frac{x}{x^2-9} = \frac{4}{x+3}$$

$$(x+3)(x-3)\left(\frac{2}{x-3} + \frac{x}{(x+3)(x-3)}\right) = (x+3)(x-3)\left(\frac{4}{x+3}\right)$$

$$2(x+3) + x = 4(x-3)$$

$$2x + 6 + x = 4x - 12$$

$$3x + 6 = 4x - 12$$

$$-x = -18$$

$$x = 18$$

27. Solving the equation:

$$\frac{3}{2} - \frac{1}{x-4} = \frac{-2}{2x-8}$$

$$2(x-4)\left(\frac{3}{2} - \frac{1}{x-4}\right) = 2(x-4)\left(\frac{-2}{2(x-4)}\right)$$

$$3(x-4) - 2 = -2$$

$$3x - 12 - 2 = -2$$

$$3x - 14 = -2$$

$$3x = 12$$

$$x = 4 \quad (\text{does not check})$$

There is no solution (4 does not check).

29. Solving the equation:

$$\frac{t-4}{t^2-3t} = \frac{-2}{t^2-9}$$

$$t(t+3)(t-3) \cdot \frac{t-4}{t(t-3)} = t(t+3)(t-3) \cdot \frac{-2}{(t+3)(t-3)}$$

$$(t+3)(t-4) = -2t$$

$$t^2 - t - 12 = -2t$$

$$t^2 + t - 12 = 0$$

$$(t+4)(t-3) = 0$$

$$t = -4 \quad (t = 3 \text{ does not check})$$

31. Solving the equation:

$$\frac{3}{y-4} - \frac{2}{y+1} = \frac{5}{y^2-3y-4}$$

$$(y-4)(y+1)\left(\frac{3}{y-4} - \frac{2}{y+1}\right) = (y-4)(y+1)\left(\frac{5}{(y-4)(y+1)}\right)$$

$$3(y+1) - 2(y-4) = 5$$

$$3y + 3 - 2y + 8 = 5$$

$$y + 11 = 5$$

$$y = -6$$

33. Solving the equation:

$$\frac{2}{1+a} = \frac{3}{1-a} + \frac{5}{a}$$

$$a(1+a)(1-a)\left(\frac{2}{1+a}\right) = a(1+a)(1-a)\left(\frac{3}{1-a} + \frac{5}{a}\right)$$

$$2a(1-a) = 3a(1+a) + 5(1+a)(1-a)$$

$$2a - 2a^2 = 3a + 3a^2 + 5 - 5a^2$$

$$-2a^2 + 2a = -2a^2 + 3a + 5$$

$$2a = 3a + 5$$

$$-a = 5$$

$$a = -5$$

35. Solving the equation:

$$\frac{3}{2x-6} - \frac{x+1}{4x-12} = 4$$

$$4(x-3)\left(\frac{3}{2(x-3)} - \frac{x+1}{4(x-3)}\right) = 4(x-3)(4)$$

$$6 - (x+1) = 16x - 48$$

$$5 - x = 16x - 48$$

$$-17x = -53$$

$$x = \frac{53}{17}$$

37. Solving the equation:

$$\frac{y+2}{y^2-y} - \frac{6}{y^2-1} = 0$$

$$y(y+1)(y-1)\left(\frac{y+2}{y(y-1)} - \frac{6}{(y+1)(y-1)}\right) = y(y+1)(y-1)(0)$$

$$(y+1)(y+2) - 6y = 0$$

$$y^2 + 3y + 2 - 6y = 0$$

$$y^2 - 3y + 2 = 0$$

$$(y-1)(y-2) = 0$$

$$y = 2 \quad (y = 1 \text{ does not check})$$

39. Solving the equation:

$$\frac{4}{2x-6} - \frac{12}{4x+12} = \frac{12}{x^2-9}$$

$$4(x+3)(x-3)\left(\frac{4}{2(x-3)} - \frac{12}{4(x+3)}\right) = 4(x+3)(x-3)\left(\frac{12}{(x+3)(x-3)}\right)$$

$$8(x+3) - 12(x-3) = 48$$

$$8x + 24 - 12x + 36 = 48$$

$$-4x + 60 = 48$$

$$-4x = -12$$

$$x = 3 \quad (x = 3 \text{ does not check})$$

There is no solution (3 does not check).

41. Solving the equation:

$$\frac{2}{y^2-7y+12} - \frac{1}{y^2-9} = \frac{4}{y^2-y-12}$$

$$(y+3)(y-3)(y-4)\left(\frac{2}{(y-3)(y-4)} - \frac{1}{(y+3)(y-3)}\right) = (y+3)(y-3)(y-4)\left(\frac{4}{(y-4)(y+3)}\right)$$

$$2(y+3) - (y-4) = 4(y-3)$$

$$2y + 6 - y + 4 = 4y - 12$$

$$y + 10 = 4y - 12$$

$$-3y = -22$$

$$y = \frac{22}{3}$$

43. **a.** Solving the equation:

$$6x - 2 = 0$$
$$6x = 2$$
$$x = \frac{1}{3}$$

b. Solving the equation:

$$\frac{6}{x} - 2 = 0$$
$$x\left(\frac{6}{x} - 2\right) = x(0)$$
$$6 - 2x = 0$$
$$6 = 2x$$
$$x = 3$$

c. Solving the equation:

$$\frac{x}{6} - 2 = -\frac{1}{2}$$
$$6\left(\frac{x}{6} - 2\right) = 6\left(-\frac{1}{2}\right)$$
$$x - 12 = -3$$
$$x = 9$$

d. Solving the equation:

$$\frac{6}{x} - 2 = -\frac{1}{2}$$
$$2x\left(\frac{6}{x} - 2\right) = 2x\left(-\frac{1}{2}\right)$$
$$12 - 4x = -x$$
$$12 = 3x$$
$$x = 4$$

e. Solving the equation:

$$\frac{6}{x^2} + 6 = \frac{20}{x}$$
$$x^2\left(\frac{6}{x^2} + 6\right) = x^2\left(\frac{20}{x}\right)$$
$$6 + 6x^2 = 20x$$
$$6x^2 - 20x + 6 = 0$$
$$3x^2 - 10x + 3 = 0$$
$$(3x - 1)(x - 3) = 0$$
$$x = \frac{1}{3}, 3$$

45. **a.** Dividing: $\dfrac{6}{x^2 - 2x - 8} \div \dfrac{x+3}{x+2} = \dfrac{6}{(x-4)(x+2)} \cdot \dfrac{x+2}{x+3} = \dfrac{6}{(x-4)(x+3)}$

b. Adding:

$$\frac{6}{x^2 - 2x - 8} + \frac{x+3}{x+2} = \frac{6}{(x-4)(x+2)} + \frac{x+3}{x+2} \cdot \frac{x-4}{x-4}$$

$$= \frac{6}{(x-4)(x+2)} + \frac{x^2 - x - 12}{(x-4)(x+2)}$$

$$= \frac{x^2 - x - 6}{(x-4)(x+2)}$$

$$= \frac{(x-3)(x+2)}{(x-4)(x+2)}$$

$$= \frac{x-3}{x-4}$$

c. Solving the equation:

$$\frac{6}{x^2 - 2x - 8} + \frac{x+3}{x+2} = 2$$

$$(x-4)(x+2)\left(\frac{6}{(x-4)(x+2)} + \frac{x+3}{x+2}\right) = (x-4)(x+2)(2)$$

$$6 + (x-4)(x+3) = 2(x-4)(x+2)$$

$$6 + x^2 - x - 12 = 2x^2 - 4x - 16$$

$$0 = x^2 - 3x - 10$$

$$0 = (x-5)(x+2)$$

$$x = 5 \qquad (x = -2 \text{ does not check})$$

47. Solving for y:

$$x = \frac{y-3}{y-1}$$

$$x(y-1) = y-3$$

$$xy - x = y - 3$$

$$xy - y = x - 3$$

$$y(x-1) = x - 3$$

$$y = \frac{x-3}{x-1}$$

49. Solving for y:

$$x = \frac{2y+1}{3y+1}$$

$$x(3y+1) = 2y+1$$

$$3xy + x = 2y + 1$$

$$3xy - 2y = -x + 1$$

$$y(3x-2) = -x + 1$$

$$y = \frac{1-x}{3x-2}$$

51. Solving for λ:

$$P = \frac{h}{\lambda}$$

$$P\lambda = h$$

$$\lambda = \frac{h}{P}$$

53. Solving for l:

$$R = \frac{wa^2}{2l}$$

$$2Rl = wa^2$$

$$l = \frac{wa^2}{2R}$$

55. Solving for b:

$$\frac{a}{b} = \frac{x}{y}$$

$$ay = bx$$

$$b = \frac{ay}{x}$$

57. Solving for b:

$$\frac{a}{a-b} = c$$

$$a = ac - bc$$

$$bc = ac - a$$

$$b = \frac{a(c-1)}{c}$$

59. Solving for x:

$$\frac{x+3}{a} = \frac{x}{b}$$

$$bx + 3b = ax$$

$$bx - ax = -3b$$

$$x(b-a) = -3b$$

$$x = \frac{-3b}{b-a} = \frac{3b}{a-b}$$

61. Solving for x:

$$\frac{1}{x} = \frac{1}{b} - \frac{1}{a}$$

$$abx\left(\frac{1}{x}\right) = abx\left(\frac{1}{b} - \frac{1}{a}\right)$$

$$ab = ax - bx$$

$$ab = x(a-b)$$

$$x = \frac{ab}{a-b}$$

63. Solving for y:

$$\frac{x}{y} - \frac{2}{z} = \frac{m}{3}$$

$$3yz\left(\frac{x}{y} - \frac{2}{z}\right) = 3yz\left(\frac{m}{3}\right)$$

$$3xz - 6y = myz$$

$$3xz = myz + 6y$$

$$3xz = y(mz + 6)$$

$$y = \frac{3xz}{mz + 6}$$

65. Substituting $y_1 = 12$ and $y_2 = 8$:

$$\frac{1}{h} = \frac{1}{12} + \frac{1}{8} = \frac{2}{24} + \frac{3}{24} = \frac{5}{24}$$

$$h = \frac{24}{5} \text{ feet}$$

67. Solving the equation:

$$\frac{3}{x+1} - \frac{1}{2} = \frac{x}{x+1}$$

$$2(x+1)\left(\frac{3}{x+1} - \frac{1}{2}\right) = 2(x+1)\left(\frac{x}{x+1}\right)$$

$$6 - (x+1) = 2x$$

$$6 - x - 1 = 2x$$

$$5 = 3x$$

$$x = \frac{5}{3}$$

The correct answer is b.

69. Solving the equation:

$$\frac{x}{x+2} + \frac{3}{x-2} = \frac{12}{x^2 - 4}$$

$$(x+2)(x-2)\left(\frac{x}{x+2} + \frac{3}{x-2}\right) = (x+2)(x-2)\left(\frac{12}{(x+2)(x-2)}\right)$$

$$x(x-2) + 3(x+2) = 12$$

$$x^2 - 2x + 3x + 6 = 12$$

$$x^2 + x - 6 = 0$$

$$(x+3)(x-2) = 0$$

$$x = -3 \qquad (x = 2 \text{ does not check})$$

So $x = 2$ is an extraneous solution. The correct answer is d.

71. Multiplying: $39.3 \cdot 60 = 2,358$

73. Dividing: $65,000 \div 5,280 \approx 12.3$

75. Multiplying: $2x\left(\frac{1}{x} + \frac{1}{2x}\right) = 2x \cdot \frac{1}{x} + 2x \cdot \frac{1}{2x} = 2 + 1 = 3$

77. Solving the equation:

$$12(x+3)+12(x-3)=3(x^2-9)$$
$$12x+36+12x-36=3x^2-27$$
$$24x=3x^2-27$$
$$3x^2-24x-27=0$$
$$3(x^2-8x-9)=0$$
$$3(x-9)(x+1)=0$$
$$x=-1,9$$

79. Solving the equation:

$$\frac{1}{10}-\frac{1}{12}=\frac{1}{x}$$
$$60x\left(\frac{1}{10}-\frac{1}{12}\right)=60x\left(\frac{1}{x}\right)$$
$$6x-5x=60$$
$$x=60$$

6.6 Applications

1. Let x and $3x$ represent the two numbers. The equation is:

$$\frac{1}{x}+\frac{1}{3x}=\frac{20}{3}$$
$$3x\left(\frac{1}{x}+\frac{1}{3x}\right)=3x\left(\frac{20}{3}\right)$$
$$3+1=20x$$
$$20x=4$$
$$x=\frac{1}{5}$$
$$3x=\frac{3}{5}$$

The numbers are $\frac{1}{5}$ and $\frac{3}{5}$.

3. Let x represent the number. The equation is:

$$x+\frac{1}{x}=\frac{10}{3}$$
$$3x\left(x+\frac{1}{x}\right)=3x\left(\frac{10}{3}\right)$$
$$3x^2+3=10x$$
$$3x^2-10x+3=0$$
$$(3x-1)(x-3)=0$$
$$x=\frac{1}{3},3$$

The number is either 3 or $\frac{1}{3}$.

5. Let x and $x + 1$ represent the two integers. The equation is:

$$\frac{1}{x} + \frac{1}{x+1} = \frac{7}{12}$$

$$12x(x+1)\left(\frac{1}{x} + \frac{1}{x+1}\right) = 12x(x+1)\left(\frac{7}{12}\right)$$

$$12(x+1) + 12x = 7x(x+1)$$

$$12x + 12 + 12x = 7x^2 + 7x$$

$$0 = 7x^2 - 17x - 12$$

$$0 = (7x+4)(x-3)$$

$$x = 3 \qquad \left(x = -\frac{4}{7} \text{ is not an integer}\right)$$

The two integers are 3 and 4.

7. Let x represent the number. The equation is:

$$\frac{7+x}{9+x} = \frac{5}{6}$$

$$6(9+x)\left(\frac{7+x}{9+x}\right) = 6(9+x)\left(\frac{5}{6}\right)$$

$$6(7+x) = 5(9+x)$$

$$42 + 6x = 45 + 5x$$

$$x = 3$$

The number is 3.

9.   **a-b.** Completing the table.

	d (miles)	r (mph)	t (hours)
Upstream	1.5	$5-x$	$\dfrac{1.5}{5-x}$
Downstream	3	$5+x$	$\dfrac{3}{5+x}$

c.   The times are the same, so the equation is $\dfrac{3}{5+x} = \dfrac{1.5}{5-x}$.

d.   Setting the times equal:

$$\frac{3}{5+x} = \frac{1.5}{5-x}$$

$$3(5-x) = 1.5(5+x)$$

$$15 - 3x = 7.5 + 1.5x$$

$$7.5 = 4.5x$$

$$x = \frac{75}{45} = \frac{5}{3}$$

The speed of the current is $\dfrac{5}{3}$ mph.

11. Let x represent the speed of the boat. Since the total time is 3 hours:

$$\frac{8}{x-2}+\frac{8}{x+2}=3$$

$$(x+2)(x-2)\left(\frac{8}{x-2}+\frac{8}{x+2}\right)=3(x+2)(x-2)$$

$$8(x+2)+8(x-2)=3x^2-12$$

$$16x=3x^2-12$$

$$0=3x^2-16x-12$$

$$0=(3x+2)(x-6)$$

$$x=6 \qquad \left(x=-\frac{2}{3} \text{ is impossible}\right)$$

The speed of the boat is 6 mph.

13. **a-b.** Completing the table.

	d (miles)	r (mph)	t (hours)
Train A	150	$x+15$	$\dfrac{150}{x+15}$
Train B	120	x	$\dfrac{120}{x}$

c. The times are the same, so the equation is $\dfrac{150}{x+15}=\dfrac{120}{x}$.

d. Setting the times equal:

$$\frac{150}{x+15}=\frac{120}{x}$$

$$150x=120(x+15)$$

$$150x=120x+1800$$

$$30x=1800$$

$$x=60$$

The speed of train A is 75 mph and the speed of train B is 60 mph.

15. The smaller plane makes the trip in 3 hours, so the 747 must take $1\frac{1}{2}$ hours to complete the trip. Thus the average

speed is given by: $\dfrac{810 \text{ miles}}{1\frac{1}{2} \text{ hours}}=540$ miles per hour

17. Let r represent the bus's usual speed. The difference of the two times is $\frac{1}{2}$ hour, therefore:

$$\frac{270}{r}-\frac{270}{r+6}=\frac{1}{2}$$

$$2r(r+6)\left(\frac{270}{r}-\frac{270}{r+6}\right)=2r(r+6)\left(\frac{1}{2}\right)$$

$$540(r+6)-540(r)=r(r+6)$$

$$540r+3240-540r=r^2+6r$$

$$0=r^2+6r-3240$$

$$0=(r-54)(r+60)$$

$$r=54 \quad (r=-60 \text{ is impossible})$$

The usual speed is 54 mph.

19. Let x represent the time to paint the room together. The rate equation is:

$$\frac{1}{4}+\frac{1}{6}=\frac{1}{x}$$

$$12x\left(\frac{1}{4}+\frac{1}{6}\right)=12x\left(\frac{1}{x}\right)$$

$$3x+2x=12$$

$$5x=12$$

$$x=\frac{12}{5}=2.4$$

It will take 2.4 hours to paint the room if Doug and Elaine are painting together.

21. Let x represent the time for Alonzo working alone to detail the car. The rate equation is:

$$\frac{1}{60}+\frac{1}{x}=\frac{1}{36}$$

$$180x\left(\frac{1}{60}+\frac{1}{x}\right)=180x\left(\frac{1}{36}\right)$$

$$3x+180=5x$$

$$180=2x$$

$$x=90$$

It will take 90 minutes to detail the car if Alonzo is working alone.

23. Let x represent the time to fill the tank if both pipes are open. The rate equation is:

$$\frac{1}{8}-\frac{1}{16}=\frac{1}{x}$$

$$16x\left(\frac{1}{8}-\frac{1}{16}\right)=16x\left(\frac{1}{x}\right)$$

$$2x-x=16$$

$$x=16$$

It will take 16 hours to fill the tank if both pipes are open.

25. Let x represent the time to fill the pool with both pipes open. The rate equation is:

$$\frac{1}{10}-\frac{1}{15}=\frac{1}{2}\bullet\frac{1}{x}$$

$$30x\left(\frac{1}{10}-\frac{1}{15}\right)=30x\left(\frac{1}{2x}\right)$$

$$3x-2x=15$$

$$x=15$$

It will take 15 hours to fill the pool with both pipes open.

27. Let x represent the time to fill the sink with the hot water faucet. The rate equation is:

$$\frac{1}{3.5}+\frac{1}{x}=\frac{1}{2.1}$$

$$7.35x\left(\frac{1}{3.5}+\frac{1}{x}\right)=7.35x\left(\frac{1}{2.1}\right)$$

$$2.1x+7.35=3.5x$$

$$7.35=1.4x$$

$$x=5.25$$

It will take 5.25 minutes to fill the sink with the hot water faucet alone.

29. Solving the equation:

$$\frac{1}{3}\left[\left(x+\frac{2}{3}x\right)+\frac{1}{3}\left(x+\frac{2}{3}x\right)\right]=10$$

$$\left(x+\frac{2}{3}x\right)+\frac{1}{3}\left(x+\frac{2}{3}x\right)=30$$

$$x+\frac{2}{3}x+\frac{1}{3}x+\frac{2}{9}x=30$$

$$\frac{20}{9}x=30$$

$$20x=270$$

$$x=\frac{27}{2}$$

31. **a.** Finding the grams of carbon: $(2.5\ \text{moles})\left(\dfrac{12.01\ \text{grams}}{1\ \text{mole}}\right)\approx 30\ \text{grams}$

b. Finding the moles of carbon: $(39\ \text{grams})\left(\dfrac{1\ \text{mole}}{12.01\ \text{grams}}\right)\approx 3.25\ \text{moles}$

33. Let x represent the number. The equation is:

$$x-\frac{1}{x}=\frac{3}{2}$$

$$2x\left(x-\frac{1}{x}\right)=2x\left(\frac{3}{2}\right)$$

$$2x^2-2=3x$$

$$2x^2-3x-2=0$$

$$(2x+1)(x-2)=0$$

$$x=-\frac{1}{2},2$$

The correct answer is d.

35. Let x represent the time to fill the pool if both pipes are used. The rate equation is:

$$\frac{1}{10}+\frac{1}{15}=\frac{1}{x}$$

$$30x\left(\frac{1}{10}+\frac{1}{15}\right)=30x\left(\frac{1}{x}\right)$$

$$3x+2x=30$$

$$5x=30$$

$$x=6$$

It will take 6 hours to fill the pool if both pipes are used. The correct answer is a.

37. The expression is undefined if $x=2$.

39. Solving the equation:

$$x^2-9=0$$

$$(x+3)(x-3)=0$$

$$x=-3,3$$

41. Reducing to lowest terms: $\dfrac{x^2-a^2}{x-a}=\dfrac{(x+a)(x-a)}{x-a}=x+a$

43. Finding the slope: $m=\dfrac{9-4}{3-1}=\dfrac{5}{2}$

45. Finding each function value:
$$f(0) = (0)^2 + 5 = 0 + 5 = 5 \qquad\qquad f(-1) = (-1)^2 + 5 = 1 + 5 = 6$$

47. Finding the x and y-intercepts:
$$y = 2(0) - 4 \qquad\qquad 0 = 2x - 4$$
$$y = 0 - 4 \qquad\qquad\qquad 4 = 2x$$
$$y = -4 \qquad\qquad\qquad\quad x = 2$$

The x-intercept is $(2,0)$ and the y-intercept is $(0,-4)$.

6.7 Rational Functions

1. Finding each function value:
$$g(0) = \frac{0+3}{0-1} = \frac{3}{-1} = -3 \qquad\qquad g(-3) = \frac{-3+3}{-3-1} = \frac{0}{-4} = 0$$
$$g(3) = \frac{3+3}{3-1} = \frac{6}{2} = 3 \qquad\qquad g(-1) = \frac{-1+3}{-1-1} = \frac{2}{-2} = -1$$
$$g(1) = \frac{1+3}{1-1} = \frac{4}{0}, \text{ which is undefined}$$

3. Finding each function value:
$$h(0) = \frac{0-3}{0+1} = \frac{-3}{1} = -3 \qquad\qquad h(-3) = \frac{-3-3}{-3+1} = \frac{-6}{-2} = 3$$
$$h(3) = \frac{3-3}{3+1} = \frac{0}{4} = 0 \qquad\qquad h(-1) = \frac{-1-3}{-1+1} = \frac{-4}{0}, \text{ which is undefined}$$
$$h(1) = \frac{1-3}{1+1} = \frac{-2}{2} = -1$$

5. The domain is $\{x \mid x \neq 1\}$. **7.** The domain is $\{x \mid x \neq 2\}$.

9. Setting the denominator equal to 0:
$$t^2 - 16 = 0$$
$$(t+4)(t-4) = 0$$
$$t = -4, 4$$

The domain is $\{t \mid t \neq -4, t \neq 4\}$.

11. a. From the graph: $f(2) = 2$ **b.** From the graph: $f(-1) = -4$

c. From the graph: $f(0)$ is undefined **d.** From the graph: $g(3) = 2$

13. a. Evaluating the difference quotient: $\dfrac{f(x) - f(a)}{x - a} = \dfrac{4x - 4a}{x - a} = \dfrac{4(x-a)}{x-a} = 4$

b. Evaluating the difference quotient: $\dfrac{f(x+h) - f(x)}{h} = \dfrac{4x + 4h - 4x}{h} = \dfrac{4h}{h} = 4$

15. a. Evaluating the difference quotient: $\dfrac{f(x) - f(a)}{x - a} = \dfrac{(5x+3) - (5a+3)}{x - a} = \dfrac{5x - 5a}{x - a} = \dfrac{5(x-a)}{x-a} = 5$

b. Evaluating the difference quotient: $\dfrac{f(x+h) - f(x)}{h} = \dfrac{5(x+h) + 3 - (5x+3)}{h} = \dfrac{5x + 5h + 3 - 5x - 3}{h} = \dfrac{5h}{h} = 5$

17. **a.** Evaluating the difference quotient: $\dfrac{f(x)-f(a)}{x-a} = \dfrac{x^2-a^2}{x-a} = \dfrac{(x+a)(x-a)}{x-a} = x+a$

b. Evaluating the difference quotient:

$$\frac{f(x+h)-f(x)}{h} = \frac{(x+h)^2 - x^2}{h} = \frac{x^2+2xh+h^2-x^2}{h} = \frac{2xh+h^2}{h} = \frac{h(2x+h)}{h} = 2x+h$$

19. **a.** Evaluating the difference quotient: $\dfrac{f(x)-f(a)}{x-a} = \dfrac{(x^2+1)-(a^2+1)}{x-a} = \dfrac{x^2-a^2}{x-a} = \dfrac{(x+a)(x-a)}{x-a} = x+a$

b. Evaluating the difference quotient:

$$\frac{f(x+h)-f(x)}{h} = \frac{(x+h)^2+1-(x^2+1)}{h} = \frac{x^2+2xh+h^2+1-x^2-1}{h} = \frac{2xh+h^2}{h} = \frac{h(2x+h)}{h} = 2x+h$$

21. **a.** Evaluating the difference quotient:

$$\frac{f(x)-f(a)}{x-a} = \frac{(x^2-3x+4)-(a^2-3a+4)}{x-a}$$

$$= \frac{x^2-a^2-3x+3a}{x-a}$$

$$= \frac{(x+a)(x-a)-3(x-a)}{x-a}$$

$$= \frac{(x-a)(x+a-3)}{x-a}$$

$$= x+a-3$$

b. Evaluating the difference quotient:

$$\frac{f(x+h)-f(x)}{h} = \frac{(x+h)^2-3(x+h)+4-(x^2-3x+4)}{h}$$

$$= \frac{x^2+2xh+h^2-3x-3h+4-x^2+3x-4}{h}$$

$$= \frac{2xh+h^2-3h}{h}$$

$$= \frac{h(2x+h-3)}{h}$$

$$= 2x+h-3$$

23. **a.** Simplifying the difference quotient: $\dfrac{f(x)-f(a)}{x-a} = \dfrac{\frac{4}{x}-\frac{4}{a}}{x-a} = \dfrac{\left(\frac{4}{x}-\frac{4}{a}\right)ax}{(x-a)ax} = \dfrac{4a-4x}{ax(x-a)} = \dfrac{-4(x-a)}{ax(x-a)} = -\dfrac{4}{ax}$

b. Simplifying the difference quotient:

$$\dfrac{f(x)-f(a)}{x-a} = \dfrac{\frac{1}{x+1}-\frac{1}{a+1}}{x-a}$$

$$= \dfrac{\left(\frac{1}{x+1}-\frac{1}{a+1}\right)(x+1)(a+1)}{(x-a)(x+1)(a+1)}$$

$$= \dfrac{a+1-x-1}{(x-a)(x+1)(a+1)}$$

$$= \dfrac{a-x}{(x-a)(x+1)(a+1)}$$

$$= -\dfrac{1}{(x+1)(a+1)}$$

c. Simplifying the difference quotient:

$$\dfrac{f(x)-f(a)}{x-a} = \dfrac{\frac{1}{x^2}-\frac{1}{a^2}}{x-a} = \dfrac{\left(\frac{1}{x^2}-\frac{1}{a^2}\right)a^2x^2}{a^2x^2(x-a)} = \dfrac{a^2-x^2}{a^2x^2(x-a)} = \dfrac{(a+x)(a-x)}{a^2x^2(x-a)} = -\dfrac{a+x}{a^2x^2}$$

25. **a.** Solving the equation:

$$f(x)+g(x) = \dfrac{5}{8}$$

$$\dfrac{1}{x-3}+\dfrac{1}{x+3} = \dfrac{5}{8}$$

$$8(x-3)(x+3)\left(\dfrac{1}{x-3}+\dfrac{1}{x+3}\right) = 8(x-3)(x+3)\left(\dfrac{5}{8}\right)$$

$$8(x+3)+8(x-3) = 5(x-3)(x+3)$$

$$8x+24+8x-24 = 5x^2-45$$

$$16x = 5x^2-45$$

$$0 = 5x^2-16x-45$$

$$0 = (5x+9)(x-5)$$

$$x = -\dfrac{9}{5}, 5$$

b. Solving the equation:

$$\frac{f(x)}{g(x)} = 5$$

$$\frac{\dfrac{1}{x-3}}{\dfrac{1}{x+3}} = 5$$

$$\frac{x+3}{x-3} = 5$$

$$x+3 = 5(x-3)$$

$$x+3 = 5x-15$$

$$18 = 4x$$

$$x = \frac{9}{2}$$

c. Solving the equation:

$$f(x) = g(x)$$

$$\frac{1}{x-3} = \frac{1}{x+3}$$

$$x+3 = x-3$$

$$3 = -3 \ \text{(false)}$$

There is no solution $(\varnothing)$.

27. Graphing the function:

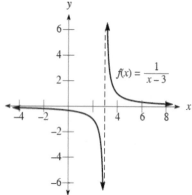

29. Graphing the function:

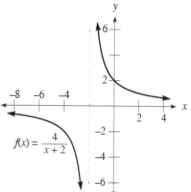

31. Graphing the function:

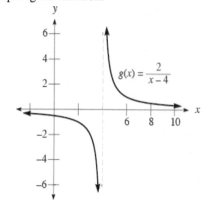

33. Graphing the function:

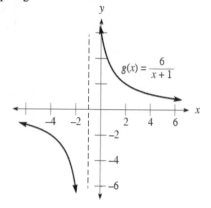

35. Sketching the graph:

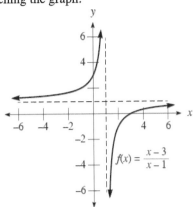

37. Sketching the graph:

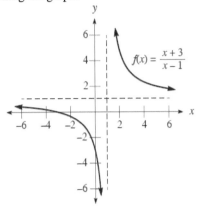

39. Sketching the graph:

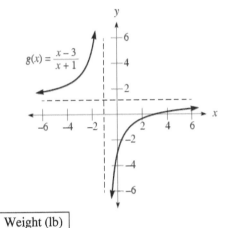

41. Completing the table:

Weeks	Weight (lb)
x	$W(x)$
0	200
1	194
4	184
12	173
24	168

43. Evaluating the function: $f(-2) = \dfrac{-2+5}{-2-4} = \dfrac{3}{-6} = -\dfrac{1}{2}$. The correct answer is b.

45. Simplifying: $\dfrac{f(x+h)-f(x)}{h} = \dfrac{(x+h)^2 - 5 - (x^2 - 5)}{h} = \dfrac{x^2 + 2xh + h^2 - 5 - x^2 + 5}{h} = \dfrac{2xh + h^2}{h} = \dfrac{h(2x+h)}{h} = 2x+h$

The correct answer is d.

47. Performing the operations: $\dfrac{2a+10}{a^3} \cdot \dfrac{a^2}{3a+15} = \dfrac{2(a+5)}{a^3} \cdot \dfrac{a^2}{3(a+5)} = \dfrac{2}{3a}$

49. Performing the operations: $(x^2 - 9)\left(\dfrac{x+2}{x+3}\right) = (x+3)(x-3)\left(\dfrac{x+2}{x+3}\right) = (x-3)(x+2)$

51. Performing the operations: $\dfrac{2x-7}{x-2} - \dfrac{x-5}{x-2} = \dfrac{2x-7-x+5}{x-2} = \dfrac{x-2}{x-2} = 1$

53. Simplifying the expression: $\dfrac{\dfrac{1}{x}-\dfrac{1}{3}}{\dfrac{1}{x}+\dfrac{1}{3}} = \dfrac{\left(\dfrac{1}{x}-\dfrac{1}{3}\right)\cdot 3x}{\left(\dfrac{1}{x}+\dfrac{1}{3}\right)\cdot 3x} = \dfrac{3-x}{3+x}$

55. Solving the equation:

$$\frac{x}{x-3}+\frac{3}{2}=\frac{3}{x-3}$$

$$2(x-3)\left(\frac{x}{x-3}+\frac{3}{2}\right)=2(x-3)\left(\frac{3}{x-3}\right)$$

$$2x+3(x-3)=6$$

$$2x+3x-9=6$$

$$5x=15$$

$$x=3 \qquad (\text{does not check})$$

There is no solution (3 does not check).

Chapter 6 Test

1. The denominator factors as $(x+5)(x-2)$, so the expression is undefined if $x=-5,2$.

2. Since the denominator is never equal to 0, the expression is defined for all real numbers.

3. Reducing the fraction: $\dfrac{x^2-y^2}{x-y} = \dfrac{(x+y)(x-y)}{x-y} = x+y$

4. Reducing the fraction: $\dfrac{2x^2-5x+3}{2x^2-x-3} = \dfrac{(2x-3)(x-1)}{(2x-3)(x+1)} = \dfrac{x-1}{x+1}$

5. Reducing the fraction: $\dfrac{7-x}{2x-14} = \dfrac{-1(x-7)}{2(x-7)} = -\dfrac{1}{2}$

6. Reducing the fraction: $\dfrac{4-a^2}{a^2-4a+4} = \dfrac{-1(a^2-4)}{a^2-4a+4} = -\dfrac{(a+2)(a-2)}{(a-2)^2} = -\dfrac{a+2}{a-2}$

7. Performing the operations: $\dfrac{a^2-16}{5a-15}\cdot\dfrac{10(a-3)^2}{a^2-7a+12} = \dfrac{(a+4)(a-4)}{5(a-3)}\cdot\dfrac{10(a-3)^2}{(a-4)(a-3)} = 2(a+4)$

8. Performing the operations:

$$\frac{a^4-81}{a^2+9}\div\frac{a^2-8a+15}{4a-20} = \frac{a^4-81}{a^2+9}\cdot\frac{4a-20}{a^2-8a+15} = \frac{(a^2+9)(a+3)(a-3)}{a^2+9}\cdot\frac{4(a-5)}{(a-5)(a-3)} = 4(a+3)$$

9. Performing the operations:

$$\frac{x^3-8}{2x^2-9x+10}\div\frac{x^2+2x+4}{2x^2+x-15} = \frac{x^3-8}{2x^2-9x+10}\cdot\frac{2x^2+x-15}{x^2+2x+4} = \frac{(x-2)(x^2+2x+4)}{(2x-5)(x-2)}\cdot\frac{(2x-5)(x+3)}{x^2+2x+4} = x+3$$

10. Performing the operations: $\dfrac{4}{21}+\dfrac{6}{35} = \dfrac{4}{21}\cdot\dfrac{5}{5}+\dfrac{6}{35}\cdot\dfrac{3}{3} = \dfrac{20}{105}+\dfrac{18}{105} = \dfrac{38}{105}$

11. Performing the operations: $\dfrac{3}{4}-\dfrac{1}{2}+\dfrac{5}{8} = \dfrac{3}{4}\cdot\dfrac{2}{2}-\dfrac{1}{2}\cdot\dfrac{4}{4}+\dfrac{5}{8} = \dfrac{6}{8}-\dfrac{4}{8}+\dfrac{5}{8} = \dfrac{7}{8}$

12. Performing the operations: $\dfrac{a}{a^2-9}+\dfrac{3}{a^2-9} = \dfrac{a+3}{a^2-9} = \dfrac{a+3}{(a+3)(a-3)} = \dfrac{1}{a-3}$

13. Performing the operations: $\dfrac{1}{x}+\dfrac{2}{x-3} = \dfrac{1}{x}\cdot\dfrac{x-3}{x-3}+\dfrac{2}{x-3}\cdot\dfrac{x}{x} = \dfrac{x-3}{x(x-3)}+\dfrac{2x}{x(x-3)} = \dfrac{3x-3}{x(x-3)} = \dfrac{3(x-1)}{x(x-3)}$

14. Performing the operations:

$$\frac{4x}{x^2+6x+5} - \frac{3x}{x^2+5x+4} = \frac{4x}{(x+5)(x+1)} - \frac{3x}{(x+4)(x+1)}$$

$$= \frac{4x}{(x+5)(x+1)} \cdot \frac{x+4}{x+4} - \frac{3x}{(x+4)(x+1)} \cdot \frac{x+5}{x+5}$$

$$= \frac{4x^2+16x}{(x+5)(x+1)(x+4)} - \frac{3x^2+15x}{(x+5)(x+1)(x+4)}$$

$$= \frac{4x^2+16x-3x^2-15x}{(x+5)(x+1)(x+4)}$$

$$= \frac{x^2+x}{(x+5)(x+1)(x+4)}$$

$$= \frac{x(x+1)}{(x+5)(x+1)(x+4)}$$

$$= \frac{x}{(x+4)(x+5)}$$

15. Performing the operations:

$$\frac{2x+8}{x^2+4x+3} - \frac{x+4}{x^2+5x+6} = \frac{2x+8}{(x+3)(x+1)} - \frac{x+4}{(x+3)(x+2)}$$

$$= \frac{2x+8}{(x+3)(x+1)} \cdot \frac{x+2}{x+2} - \frac{x+4}{(x+3)(x+2)} \cdot \frac{x+1}{x+1}$$

$$= \frac{2x^2+12x+16}{(x+1)(x+2)(x+3)} - \frac{x^2+5x+4}{(x+1)(x+2)(x+3)}$$

$$= \frac{2x^2+12x+16-x^2-5x-4}{(x+1)(x+2)(x+3)}$$

$$= \frac{x^2+7x+12}{(x+1)(x+2)(x+3)}$$

$$= \frac{(x+3)(x+4)}{(x+1)(x+2)(x+3)}$$

$$= \frac{x+4}{(x+1)(x+2)}$$

16. Simplifying the complex fraction: $\dfrac{3-\dfrac{1}{a+3}}{3+\dfrac{1}{a+3}} = \dfrac{\left(3-\dfrac{1}{a+3}\right)(a+3)}{\left(3+\dfrac{1}{a+3}\right)(a+3)} = \dfrac{3(a+3)-1}{3(a+3)+1} = \dfrac{3a+9-1}{3a+9+1} = \dfrac{3a+8}{3a+10}$

17. Simplifying the complex fraction: $\dfrac{1-\dfrac{9}{x^2}}{1+\dfrac{1}{x}-\dfrac{6}{x^2}} = \dfrac{\left(1-\dfrac{9}{x^2}\right) \cdot x^2}{\left(1+\dfrac{1}{x}-\dfrac{6}{x^2}\right) \cdot x^2} = \dfrac{x^2-9}{x^2+x-6} = \dfrac{(x+3)(x-3)}{(x+3)(x-2)} = \dfrac{x-3}{x-2}$

18. Solving the equation:

$$\frac{1}{x} + 3 = \frac{4}{3}$$

$$3x\left(\frac{1}{x} + 3\right) = 3x\left(\frac{4}{3}\right)$$

$$3 + 9x = 4x$$

$$5x = -3$$

$$x = -\frac{3}{5}$$

19. Solving the equation:

$$\frac{x}{x-3} + 3 = \frac{3}{x-3}$$

$$(x-3)\left(\frac{x}{x-3} + 3\right) = (x-3)\left(\frac{3}{x-3}\right)$$

$$x + 3(x-3) = 3$$

$$x + 3x - 9 = 3$$

$$4x = 12$$

$$x = 3 \quad (x = 3 \text{ does not check})$$

There is no solution (3 does not check).

20. Solving the equation:

$$\frac{y+3}{2y} + \frac{5}{y-1} = \frac{1}{2}$$

$$2y(y-1)\left(\frac{y+3}{2y} + \frac{5}{y-1}\right) = 2y(y-1)\left(\frac{1}{2}\right)$$

$$(y-1)(y+3) + 10y = y(y-1)$$

$$y^2 + 2y - 3 + 10y = y^2 - y$$

$$12y - 3 = -y$$

$$13y = 3$$

$$y = \frac{3}{13}$$

21. Solving the equation:

$$1 - \frac{1}{x} = \frac{6}{x^2}$$

$$x^2\left(1 - \frac{1}{x}\right) = x^2\left(\frac{6}{x^2}\right)$$

$$x^2 - x = 6$$

$$x^2 - x - 6 = 0$$

$$(x+2)(x-3) = 0$$

$$x = -2, 3$$

22. Let x represent the number. The equation is:

$$\frac{10}{23-x} = \frac{1}{3}$$

$$30 = 23 - x$$

$$x = -7$$

The number is -7.

23. Let x represent the speed of the boat. Since the total time is 3 hours:

$$\frac{8}{x-2} + \frac{8}{x+2} = 3$$

$$3(x-2)(x+2)\left(\frac{8}{x-2} + \frac{8}{x+2}\right) = 3(x-2)(x+2) \cdot 3$$

$$24(x+2) + 24(x-2) = 9(x^2 - 4)$$

$$48x = 9x^2 - 36$$

$$0 = 9x^2 - 48x - 36$$

$$0 = 3(3x^2 - 16x - 12)$$

$$0 = 3(3x+2)(x-6)$$

$$x = 6 \quad \left(x = -\frac{2}{3} \text{ is impossible}\right)$$

The speed of the boat is 6 mph.

24. Let x represent the time to fill the pool with both the pipe and drain open. The rate equation is:

$$\frac{1}{10} - \frac{1}{15} = \frac{1}{2} \cdot \frac{1}{x}$$

$$30x\left(\frac{1}{10} - \frac{1}{15}\right) = 30x\left(\frac{1}{2x}\right)$$

$$3x - 2x = 15$$

$$x = 15$$

The pool can be filled in 15 hours with both the pipe and drain open.

25. The domain is $\{x \mid x \ne -2\}$.

26. Setting the denominator equal to 0:

$$t^2 - 36 = 0$$

$$(t+6)(t-6) = 0$$

$$t = -6, 6$$

The domain is $\{t \mid t \ne -6, t \ne 6\}$.

27. Evaluating the difference quotient: $\dfrac{f(x) - f(a)}{x - a} = \dfrac{(4x-3) - (4a-3)}{x-a} = \dfrac{4x - 4a}{x-a} = \dfrac{4(x-a)}{x-a} = 4$

28. Evaluating the difference quotient:

$$\frac{f(x+h) - f(x)}{h} = \frac{(x+h)^2 + 2(x+h) - 5 - (x^2 + 2x - 5)}{h}$$

$$= \frac{x^2 + 2xh + h^2 + 2x + 2h - 5 - x^2 - 2x + 5}{h}$$

$$= \frac{2xh + h^2 + 2h}{h}$$

$$= \frac{h(2x + h + 2)}{h}$$

$$= 2x + h + 2$$

29. Graphing the function:

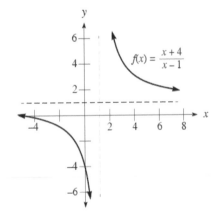

Chapter 7
Roots and Rational Exponents

7.1 Roots and Radical Functions

1. Finding the root: $\sqrt{144} = 12$

3. Finding the root: $\sqrt{-144}$ is not a real number

5. Finding the root: $-\sqrt{49} = -7$

7. Finding the root: $\sqrt[3]{-27} = -3$

9. Finding the root: $-\sqrt[3]{-27} = -(-3) = 3$

11. Finding the root: $-\sqrt[4]{16} = -2$

13. Finding the root: $\sqrt{0.04} = 0.2$

15. Finding the root: $\sqrt[3]{0.008} = 0.2$

17. Finding the root: $\sqrt{\dfrac{1}{36}} = \dfrac{1}{6}$

19. Finding the root: $\sqrt[3]{\dfrac{1}{8}} = \dfrac{1}{2}$

21. Simplifying: $\left(\sqrt{5}\right)^2 = 5$

23. Simplifying: $\left(\sqrt[3]{2}\right)^3 = 2$

25. Simplifying: $\left(\sqrt[4]{10}\right)^4 = 10$

27. Simplifying: $\left(\sqrt{7x}\right)^2 = 7x$

29. Simplifying: $\sqrt{36a^8} = 6a^4$

31. Simplifying: $\sqrt[3]{27a^{12}} = 3a^4$

33. Simplifying: $\sqrt[3]{x^3 y^6} = xy^2$

35. Simplifying: $\sqrt[5]{32x^{10}y^5} = 2x^2 y$

37. Simplifying: $\sqrt[4]{16a^{12}b^{20}} = 2a^3 b^5$

39. **a.** Simplifying: $\sqrt{25} = \sqrt{5^2} = 5$

     b. Simplifying: $\sqrt{0.25} = \sqrt{0.5^2} = 0.5$

     c. Simplifying: $\sqrt{2,500} = \sqrt{50^2} = 50$

     d. Simplifying: $\sqrt{0.0025} = \sqrt{0.05^2} = 0.05$

41. **a.** Simplifying: $\sqrt{16a^4 b^8} = \sqrt{\left(4a^2 b^4\right)^2} = 4a^2 b^4$

     b. Simplifying: $\sqrt[4]{16a^4 b^8} = \sqrt[4]{\left(2ab^2\right)^4} = 2ab^2$

43. Graphing the equation:

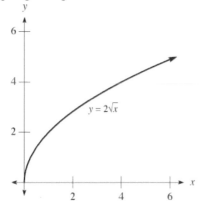

45. Graphing the equation:

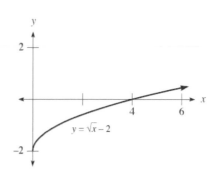

47. Graphing the equation:

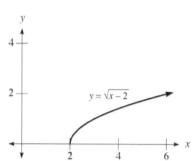

49. Graphing the equation:

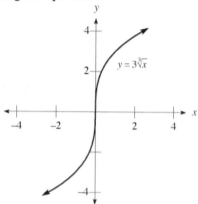

51. Graphing the equation:

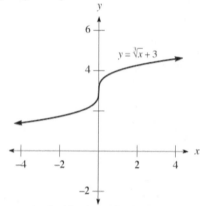

53. Graphing the equation:

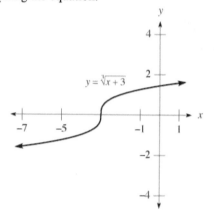

55. The quantity inside the radical must be non-negative, so:
$$x + 3 \geq 0$$
$$x \geq -3$$
The domain is $\{x \mid x \geq -3\} = [-3, \infty)$.

57. The quantity inside the radical must be non-negative, so $x \geq 0$. The domain is $\{x \mid x \geq 0\} = [0, \infty)$.

59. The quantity inside the radical must be non-negative, so:
$$2x - 10 \geq 0$$
$$2x \geq 10$$
$$x \geq 5$$
The domain is $\{x \mid x \geq 5\} = [5, \infty)$.

61. The quantity inside the radical must be non-negative, so:
$$5 - x \geq 0$$
$$-x \geq -5$$
$$x \leq 5$$
The domain is $\{x \mid x \leq 5\} = (-\infty, 5]$.

63. The cube root has no domain restrictions, so the domain is $\{x \mid x \text{ is any real number}\} = (-\infty, \infty)$.

65. The cube root has no domain restrictions, so the domain is $\{x \mid x \text{ is any real number}\} = (-\infty, \infty)$.

67. **a.** Each side of the square is: $60 + 300 + 60 = 420$ picometers

b. Let d represent the length of the diagonal. Using the Pythagorean theorem:

$$420^2 + 420^2 = d^2$$
$$d^2 = 352,800$$
$$d = \sqrt{352,800} \approx 594 \text{ picometers}$$

c. Converting to meters: $594 \text{ pm} \cdot \dfrac{1 \text{ m}}{10^{12} \text{ pm}} = 5.94 \times 10^{-10} \text{ m}$

69. Answers will vary.

71. Simplifying: $-\sqrt{64} = -8$. The correct answer is d.

73. Since $f(-3) = \sqrt{-3+4} = \sqrt{1} = 1$, the point $(-3,1)$ lies on the graph. The correct answer is c.

75. Simplifying: $\sqrt{25} = 5$

77. Simplifying: $\sqrt{16x^4 y^2} = 4x^2 y$

79. Simplifying: $\sqrt[3]{27} = 3$

81. Simplifying: $\sqrt[3]{8a^3 b^3} = 2ab$

83. Simplifying: $-5^2 = -(5 \cdot 5) = -25$

85. Simplifying: $5^{-2} = \dfrac{1}{5^2} = \dfrac{1}{25}$

87. Simplifying: $x^2 \cdot x^5 = x^{2+5} = x^7$

89. Simplifying: $\dfrac{x^5}{x^2} = x^{5-2} = x^3$

7.2 Rational Exponents

1. Writing as a root and simplifying: $36^{1/2} = \sqrt{36} = 6$

3. Writing as a root and simplifying: $-9^{1/2} = -\sqrt{9} = -3$

5. Writing as a root and simplifying: $8^{1/3} = \sqrt[3]{8} = 2$

7. Writing as a root and simplifying: $(-8)^{1/3} = \sqrt[3]{-8} = -2$

9. Writing as a root and simplifying: $32^{1/5} = \sqrt[5]{32} = 2$

11. Writing as a root and simplifying: $\left(\dfrac{81}{25}\right)^{1/2} = \sqrt{\dfrac{81}{25}} = \dfrac{9}{5}$

13. Writing as a root and simplifying: $\left(\dfrac{64}{125}\right)^{1/3} = \sqrt[3]{\dfrac{64}{125}} = \dfrac{4}{5}$

15. Writing as an exponent: $\sqrt{5} = 5^{1/2}$

17. Writing as an exponent: $\sqrt{3x} = (3x)^{1/2}$

19. Writing as an exponent: $\sqrt[3]{9} = 9^{1/3}$

21. Writing as an exponent: $\sqrt[3]{4x^2} = \left(4x^2\right)^{1/3}$

23. Simplifying: $27^{2/3} = \left(27^{1/3}\right)^2 = 3^2 = 9$

25. Simplifying: $25^{3/2} = \left(25^{1/2}\right)^3 = 5^3 = 125$

27. Simplifying: $16^{3/4} = \left(16^{1/4}\right)^3 = 2^3 = 8$

29. Simplifying: $27^{-1/3} = \left(27^{1/3}\right)^{-1} = 3^{-1} = \dfrac{1}{3}$

31. Simplifying: $81^{-3/4} = \left(81^{1/4}\right)^{-3} = 3^{-3} = \dfrac{1}{3^3} = \dfrac{1}{27}$

33. Simplifying: $\left(\dfrac{25}{36}\right)^{-1/2} = \left(\dfrac{36}{25}\right)^{1/2} = \dfrac{6}{5}$

35. Simplifying: $\left(\dfrac{81}{16}\right)^{-3/4} = \left(\dfrac{16}{81}\right)^{3/4} = \left[\left(\dfrac{16}{81}\right)^{1/4}\right]^3 = \left(\dfrac{2}{3}\right)^3 = \dfrac{8}{27}$

37. Simplifying: $16^{1/2} + 27^{1/3} = 4 + 3 = 7$

39. Simplifying: $8^{-2/3} + 4^{-1/2} = \left(8^{1/3}\right)^{-2} + \left(4^{1/2}\right)^{-1} = 2^{-2} + 2^{-1} = \dfrac{1}{4} + \dfrac{1}{2} = \dfrac{3}{4}$

41. Using properties of exponents: $x^{3/5} \cdot x^{1/5} = x^{3/5+1/5} = x^{4/5}$

43. Using properties of exponents: $y^{1/2} \cdot y^{1/4} = y^{1/2+1/4} = y^{2/4+1/4} = y^{3/4}$

45. Using properties of exponents: $\left(a^{3/4}\right)^{4/3} = a^{3/4 \cdot 4/3} = a$

47. Using properties of exponents: $\dfrac{x^{1/5}}{x^{3/5}} = x^{1/5-3/5} = x^{-2/5} = \dfrac{1}{x^{2/5}}$

49. Using properties of exponents: $\dfrac{x^{5/6}}{x^{2/3}} = x^{5/6-2/3} = x^{5/6-4/6} = x^{1/6}$

51. Using properties of exponents: $\left(x^{3/5}y^{5/6}z^{1/3}\right)^{3/5} = x^{3/5 \cdot 3/5}y^{5/6 \cdot 3/5}z^{1/3 \cdot 3/5} = x^{9/25}y^{1/2}z^{1/5}$

53. Using properties of exponents: $\dfrac{a^{3/4}b^2}{a^{7/8}b^{1/4}} = a^{3/4-7/8}b^{2-1/4} = a^{6/8-7/8}b^{8/4-1/4} = a^{-1/8}b^{7/4} = \dfrac{b^{7/4}}{a^{1/8}}$

55. Using properties of exponents: $\dfrac{\left(y^{2/3}\right)^{3/4}}{\left(y^{1/3}\right)^{3/5}} = \dfrac{y^{1/2}}{y^{1/5}} = y^{1/2-1/5} = y^{5/10-2/10} = y^{3/10}$

57. Using properties of exponents: $\dfrac{x \cdot x^{2/3}}{\left(x^{5/6}\right)^3} = \dfrac{x^{1+2/3}}{x^{5/6 \cdot 3}} = \dfrac{x^{5/3}}{x^{5/2}} = x^{5/3-5/2} = x^{10/6-15/6} = x^{-5/6} = \dfrac{1}{x^{5/6}}$

59. Using properties of exponents: $\left(\dfrac{a^{-1/4}}{b^{1/2}}\right)^8 = \dfrac{a^{-1/4 \cdot 8}}{b^{1/2 \cdot 8}} = \dfrac{a^{-2}}{b^4} = \dfrac{1}{a^2 b^4}$

61. Writing with rational exponents and simplifying: $\sqrt{25a^6} = \left(25a^6\right)^{1/2} = 25^{1/2}\left(a^6\right)^{1/2} = 5a^3$

63. Writing with rational exponents and simplifying: $\sqrt{x^2 y^{10}} = \left(x^2 y^{10}\right)^{1/2} = \left(x^2\right)^{1/2}\left(y^{10}\right)^{1/2} = xy^5$

65. Writing with rational exponents and simplifying: $\sqrt[3]{27b^9} = \left(27b^9\right)^{1/3} = 27^{1/3}\left(b^9\right)^{1/3} = 3b^3$

67. Writing with rational exponents and simplifying: $\sqrt[3]{x^6 y^{21}} = \left(x^6 y^{21}\right)^{1/3} = \left(x^6\right)^{1/3}\left(y^{21}\right)^{1/3} = x^2 y^7$

69. Writing with rational exponents and simplifying: $\sqrt[4]{81a^8 b^{20}} = \left(81a^8 b^{20}\right)^{1/4} = 81^{1/4}\left(a^8\right)^{1/4}\left(b^{20}\right)^{1/4} = 3a^2 b^5$

71. Simplifying each expression:
$$\left(9^{1/2} + 4^{1/2}\right)^2 = (3+2)^2 = 5^2 = 25$$
$$9 + 4 = 13$$
Note that the values are not equal.

73. Rewriting with exponents: $\sqrt{\sqrt{a}} = \sqrt{a^{1/2}} = \left(a^{1/2}\right)^{1/2} = a^{1/4} = \sqrt[4]{a}$

75. Substituting $r = 250$: $v = \left(\dfrac{5 \cdot 250}{2}\right)^{1/2} = 625^{1/2} = 25$. The maximum speed is 25 mph.

77. Writing as an exponent: $\sqrt{8x} = (8x)^{1/2}$. The correct answer is a.

79. Writing with rational exponents and simplifying: $\sqrt{64x^6 y^{12}} = \left(64x^6 y^{12}\right)^{1/2} = 64^{1/2}\left(x^6\right)^{1/2}\left(y^{12}\right)^{1/2} = 8x^3 y^6$
The correct answer is b.

81. Simplifying: $\sqrt{6^2} = 6$

83. Simplifying: $\sqrt{(5y)^2} = 5y$

85. Simplifying: $\sqrt[3]{2^3} = 2$

87. Filling in the blank: $50 = 25 \cdot 2$

89. Filling in the blank: $48x^4 y^3 = 48x^4 y^2 \cdot y$

91. Filling in the blank: $12x^7 y^6 = 4x^6 y^6 \cdot 3x$

7.3 Simplified Form for Radicals

1. Simplifying the radical: $\sqrt{8} = \sqrt{4 \cdot 2} = 2\sqrt{2}$

3. Simplifying the radical: $\sqrt{98} = \sqrt{49 \cdot 2} = 7\sqrt{2}$

5. Simplifying the radical: $\sqrt{288} = \sqrt{144 \cdot 2} = 12\sqrt{2}$

7. Simplifying the radical: $\sqrt{80} = \sqrt{16 \cdot 5} = 4\sqrt{5}$

9. Simplifying the radical: $\sqrt{48} = \sqrt{16 \cdot 3} = 4\sqrt{3}$

11. Simplifying the radical: $\sqrt{675} = \sqrt{225 \cdot 3} = 15\sqrt{3}$

13. Simplifying the radical: $\sqrt[3]{54} = \sqrt[3]{27 \cdot 2} = 3\sqrt[3]{2}$

15. Simplifying the radical: $\sqrt[3]{128} = \sqrt[3]{64 \cdot 2} = 4\sqrt[3]{2}$

17. Simplifying the radical: $\sqrt[3]{432} = \sqrt[3]{216 \cdot 2} = 6\sqrt[3]{2}$

19. Simplifying the radical: $\sqrt[5]{64} = \sqrt[5]{32 \cdot 2} = 2\sqrt[5]{2}$

21. Simplifying the radical: $\sqrt{18x^3} = \sqrt{9x^2 \cdot 2x} = 3x\sqrt{2x}$

23. Simplifying the radical: $\sqrt[4]{32y^7} = \sqrt[4]{16y^4 \cdot 2y^3} = 2y\sqrt[4]{2y^3}$

25. Simplifying the radical: $\sqrt[3]{40x^4y^7} = \sqrt[3]{8x^3y^6 \cdot 5xy} = 2xy^2\sqrt[3]{5xy}$

27. Simplifying the radical: $\sqrt{48a^2b^3c^4} = \sqrt{16a^2b^2c^4 \cdot 3b} = 4abc^2\sqrt{3b}$

29. Simplifying the radical: $\sqrt[3]{48a^2b^3c^4} = \sqrt[3]{8b^3c^3 \cdot 6a^2c} = 2bc\sqrt[3]{6a^2c}$

31. Simplifying the radical: $\sqrt[5]{64x^8y^{12}} = \sqrt[5]{32x^5y^{10} \cdot 2x^3y^2} = 2xy^2\sqrt[5]{2x^3y^2}$

33. Simplifying the radical: $\sqrt[5]{243x^7y^{10}z^5} = \sqrt[5]{243x^5y^{10}z^5 \cdot x^2} = 3xy^2z\sqrt[5]{x^2}$

35. Substituting into the expression: $\sqrt{b^2 - 4ac} = \sqrt{(-6)^2 - 4(2)(3)} = \sqrt{36 - 24} = \sqrt{12} = 2\sqrt{3}$

37. Substituting into the expression: $\sqrt{b^2 - 4ac} = \sqrt{(2)^2 - 4(1)(6)} = \sqrt{4 - 24} = \sqrt{-20}$, which is not a real number

39. Substituting into the expression: $\sqrt{b^2 - 4ac} = \sqrt{\left(-\frac{1}{2}\right)^2 - 4\left(\frac{1}{2}\right)\left(-\frac{5}{4}\right)} = \sqrt{\frac{1}{4} + \frac{5}{2}} = \sqrt{\frac{11}{4}} = \frac{\sqrt{11}}{2}$

41. Simplifying: $\dfrac{\sqrt{20}}{4} = \dfrac{\sqrt{4 \cdot 5}}{4} = \dfrac{2\sqrt{5}}{4} = \dfrac{\sqrt{5}}{2}$

43. Simplifying: $\dfrac{\sqrt{12}}{4} = \dfrac{\sqrt{4 \cdot 3}}{4} = \dfrac{2\sqrt{3}}{4} = \dfrac{\sqrt{3}}{2}$

45. Simplifying: $\dfrac{4 + \sqrt{12}}{2} = \dfrac{4 + \sqrt{4 \cdot 3}}{2} = \dfrac{4 + 2\sqrt{3}}{2} = \dfrac{2(2 + \sqrt{3})}{2} = 2 + \sqrt{3}$

47. Simplifying: $\dfrac{9 + \sqrt{27}}{3} = \dfrac{9 + \sqrt{9 \cdot 3}}{3} = \dfrac{9 + 3\sqrt{3}}{3} = \dfrac{3(3 + \sqrt{3})}{3} = 3 + \sqrt{3}$

49. Simplifying: $\dfrac{10 + \sqrt{75}}{5} = \dfrac{10 + \sqrt{25 \cdot 3}}{5} = \dfrac{10 + 5\sqrt{3}}{5} = \dfrac{5(2 + \sqrt{3})}{5} = 2 + \sqrt{3}$

51. Simplifying: $\dfrac{-2 - \sqrt{27}}{6} = \dfrac{-2 - \sqrt{9 \cdot 3}}{6} = \dfrac{-2 - 3\sqrt{3}}{6}$

53. Simplifying: $\dfrac{-4 - \sqrt{8}}{2} = \dfrac{-4 - \sqrt{4 \cdot 2}}{2} = \dfrac{-4 - 2\sqrt{2}}{2} = \dfrac{2(-2 - \sqrt{2})}{2} = -2 - \sqrt{2}$

55. Simplifying: $\sqrt{\dfrac{7}{25}} = \dfrac{\sqrt{7}}{\sqrt{25}} = \dfrac{\sqrt{7}}{5}$

57. Simplifying: $\sqrt{\dfrac{5x}{36}} = \dfrac{\sqrt{5x}}{\sqrt{36}} = \dfrac{\sqrt{5x}}{6}$

59. Simplifying: $\sqrt[3]{\dfrac{3}{64}} = \dfrac{\sqrt[3]{3}}{\sqrt[3]{64}} = \dfrac{\sqrt[3]{3}}{4}$

61. Simplifying: $\sqrt[3]{\dfrac{2a}{b^3}} = \dfrac{\sqrt[3]{2a}}{\sqrt[3]{b^3}} = \dfrac{\sqrt[3]{2a}}{b}$

63. Simplifying: $\sqrt[4]{\dfrac{9}{16}} = \dfrac{\sqrt[4]{9}}{\sqrt[4]{16}} = \dfrac{\sqrt[4]{9}}{2}$

65. Simplifying: $\dfrac{\sqrt{15}}{\sqrt{3}} = \sqrt{\dfrac{15}{3}} = \sqrt{5}$

67. Simplifying: $\dfrac{\sqrt[3]{12}}{\sqrt[3]{4}} = \sqrt[3]{\dfrac{12}{4}} = \sqrt[3]{3}$

69. Simplifying: $\sqrt{\dfrac{12x^2}{25}} = \dfrac{\sqrt{4x^2 \cdot 3}}{\sqrt{25}} = \dfrac{2x\sqrt{3}}{5}$

71. Simplifying: $\sqrt{\dfrac{3x^3}{4y^6}} = \dfrac{\sqrt{x^2 \cdot 3x}}{\sqrt{4y^6}} = \dfrac{x\sqrt{3x}}{2y^3}$

73. Simplifying: $\sqrt[3]{\dfrac{15b^4}{8a^3}} = \dfrac{\sqrt[3]{b^3 \cdot 15b}}{\sqrt[3]{8a^3}} = \dfrac{b\sqrt[3]{15b}}{2a}$

75. Simplifying: $\sqrt[4]{\dfrac{9x^6 y^{10}}{16z^8}} = \dfrac{\sqrt[4]{x^4 y^8 \cdot 9x^2 y^2}}{\sqrt[4]{16z^8}} = \dfrac{xy^2 \sqrt[4]{9x^2 y^2}}{2z^2}$

77. Simplifying: $\sqrt{25x^2} = 5|x|$

79. Simplifying: $\sqrt{27x^3 y^2} = \sqrt{9x^2 y^2 \cdot 3x} = 3|xy|\sqrt{3x}$

81. Simplifying: $\sqrt{x^2 - 10x + 25} = \sqrt{(x-5)^2} = |x-5|$

83. Simplifying: $\sqrt{4x^2 + 12x + 9} = \sqrt{(2x+3)^2} = |2x+3|$

85. Simplifying: $\sqrt{4a^4 + 16a^3 + 16a^2} = \sqrt{4a^2 \left(a^2 + 4a + 4\right)} = \sqrt{4a^2 (a+2)^2} = 2|a(a+2)|$

87. Simplifying: $\sqrt{4x^3 - 8x^2} = \sqrt{4x^2 (x-2)} = 2|x|\sqrt{x-2}$

89. Substituting $a = 9$ and $b = 16$:
$$\sqrt{a+b} = \sqrt{9+16} = \sqrt{25} = 5$$
$$\sqrt{a} + \sqrt{b} = \sqrt{9} + \sqrt{16} = 3 + 4 = 7$$
Thus $\sqrt{a+b} \neq \sqrt{a} + \sqrt{b}$.

91. Substituting $w = 10$ and $l = 15$: $d = \sqrt{l^2 + w^2} = \sqrt{15^2 + 10^2} = \sqrt{225 + 100} = \sqrt{325} = \sqrt{25 \cdot 13} = 5\sqrt{13}$ feet

93. Using x as the length of the sides, the hypotenuse d is given by:
$$x^2 + x^2 = d^2$$
$$d^2 = 2x^2$$
$$d = x\sqrt{2}$$
Therefore the ratio is: $\dfrac{x\sqrt{2}}{x} = \sqrt{2}$

95. **a.** Since the diagonal of the base is $5\sqrt{2}$, the ratio is: $\dfrac{5\sqrt{2}}{5} = \sqrt{2}$

b. Since the area of the base is 25, the ratio is: $\dfrac{25}{5\sqrt{2}} = \dfrac{5}{\sqrt{2}}$

c. Since the area of the base is 25 and the perimeter is 20, the ratio is: $\dfrac{25}{20} = \dfrac{5}{4}$

97. Using a calculator: $\dfrac{1+\sqrt{5}}{2} \approx 1.618$

99. Answers will vary.   **101.** Answers will vary.

103. Simplifying the radical: $\sqrt{48} = \sqrt{16 \cdot 3} = 4\sqrt{3}$. The correct answer is b.

105. Simplifying: $\dfrac{2+\sqrt{48}}{6} = \dfrac{2+\sqrt{16 \cdot 3}}{6} = \dfrac{2+4\sqrt{3}}{6} = \dfrac{2\left(1+2\sqrt{3}\right)}{6} = \dfrac{1+2\sqrt{3}}{3}$. The correct answer is a.

107. Simplifying: $5x - 4x + 6x = 7x$

109. Simplifying: $35xy^2 - 8xy^2 = 27xy^2$

111. Simplifying: $\dfrac{1}{2}x + \dfrac{1}{3}x = \dfrac{3}{6}x + \dfrac{2}{6}x = \dfrac{5}{6}x$

113. Simplifying: $\sqrt{18} = \sqrt{9 \cdot 2} = 3\sqrt{2}$

115. Simplifying: $\sqrt{75xy^3} = \sqrt{25y^2 \cdot 3xy} = 5y\sqrt{3xy}$

117. Simplifying: $\sqrt[3]{8a^4 b^2} = \sqrt[3]{8a^3 \cdot ab^2} = 2a\sqrt[3]{ab^2}$

7.4 Addition and Subtraction of Radical Expressions

1. Combining radicals: $3\sqrt{5} + 4\sqrt{5} = 7\sqrt{5}$

3. Combining radicals: $3x\sqrt{7} - 4x\sqrt{7} = -x\sqrt{7}$

5. Combining radicals: $5\sqrt[3]{10} - 4\sqrt[3]{10} = \sqrt[3]{10}$

7. Combining radicals: $8\sqrt[5]{6} - 2\sqrt[5]{6} + 3\sqrt[5]{6} = 9\sqrt[5]{6}$

9. Combining radicals: $3x\sqrt{2} - 4x\sqrt{2} + x\sqrt{2} = 0$

11. Combining radicals: $4\sqrt{2} + \sqrt{3} + 3\sqrt{2} + 2\sqrt{3} = 7\sqrt{2} + 3\sqrt{3}$

13. Combining radicals: $6\sqrt{x} - 5\sqrt{y} - 4\sqrt{x} - 7\sqrt{y} = 2\sqrt{x} - 12\sqrt{y}$

15. Combining radicals: $5\sqrt{3} + 4\sqrt[3]{3} + \sqrt{3} - 3\sqrt[3]{3} = 6\sqrt{3} + \sqrt[3]{3}$

17. Combining radicals: $\sqrt{20} - \sqrt{80} + \sqrt{45} = 2\sqrt{5} - 4\sqrt{5} + 3\sqrt{5} = \sqrt{5}$

19. Combining radicals: $4\sqrt{8} - 2\sqrt{50} - 5\sqrt{72} = 8\sqrt{2} - 10\sqrt{2} - 30\sqrt{2} = -32\sqrt{2}$

21. Combining radicals: $5x\sqrt{8} + 3\sqrt{32x^2} - 5\sqrt{50x^2} = 10x\sqrt{2} + 12x\sqrt{2} - 25x\sqrt{2} = -3x\sqrt{2}$

23. Combining radicals: $5\sqrt[3]{16} - 4\sqrt[3]{54} = 10\sqrt[3]{2} - 12\sqrt[3]{2} = -2\sqrt[3]{2}$

25. Combining radicals: $\sqrt[3]{x^4 y^2} + 7x\sqrt[3]{xy^2} = x\sqrt[3]{xy^2} + 7x\sqrt[3]{xy^2} = 8x\sqrt[3]{xy^2}$

27. Combining radicals: $5a^2\sqrt{27ab^3} - 6b\sqrt{12a^5 b} = 15a^2 b\sqrt{3ab} - 12a^2 b\sqrt{3ab} = 3a^2 b\sqrt{3ab}$

29. Combining radicals: $b\sqrt[3]{24a^5 b} + 3a\sqrt[3]{81a^2 b^4} = 2ab\sqrt[3]{3a^2 b} + 9ab\sqrt[3]{3a^2 b} = 11ab\sqrt[3]{3a^2 b}$

31. Combining radicals: $5x\sqrt[4]{3y^5} + y\sqrt[4]{243x^4 y} + \sqrt[4]{48x^4 y^5} = 5xy\sqrt[4]{3y} + 3xy\sqrt[4]{3y} + 2xy\sqrt[4]{3y} = 10xy\sqrt[4]{3y}$

33. Combining radicals: $\dfrac{\sqrt{3}}{2} + \dfrac{\sqrt{27}}{2} = \dfrac{\sqrt{3}}{2} + \dfrac{3\sqrt{3}}{2} = \dfrac{4\sqrt{3}}{2} = 2\sqrt{3}$

35. Combining radicals: $\sqrt{\dfrac{5}{36}} + \dfrac{\sqrt{45}}{6} = \dfrac{\sqrt{5}}{6} + \dfrac{3\sqrt{5}}{6} = \dfrac{4\sqrt{5}}{6} = \dfrac{2\sqrt{5}}{3}$

37. Combining radicals: $\dfrac{\sqrt{x}}{3} - \dfrac{\sqrt{x}}{2} = \dfrac{2\sqrt{x}}{6} - \dfrac{3\sqrt{x}}{6} = -\dfrac{\sqrt{x}}{6}$

39. Combining radicals: $\dfrac{\sqrt{18}}{6} + \sqrt{\dfrac{2}{9}} = \dfrac{3\sqrt{2}}{6} + \dfrac{\sqrt{2}}{3} = \dfrac{3\sqrt{2}}{6} + \dfrac{2\sqrt{2}}{6} = \dfrac{5\sqrt{2}}{6}$

41. Combining radicals: $2x\sqrt{8} + 3y\sqrt{50} = 4x\sqrt{2} + 15y\sqrt{2} = (4x + 15y)\sqrt{2}$

43. Combining radicals: $2\sqrt[3]{16x^3} - \sqrt[3]{54} = 2 \cdot 2x\sqrt[3]{2} - 3\sqrt[3]{2} = (4x - 3)\sqrt[3]{2}$

45. Using a calculator:

$\sqrt{12} \approx 3.464$ $2\sqrt{3} \approx 3.464$

47. It is equal to the decimal approximation for $\sqrt{50}$:

$\sqrt{8} + \sqrt{18} \approx 7.071 \approx \sqrt{50}$ $\sqrt{26} \approx 5.099$

49. Correcting the right side: $3\sqrt{2x} + 5\sqrt{2x} = 8\sqrt{2x}$

51. Correcting the right side: $\sqrt{9 + 16} = \sqrt{25} = 5$

53. The correct answer is a, since these radicals are similar.

55. Simplifying: $3 \cdot 2 = 6$

57. Simplifying: $(x + y)(4x - y) = 4x^2 - xy + 4xy - y^2 = 4x^2 + 3xy - y^2$

59. Simplifying: $(x + 3)^2 = x^2 + 2(3x) + 3^2 = x^2 + 6x + 9$

61. Simplifying: $(x - 2)(x + 2) = x^2 - 2^2 = x^2 - 4$

63. Simplifying: $2\sqrt{18} = 2\sqrt{9 \cdot 2} = 2 \cdot 3\sqrt{2} = 6\sqrt{2}$

65. Simplifying: $\left(\sqrt{6}\right)^2 = 6$

67. Simplifying: $\left(3\sqrt{x}\right)^2 = 9x$

7.5 Multiplication and Division of Radical Expressions

1. Multiplying: $\sqrt{6}\sqrt{3} = \sqrt{18} = 3\sqrt{2}$

3. Multiplying: $\left(2\sqrt{3}\right)\left(5\sqrt{7}\right) = 10\sqrt{21}$

5. Multiplying: $\left(4\sqrt{6}\right)\left(2\sqrt{15}\right)\left(3\sqrt{10}\right) = 24\sqrt{900} = 24 \cdot 30 = 720$

7. Multiplying: $\left(3\sqrt[3]{3}\right)\left(6\sqrt[3]{9}\right) = 18\sqrt[3]{27} = 18 \cdot 3 = 54$

9. Multiplying: $\sqrt{3}\left(\sqrt{2} - 3\sqrt{3}\right) = \sqrt{6} - 3\sqrt{9} = \sqrt{6} - 9$

11. Multiplying: $6\sqrt[3]{4}\left(2\sqrt[3]{2} + 1\right) = 12\sqrt[3]{8} + 6\sqrt[3]{4} = 24 + 6\sqrt[3]{4}$

13. Multiplying: $\left(\sqrt{3} + \sqrt{2}\right)\left(3\sqrt{3} - \sqrt{2}\right) = 3\sqrt{9} - \sqrt{6} + 3\sqrt{6} - \sqrt{4} = 9 + 2\sqrt{6} - 2 = 7 + 2\sqrt{6}$

15. Multiplying: $\left(\sqrt{x} + 5\right)\left(\sqrt{x} - 3\right) = x - 3\sqrt{x} + 5\sqrt{x} - 15 = x + 2\sqrt{x} - 15$

17. Multiplying: $\left(3\sqrt{6} + 4\sqrt{2}\right)\left(\sqrt{6} + 2\sqrt{2}\right) = 3\sqrt{36} + 4\sqrt{12} + 6\sqrt{12} + 8\sqrt{4} = 18 + 8\sqrt{3} + 12\sqrt{3} + 16 = 34 + 20\sqrt{3}$

19. Multiplying: $\left(\sqrt{3} + 4\right)^2 = \left(\sqrt{3} + 4\right)\left(\sqrt{3} + 4\right) = \sqrt{9} + 4\sqrt{3} + 4\sqrt{3} + 16 = 19 + 8\sqrt{3}$

21. Multiplying: $\left(\sqrt{x} - 3\right)^2 = \left(\sqrt{x} - 3\right)\left(\sqrt{x} - 3\right) = x - 3\sqrt{x} - 3\sqrt{x} + 9 = x - 6\sqrt{x} + 9$

23. Multiplying: $\left(2\sqrt{a} - 3\sqrt{b}\right)^2 = \left(2\sqrt{a} - 3\sqrt{b}\right)\left(2\sqrt{a} - 3\sqrt{b}\right) = 4a - 6\sqrt{ab} - 6\sqrt{ab} + 9b = 4a - 12\sqrt{ab} + 9b$

25. Multiplying: $\left(\sqrt{x-4} + 2\right)^2 = \left(\sqrt{x-4} + 2\right)\left(\sqrt{x-4} + 2\right) = x - 4 + 2\sqrt{x-4} + 2\sqrt{x-4} + 4 = x + 4\sqrt{x-4}$

27. Multiplying: $\left(\sqrt{x-5} - 3\right)^2 = \left(\sqrt{x-5} - 3\right)\left(\sqrt{x-5} - 3\right) = x - 5 - 3\sqrt{x-5} - 3\sqrt{x-5} + 9 = x + 4 - 6\sqrt{x-5}$

29. Multiplying: $\left(\sqrt{3} - \sqrt{2}\right)\left(\sqrt{3} + \sqrt{2}\right) = \left(\sqrt{3}\right)^2 - \left(\sqrt{2}\right)^2 = 3 - 2 = 1$

31. Multiplying: $\left(\sqrt{a} + 7\right)\left(\sqrt{a} - 7\right) = \left(\sqrt{a}\right)^2 - (7)^2 = a - 49$

33. Multiplying: $\left(5 - \sqrt{x}\right)\left(5 + \sqrt{x}\right) = (5)^2 - \left(\sqrt{x}\right)^2 = 25 - x$

35. Multiplying: $\left(\sqrt{x-4} + 2\right)\left(\sqrt{x-4} - 2\right) = \left(\sqrt{x-4}\right)^2 - (2)^2 = x - 4 - 4 = x - 8$

37. Multiplying: $\left(\sqrt{3} + 1\right)^3 = \left(\sqrt{3} + 1\right)\left(3 + 2\sqrt{3} + 1\right) = \left(\sqrt{3} + 1\right)\left(4 + 2\sqrt{3}\right) = 4\sqrt{3} + 4 + 6 + 2\sqrt{3} = 10 + 6\sqrt{3}$

39. Simplifying: $\dfrac{\sqrt{30}}{\sqrt{6}} = \sqrt{\dfrac{30}{6}} = \sqrt{5}$

41. Simplifying: $\dfrac{6\sqrt{10}}{3\sqrt{2}} = 2\sqrt{\dfrac{10}{2}} = 2\sqrt{5}$

43. Simplifying: $\dfrac{\sqrt[3]{12}}{\sqrt[3]{3}} = \sqrt[3]{\dfrac{12}{3}} = \sqrt[3]{4}$

45. Simplifying: $\dfrac{2\sqrt[3]{18}}{12\sqrt[3]{9}} = \dfrac{\sqrt[3]{18}}{6\sqrt[3]{9}} = \dfrac{\sqrt[3]{2}}{6}$

47. Simplifying: $\dfrac{3x\sqrt{24}}{9\sqrt{2}} = \dfrac{x\sqrt{12}}{3} = \dfrac{2x\sqrt{3}}{3}$

49. Simplifying: $\dfrac{11\sqrt{40ab^3}}{2\sqrt{5ab}} = \dfrac{11\sqrt{8b^2}}{2} = \dfrac{22b\sqrt{2}}{2} = 11b\sqrt{2}$

51. Rationalizing the denominator: $\dfrac{2}{\sqrt{3}} = \dfrac{2}{\sqrt{3}} \cdot \dfrac{\sqrt{3}}{\sqrt{3}} = \dfrac{2\sqrt{3}}{3}$

53. Rationalizing the denominator: $\dfrac{5}{\sqrt{6}} = \dfrac{5}{\sqrt{6}} \cdot \dfrac{\sqrt{6}}{\sqrt{6}} = \dfrac{5\sqrt{6}}{6}$

55. Rationalizing the denominator: $\sqrt{\dfrac{1}{2}} = \dfrac{1}{\sqrt{2}} \cdot \dfrac{\sqrt{2}}{\sqrt{2}} = \dfrac{\sqrt{2}}{2}$

57. Rationalizing the denominator: $\sqrt{\dfrac{1}{5}} = \dfrac{1}{\sqrt{5}} \cdot \dfrac{\sqrt{5}}{\sqrt{5}} = \dfrac{\sqrt{5}}{5}$

59. Rationalizing the denominator: $\dfrac{4}{\sqrt[3]{2}} = \dfrac{4}{\sqrt[3]{2}} \cdot \dfrac{\sqrt[3]{4}}{\sqrt[3]{4}} = \dfrac{4\sqrt[3]{4}}{2} = 2\sqrt[3]{4}$

61. Rationalizing the denominator: $\dfrac{2}{\sqrt[3]{9}} = \dfrac{2}{\sqrt[3]{9}} \cdot \dfrac{\sqrt[3]{3}}{\sqrt[3]{3}} = \dfrac{2\sqrt[3]{3}}{3}$

63. Rationalizing the denominator: $\sqrt[4]{\dfrac{3}{2x^2}} = \dfrac{\sqrt[4]{3}}{\sqrt[4]{2x^2}} \cdot \dfrac{\sqrt[4]{8x^2}}{\sqrt[4]{8x^2}} = \dfrac{\sqrt[4]{24x^2}}{2x}$

65. Rationalizing the denominator: $\sqrt[4]{\dfrac{8}{y}} = \dfrac{\sqrt[4]{8}}{\sqrt[4]{y}} \cdot \dfrac{\sqrt[4]{y^3}}{\sqrt[4]{y^3}} = \dfrac{\sqrt[4]{8y^3}}{y}$

67. Rationalizing the denominator: $\sqrt[3]{\dfrac{4x}{3y}} = \dfrac{\sqrt[3]{4x}}{\sqrt[3]{3y}} \cdot \dfrac{\sqrt[3]{9y^2}}{\sqrt[3]{9y^2}} = \dfrac{\sqrt[3]{36xy^2}}{3y}$

69. Rationalizing the denominator: $\sqrt[3]{\dfrac{2x}{9y}} = \dfrac{\sqrt[3]{2x}}{\sqrt[3]{9y}} \cdot \dfrac{\sqrt[3]{3y^2}}{\sqrt[3]{3y^2}} = \dfrac{\sqrt[3]{6xy^2}}{3y}$

71. Simplifying: $\sqrt{\dfrac{27x^3}{5y}} = \dfrac{\sqrt{27x^3}}{\sqrt{5y}} \cdot \dfrac{\sqrt{5y}}{\sqrt{5y}} = \dfrac{\sqrt{135x^3y}}{5y} = \dfrac{3x\sqrt{15xy}}{5y}$

73. Simplifying: $\sqrt{\dfrac{75x^3y^2}{2z}} = \dfrac{\sqrt{75x^3y^2}}{\sqrt{2z}} \cdot \dfrac{\sqrt{2z}}{\sqrt{2z}} = \dfrac{\sqrt{150x^3y^2z}}{2z} = \dfrac{5xy\sqrt{6xz}}{2z}$

75. **a.** Rationalizing the denominator: $\dfrac{1}{\sqrt{2}} = \dfrac{1}{\sqrt{2}} \cdot \dfrac{\sqrt{2}}{\sqrt{2}} = \dfrac{\sqrt{2}}{2}$

  b. Rationalizing the denominator: $\dfrac{1}{\sqrt[3]{2}} = \dfrac{1}{\sqrt[3]{2}} \cdot \dfrac{\sqrt[3]{4}}{\sqrt[3]{4}} = \dfrac{\sqrt[3]{4}}{2}$

  c. Rationalizing the denominator: $\dfrac{1}{\sqrt[4]{2}} = \dfrac{1}{\sqrt[4]{2}} \cdot \dfrac{\sqrt[4]{8}}{\sqrt[4]{8}} = \dfrac{\sqrt[4]{8}}{2}$

77. Combining radicals: $\dfrac{\sqrt{2}}{2} + \dfrac{1}{\sqrt{2}} = \dfrac{\sqrt{2}}{2} + \dfrac{1}{\sqrt{2}} \cdot \dfrac{\sqrt{2}}{\sqrt{2}} = \dfrac{\sqrt{2}}{2} + \dfrac{\sqrt{2}}{2} = \sqrt{2}$

79. Combining radicals: $\dfrac{\sqrt{5}}{3} + \dfrac{1}{\sqrt{5}} = \dfrac{\sqrt{5}}{3} + \dfrac{1}{\sqrt{5}} \cdot \dfrac{\sqrt{5}}{\sqrt{5}} = \dfrac{\sqrt{5}}{3} + \dfrac{\sqrt{5}}{5} = \dfrac{5\sqrt{5}}{15} + \dfrac{3\sqrt{5}}{15} = \dfrac{8\sqrt{5}}{15}$

81. Combining radicals: $\sqrt{x} - \dfrac{1}{\sqrt{x}} = \sqrt{x} - \dfrac{1}{\sqrt{x}} \cdot \dfrac{\sqrt{x}}{\sqrt{x}} = \sqrt{x} - \dfrac{\sqrt{x}}{x} = \dfrac{x\sqrt{x}}{x} - \dfrac{\sqrt{x}}{x} = \dfrac{(x-1)\sqrt{x}}{x}$

83. Combining radicals: $\dfrac{\sqrt{18}}{6} + \sqrt{\dfrac{1}{2}} + \dfrac{\sqrt{2}}{2} = \dfrac{3\sqrt{2}}{6} + \dfrac{1}{\sqrt{2}} \cdot \dfrac{\sqrt{2}}{\sqrt{2}} + \dfrac{\sqrt{2}}{2} = \dfrac{\sqrt{2}}{2} + \dfrac{\sqrt{2}}{2} + \dfrac{\sqrt{2}}{2} = \dfrac{3\sqrt{2}}{2}$

85. Combining radicals: $\sqrt{6} - \sqrt{\dfrac{2}{3}} + \sqrt{\dfrac{1}{6}} = \sqrt{6} - \dfrac{\sqrt{2}}{\sqrt{3}} \cdot \dfrac{\sqrt{3}}{\sqrt{3}} + \dfrac{1}{\sqrt{6}} \cdot \dfrac{\sqrt{6}}{\sqrt{6}} = \sqrt{6} - \dfrac{\sqrt{6}}{3} + \dfrac{\sqrt{6}}{6} = \dfrac{6\sqrt{6}}{6} - \dfrac{2\sqrt{6}}{6} + \dfrac{\sqrt{6}}{6} = \dfrac{5\sqrt{6}}{6}$

87. Combining radicals: $\sqrt[3]{25} + \dfrac{3}{\sqrt[3]{5}} = \sqrt[3]{25} + \dfrac{3}{\sqrt[3]{5}} \cdot \dfrac{\sqrt[3]{25}}{\sqrt[3]{25}} = \sqrt[3]{25} + \dfrac{3\sqrt[3]{25}}{5} = \dfrac{5\sqrt[3]{25}}{5} + \dfrac{3\sqrt[3]{25}}{5} = \dfrac{8\sqrt[3]{25}}{5}$

89. Rationalizing the denominator: $\dfrac{\sqrt{2}}{\sqrt{6} - \sqrt{2}} = \dfrac{\sqrt{2}}{\sqrt{6} - \sqrt{2}} \cdot \dfrac{\sqrt{6} + \sqrt{2}}{\sqrt{6} + \sqrt{2}} = \dfrac{\sqrt{12} + 2}{6 - 2} = \dfrac{2\sqrt{3} + 2}{4} = \dfrac{1 + \sqrt{3}}{2}$

91. Rationalizing the denominator: $\dfrac{\sqrt{5}}{\sqrt{5}+1} = \dfrac{\sqrt{5}}{\sqrt{5}+1} \cdot \dfrac{\sqrt{5}-1}{\sqrt{5}-1} = \dfrac{5-\sqrt{5}}{5-1} = \dfrac{5-\sqrt{5}}{4}$

93. Rationalizing the denominator: $\dfrac{\sqrt{x}}{\sqrt{x}-3} = \dfrac{\sqrt{x}}{\sqrt{x}-3} \cdot \dfrac{\sqrt{x}+3}{\sqrt{x}+3} = \dfrac{x+3\sqrt{x}}{x-9}$

95. Rationalizing the denominator: $\dfrac{\sqrt{5}}{2\sqrt{5}-3} = \dfrac{\sqrt{5}}{2\sqrt{5}-3} \cdot \dfrac{2\sqrt{5}+3}{2\sqrt{5}+3} = \dfrac{2\sqrt{25}+3\sqrt{5}}{20-9} = \dfrac{10+3\sqrt{5}}{11}$

97. Rationalizing the denominator: $\dfrac{3}{\sqrt{x}-\sqrt{y}} = \dfrac{3}{\sqrt{x}-\sqrt{y}} \cdot \dfrac{\sqrt{x}+\sqrt{y}}{\sqrt{x}+\sqrt{y}} = \dfrac{3\sqrt{x}+3\sqrt{y}}{x-y}$

99. Rationalizing the denominator: $\dfrac{\sqrt{6}+\sqrt{2}}{\sqrt{6}-\sqrt{2}} = \dfrac{\sqrt{6}+\sqrt{2}}{\sqrt{6}-\sqrt{2}} \cdot \dfrac{\sqrt{6}+\sqrt{2}}{\sqrt{6}+\sqrt{2}} = \dfrac{6+2\sqrt{12}+2}{6-2} = \dfrac{8+4\sqrt{3}}{4} = 2+\sqrt{3}$

101. Rationalizing the denominator: $\dfrac{\sqrt{7}-2}{\sqrt{7}+2} = \dfrac{\sqrt{7}-2}{\sqrt{7}+2} \cdot \dfrac{\sqrt{7}-2}{\sqrt{7}-2} = \dfrac{7-4\sqrt{7}+4}{7-4} = \dfrac{11-4\sqrt{7}}{3}$

103. a. Adding: $\left(\sqrt{x}+2\right)+\left(\sqrt{x}-2\right) = \sqrt{x}+2+\sqrt{x}-2 = 2\sqrt{x}$

     b. Multiplying: $\left(\sqrt{x}+2\right)\left(\sqrt{x}-2\right) = x+2\sqrt{x}-2\sqrt{x}-4 = x-4$

     c. Squaring: $\left(\sqrt{x}+2\right)^2 = \left(\sqrt{x}+2\right)\left(\sqrt{x}+2\right) = x+2\sqrt{x}+2\sqrt{x}+4 = x+4\sqrt{x}+4$

     d. Dividing: $\dfrac{\sqrt{x}+2}{\sqrt{x}-2} = \dfrac{\sqrt{x}+2}{\sqrt{x}-2} \cdot \dfrac{\sqrt{x}+2}{\sqrt{x}+2} = \dfrac{x+4\sqrt{x}+4}{x-4}$

105. a. Adding: $\sqrt{2}+\left(\sqrt{6}+\sqrt{2}\right) = \sqrt{2}+\sqrt{6}+\sqrt{2} = \sqrt{6}+2\sqrt{2}$

     b. Multiplying: $\sqrt{2}\left(\sqrt{6}+\sqrt{2}\right) = \sqrt{12}+\sqrt{4} = 2+2\sqrt{3}$

     c. Dividing: $\dfrac{\sqrt{6}+\sqrt{2}}{\sqrt{2}} = \dfrac{\sqrt{6}+\sqrt{2}}{\sqrt{2}} \cdot \dfrac{\sqrt{2}}{\sqrt{2}} = \dfrac{\sqrt{12}+2}{2} = \dfrac{2+2\sqrt{3}}{2} = 1+\sqrt{3}$

     d. Dividing: $\dfrac{\sqrt{2}}{\sqrt{6}+\sqrt{2}} = \dfrac{\sqrt{2}}{\sqrt{6}+\sqrt{2}} \cdot \dfrac{\sqrt{6}-\sqrt{2}}{\sqrt{6}-\sqrt{2}} = \dfrac{\sqrt{12}-2}{6-2} = \dfrac{-2+2\sqrt{3}}{4} = \dfrac{-1+\sqrt{3}}{2}$

107. Simplifying the product: $\left(\sqrt[3]{2}+\sqrt[3]{3}\right)\left(\sqrt[3]{4}-\sqrt[3]{6}+\sqrt[3]{9}\right) = \sqrt[3]{8}-\sqrt[3]{12}+\sqrt[3]{18}+\sqrt[3]{12}-\sqrt[3]{18}+\sqrt[3]{27} = 2+3 = 5$

109. The correct statement is: $5\left(2\sqrt{3}\right) = 10\sqrt{3}$

111. The correct statement is: $\left(\sqrt{x}+3\right)^2 = \left(\sqrt{x}+3\right)\left(\sqrt{x}+3\right) = x+6\sqrt{x}+9$

113. The correct statement is: $\left(5\sqrt{3}\right)^2 = \left(5\sqrt{3}\right)\left(5\sqrt{3}\right) = 25 \cdot 3 = 75$

115. Substituting $h=50$: $t = \dfrac{\sqrt{100-50}}{4} = \dfrac{\sqrt{50}}{4} = \dfrac{5\sqrt{2}}{4}$ seconds

     Substituting $h=0$: $t = \dfrac{\sqrt{100-0}}{4} = \dfrac{\sqrt{100}}{4} = \dfrac{10}{4} = \dfrac{5}{2}$ seconds

117. Since the large rectangle is a golden rectangle and $AC=6$, then $CE = 6\left(\dfrac{1+\sqrt{5}}{2}\right) = 3+3\sqrt{5}$. Since $CD=6$, then

$DE = 3+3\sqrt{5}-6 = 3\sqrt{5}-3$. Now computing the ratio:

$\dfrac{EF}{DE} = \dfrac{6}{3\sqrt{5}-3} \cdot \dfrac{3\sqrt{5}+3}{3\sqrt{5}+3} = \dfrac{18\left(\sqrt{5}+1\right)}{45-9} = \dfrac{18\left(\sqrt{5}+1\right)}{36} = \dfrac{1+\sqrt{5}}{2}$

Therefore the smaller rectangle $BDEF$ is also a golden rectangle.

119. Since the large rectangle is a golden rectangle and $AC = 2x$, then $CE = 2x\left(\dfrac{1+\sqrt{5}}{2}\right) = x\left(1+\sqrt{5}\right)$. Since $CD = 2x$, then

$DE = x\left(1+\sqrt{5}\right) - 2x = x\left(-1+\sqrt{5}\right)$. Now computing the ratio:

$$\frac{EF}{DE} = \frac{2x}{x\left(-1+\sqrt{5}\right)} = \frac{2}{-1+\sqrt{5}} \cdot \frac{-1-\sqrt{5}}{-1-\sqrt{5}} = \frac{-2\left(\sqrt{5}+1\right)}{1-5} = \frac{-2\left(\sqrt{5}+1\right)}{-4} = \frac{1+\sqrt{5}}{2}$$

Therefore the smaller rectangle $BDEF$ is also a golden rectangle.

121. Multiplying: $3\sqrt{6} \cdot 4\sqrt{10} = 12\sqrt{60} = 12\sqrt{4 \cdot 15} = 24\sqrt{15}$. The correct answer is a.

123. Dividing: $\dfrac{8\sqrt{12}}{12\sqrt{2}} = \dfrac{2\sqrt{12}}{3\sqrt{2}} = \dfrac{2\sqrt{6}}{3}$. The correct answer is a.

125. Simplifying: $(t+5)^2 = t^2 + 2(5t) + 5^2 = t^2 + 10t + 25$

127. Simplifying: $\sqrt{x} \cdot \sqrt{x} = \sqrt{x^2} = x$

129. Solving the equation:
$$3x + 4 = 5^2$$
$$3x + 4 = 25$$
$$3x = 21$$
$$x = 7$$

131. Solving the equation:
$$t^2 + 7t + 12 = 0$$
$$(t+4)(t+3) = 0$$
$$t = -4, -3$$

133. Solving the equation:
$$t^2 + 10t + 25 = t + 7$$
$$t^2 + 9t + 18 = 0$$
$$(t+6)(t+3) = 0$$
$$t = -6, -3$$

135. Solving the equation:
$$(x+4)^2 = x + 6$$
$$x^2 + 8x + 16 = x + 6$$
$$x^2 + 7x + 10 = 0$$
$$(x+5)(x+2) = 0$$
$$x = -5, -2$$

137. Substituting $x = 7$: $\sqrt{3(7)+4} = \sqrt{25} = 5$. Yes, it is a solution.

139. Substituting $t = -6$:
$$-6 + 5 = \sqrt{-6+7}$$
$$-1 = 1$$
No, it is not a solution.

7.6 Equations Involving Radicals

1. Solving the equation:
$$\sqrt{2x+1} = 3$$
$$\left(\sqrt{2x+1}\right)^2 = 3^2$$
$$2x + 1 = 9$$
$$2x = 8$$
$$x = 4$$

3. Solving the equation:
$$\sqrt{4x+1} = -5$$
$$\left(\sqrt{4x+1}\right)^2 = (-5)^2$$
$$4x + 1 = 25$$
$$4x = 24$$
$$x = 6$$
Since this value does not check, there is no solution.

5. Solving the equation:
$$\sqrt{2y-1} = 3$$
$$\left(\sqrt{2y-1}\right)^2 = 3^2$$
$$2y - 1 = 9$$
$$2y = 10$$
$$y = 5$$

7. Solving the equation:
$$\sqrt{5x-7} = -1$$
$$\left(\sqrt{5x-7}\right)^2 = (-1)^2$$
$$5x - 7 = 1$$
$$5x = 8$$
$$x = \frac{8}{5}$$

9. Solving the equation:
$$\sqrt{2x-3} - 2 = 4$$
$$\sqrt{2x-3} = 6$$
$$\left(\sqrt{2x-3}\right)^2 = 6^2$$
$$2x-3 = 36$$
$$2x = 39$$
$$x = \frac{39}{2}$$

11. Solving the equation:
$$\sqrt{4a+1} + 3 = 2$$
$$\sqrt{4a+1} = -1$$
$$\left(\sqrt{4a+1}\right)^2 = (-1)^2$$
$$4a+1 = 1$$
$$4a = 0$$
$$a = 0$$

Since this value does not check, there is no solution.

13. Solving the equation:
$$\sqrt[4]{3x+1} = 2$$
$$\left(\sqrt[4]{3x+1}\right)^4 = 2^4$$
$$3x+1 = 16$$
$$3x = 15$$
$$x = 5$$

15. Solving the equation:
$$\sqrt[3]{2x-5} = 1$$
$$\left(\sqrt[3]{2x-5}\right)^3 = 1^3$$
$$2x-5 = 1$$
$$2x = 6$$
$$x = 3$$

17. Solving the equation:
$$\sqrt[3]{3a+5} = -3$$
$$\left(\sqrt[3]{3a+5}\right)^3 = (-3)^3$$
$$3a+5 = -27$$
$$3a = -32$$
$$a = -\frac{32}{3}$$

19. Solving the equation:
$$\sqrt{y-3} = y-3$$
$$\left(\sqrt{y-3}\right)^2 = (y-3)^2$$
$$y-3 = y^2 - 6y + 9$$
$$0 = y^2 - 7y + 12$$
$$0 = (y-3)(y-4)$$
$$y = 3,4$$

21. Solving the equation:
$$\sqrt{a+2} = a+2$$
$$\left(\sqrt{a+2}\right)^2 = (a+2)^2$$
$$a+2 = a^2 + 4a + 4$$
$$0 = a^2 + 3a + 2$$
$$0 = (a+2)(a+1)$$
$$a = -2,-1$$

23. Solving the equation:
$$\sqrt{2x+4} = \sqrt{1-x}$$
$$\left(\sqrt{2x+4}\right)^2 = \left(\sqrt{1-x}\right)^2$$
$$2x+4 = 1-x$$
$$3x = -3$$
$$x = -1$$

25. Solving the equation:
$$\sqrt{4a+7} = -\sqrt{a+2}$$
$$\left(\sqrt{4a+7}\right)^2 = \left(-\sqrt{a+2}\right)^2$$
$$4a+7 = a+2$$
$$3a = -5$$
$$a = -\frac{5}{3}$$

Since this value does not check, there is no solution.

27. Solving the equation:
$$\sqrt[4]{5x-8} = \sqrt[4]{4x-1}$$
$$\left(\sqrt[4]{5x-8}\right)^4 = \left(\sqrt[4]{4x-1}\right)^4$$
$$5x-8 = 4x-1$$
$$x = 7$$

29. Solving the equation:
$$x+1 = \sqrt{5x+1}$$
$$(x+1)^2 = \left(\sqrt{5x+1}\right)^2$$
$$x^2 + 2x + 1 = 5x + 1$$
$$x^2 - 3x = 0$$
$$x(x-3) = 0$$
$$x = 0,3$$

31. Solving the equation:
$$t+5 = \sqrt{2t+9}$$
$$(t+5)^2 = \left(\sqrt{2t+9}\right)^2$$
$$t^2 + 10t + 25 = 2t + 9$$
$$t^2 + 8t + 16 = 0$$
$$(t+4)^2 = 0$$
$$t = -4$$

33. Solving the equation:
$$\sqrt{y-8} = \sqrt{8-y}$$
$$\left(\sqrt{y-8}\right)^2 = \left(\sqrt{8-y}\right)^2$$
$$y-8 = 8-y$$
$$2y = 16$$
$$y = 8$$

35. Solving the equation:
$$\sqrt[3]{3x+5} = \sqrt[3]{5-2x}$$
$$\left(\sqrt[3]{3x+5}\right)^3 = \left(\sqrt[3]{5-2x}\right)^3$$
$$3x+5 = 5-2x$$
$$5x = 0$$
$$x = 0$$

37. Solving the equation:
$$\sqrt{x-8} = \sqrt{x} - 2$$
$$\left(\sqrt{x-8}\right)^2 = \left(\sqrt{x}-2\right)^2$$
$$x-8 = x - 4\sqrt{x} + 4$$
$$-12 = -4\sqrt{x}$$
$$\sqrt{x} = 3$$
$$x = 9$$

39. Solving the equation:
$$\sqrt{x+1} = \sqrt{x} + 1$$
$$\left(\sqrt{x+1}\right)^2 = \left(\sqrt{x}+1\right)^2$$
$$x+1 = x + 2\sqrt{x} + 1$$
$$0 = 2\sqrt{x}$$
$$\sqrt{x} = 0$$
$$x = 0$$

41. Solving the equation:
$$\sqrt{x+8} = \sqrt{x-4} + 2$$
$$\left(\sqrt{x+8}\right)^2 = \left(\sqrt{x-4}+2\right)^2$$
$$x+8 = x-4 + 4\sqrt{x-4} + 4$$
$$8 = 4\sqrt{x-4}$$
$$\sqrt{x-4} = 2$$
$$x-4 = 4$$
$$x = 8$$

43. Solving the equation:
$$\sqrt{x-5} - 3 = \sqrt{x-8}$$
$$\left(\sqrt{x-5}-3\right)^2 = \left(\sqrt{x-8}\right)^2$$
$$x-5 - 6\sqrt{x-5} + 9 = x-8$$
$$-6\sqrt{x-5} = -12$$
$$\sqrt{x-5} = 2$$
$$x-5 = 4$$
$$x = 9$$
Since this value does not check, there is no solution.

45. a. Solving the equation:
$$\sqrt{y} - 4 = 6$$
$$\sqrt{y} = 10$$
$$\left(\sqrt{y}\right)^2 = 10^2$$
$$y = 100$$

b. Solving the equation:
$$\sqrt{y-4} = 6$$
$$\left(\sqrt{y-4}\right)^2 = 6^2$$
$$y-4 = 36$$
$$y = 40$$

c. Solving the equation:
$$\sqrt{y-4} = -6$$
$$\left(\sqrt{y-4}\right)^2 = (-6)^2$$
$$y-4 = 36$$
$$y = 40$$

There is no solution (40 does not check).

d. Solving the equation:
$$\sqrt{y-4} = y-6$$
$$\left(\sqrt{y-4}\right)^2 = (y-6)^2$$
$$y-4 = y^2 - 12y + 36$$
$$0 = y^2 - 13y + 40$$
$$0 = (y-5)(y-8)$$
$$y = 5, 8$$

The solution is 8 (5 does not check).

47. **a.** Solving the equation:

$$x - 3 = 0$$
$$x = 3$$

b. Solving the equation:

$$\sqrt{x} - 3 = 0$$
$$\left(\sqrt{x}\right)^2 = 3^2$$
$$x = 9$$

c. Solving the equation:

$$\sqrt{x - 3} = 0$$
$$\left(\sqrt{x - 3}\right)^2 = 0^2$$
$$x - 3 = 0$$
$$x = 3$$

d. Solving the equation:

$$\sqrt{x} + 3 = 0$$
$$\sqrt{x} = -3$$
$$\left(\sqrt{x}\right)^2 = (-3)^2$$
$$x = 9$$

There is no solution (9 does not check).

e. Solving the equation:

$$\sqrt{x} + 3 = 5$$
$$\sqrt{x} = 2$$
$$\left(\sqrt{x}\right)^2 = 2^2$$
$$x = 4$$

f. Solving the equation:

$$\sqrt{x} + 3 = -5$$
$$\sqrt{x} = -8$$
$$\left(\sqrt{x}\right)^2 = (-8)^2$$
$$x = 64$$

There is no solution (64 does not check).

g. Solving the equation:

$$x - 3 = \sqrt{5 - x}$$
$$(x - 3)^2 = \left(\sqrt{5 - x}\right)^2$$
$$x^2 - 6x + 9 = 5 - x$$
$$x^2 - 5x + 4 = 0$$
$$(x - 1)(x - 4) = 0$$
$$x = 1, 4$$

The solution is 4 (1 does not check).

49. Solving the equation:

$$(5x - 2)^{1/2} = 3$$
$$\sqrt{5x - 2} = 3$$
$$\left(\sqrt{5x - 2}\right)^2 = 3^2$$
$$5x - 2 = 9$$
$$5x = 11$$
$$x = \frac{11}{5}$$

51. Solving the equation:

$$(4x + 1)^{1/3} = 2$$
$$\sqrt[3]{4x + 1} = 2$$
$$\left(\sqrt[3]{4x + 1}\right)^3 = 2^3$$
$$4x + 1 = 8$$
$$4x = 7$$
$$x = \frac{7}{4}$$

53. Solving the equation:

$$(x+2)^{2/3} = 1$$
$$\sqrt[3]{(x+2)^2} = 1$$
$$\left(\sqrt[3]{(x+2)^2}\right)^3 = 1^3$$
$$(x+2)^2 = 1$$
$$x^2 + 4x + 4 = 1$$
$$x^2 + 4x + 3 = 0$$
$$(x+3)(x+1) = 0$$
$$x = -3, -1$$

55. Solving for h:

$$t = \frac{\sqrt{100-h}}{4}$$
$$4t = \sqrt{100-h}$$
$$16t^2 = 100 - h$$
$$h = 100 - 16t^2$$

57. Solving for L:

$$2 = 2\left(\frac{22}{7}\right)\sqrt{\frac{L}{32}}$$
$$\frac{7}{22} = \sqrt{\frac{L}{32}}$$
$$\left(\frac{7}{22}\right)^2 = \frac{L}{32}$$
$$L = 32\left(\frac{7}{22}\right)^2 \approx 3.24 \text{ feet}$$

59. Solving the equation:

$$\sqrt{3x-2} - 3 = 1$$
$$\sqrt{3x-2} = 4$$
$$\left(\sqrt{3x-2}\right)^2 = 4^2$$
$$3x - 2 = 16$$
$$3x = 18$$
$$x = 6$$

The correct answer is d.

61. Solving the equation:

$$\sqrt[3]{2x-3} = -4$$
$$\left(\sqrt[3]{2x-3}\right)^3 = (-4)^3$$
$$2x - 3 = -64$$
$$2x = -61$$
$$x = -\frac{61}{2}$$

The correct answer is d.

63. Simplifying: $\sqrt{25} = 5$

65. Simplifying: $\sqrt{12} = \sqrt{4 \cdot 3} = 2\sqrt{3}$

67. Simplifying: $(-1)^{15} = -1$

69. Simplifying: $(-1)^{50} = 1$

71. Solving the equation:

$$3x = 12$$
$$x = 4$$

73. Solving the equation:

$$4x - 3 = 5$$
$$4x = 8$$
$$x = 2$$

75. Performing the operations: $(3+4x)+(7-6x) = 10 - 2x$

77. Performing the operations: $(7+3x)-(5+6x) = 7+3x-5-6x = 2-3x$

79. Performing the operations: $(3-4x)(2+5x) = 6+15x-8x-20x^2 = 6+7x-20x^2$

81. Performing the operations: $2x(4-6x) = 8x - 12x^2$

83. Performing the operations: $(2+3x)^2 = 2^2 + 2(2)(3x) + (3x)^2 = 4+12x+9x^2$

85. Performing the operations: $(2-3x)(2+3x) = 2^2 - (3x)^2 = 4 - 9x^2$

7.7 Complex Numbers

1. Writing in terms of i: $\sqrt{-36} = 6i$

3. Writing in terms of i: $-\sqrt{-25} = -5i$

5. Writing in terms of i: $\sqrt{-72} = 6i\sqrt{2}$

7. Writing in terms of i: $-\sqrt{-12} = -2i\sqrt{3}$

9. Rewriting the expression: $i^{28} = \left(i^4\right)^7 = (1)^7 = 1$

11. Rewriting the expression: $i^{26} = i^{24}i^2 = \left(i^4\right)^6 i^2 = (1)^6(-1) = -1$

13. Rewriting the expression: $i^{75} = i^{72}i^3 = \left(i^4\right)^{18} i^2 i = (1)^{18}(-1)i = -i$

15. Setting real and imaginary parts equal:
$$2x = 6 \qquad 3y = -3$$
$$x = 3 \qquad y = -1$$

17. Setting real and imaginary parts equal:
$$-x = 2 \qquad 10y = -5$$
$$x = -2 \qquad y = -\frac{1}{2}$$

19. Setting real and imaginary parts equal:
$$2x = -16 \qquad -2y = 10$$
$$x = -8 \qquad y = -5$$

21. Setting real and imaginary parts equal:
$$2x - 4 = 10 \qquad -6y = -3$$
$$2x = 14 \qquad y = \frac{1}{2}$$
$$x = 7$$

23. Setting real and imaginary parts equal:
$$7x - 1 = 2 \qquad 5y + 2 = 4$$
$$7x = 3 \qquad 5y = 2$$
$$x = \frac{3}{7} \qquad y = \frac{2}{5}$$

25. Combining the numbers: $(2+3i)+(3+6i) = 5+9i$

27. Combining the numbers: $(3-5i)+(2+4i) = 5-i$

29. Combining the numbers: $(5+2i)-(3+6i) = 5+2i-3-6i = 2-4i$

31. Combining the numbers: $(3-5i)-(2+i) = 3-5i-2-i = 1-6i$

33. Combining the numbers: $\left[(3+2i)-(6+i)\right]+(5+i) = 3+2i-6-i+5+i = 2+2i$

35. Combining the numbers: $\left[(7-i)-(2+4i)\right]-(6+2i) = 7-i-2-4i-6-2i = -1-7i$

37. Combining the numbers:
$$(3+2i)-\left[(3-4i)-(6+2i)\right] = (3+2i)-(3-4i-6-2i) = (3+2i)-(-3-6i) = 3+2i+3+6i = 6+8i$$

39. Combining the numbers: $(4-9i)+\left[(2-7i)-(4+8i)\right] = (4-9i)+(2-7i-4-8i) = (4-9i)+(-2-15i) = 2-24i$

41. Finding the product: $3i(4+5i) = 12i+15i^2 = -15+12i$

43. Finding the product: $6i(4-3i) = 24i-18i^2 = 18+24i$

45. Finding the product: $(3+2i)(4+i) = 12+8i+3i+2i^2 = 12+11i-2 = 10+11i$

47. Finding the product: $(4+9i)(3-i) = 12+27i-4i-9i^2 = 12+23i+9 = 21+23i$

49. Finding the product: $(-1+2i)(6-5i) = -6+5i+12i-10i^2 = -6+17i+10 = 4+17i$

51. Finding the product: $(2-i)^3 = (2-i)(2-i)^2 = (2-i)(4-4i-1) = (2-i)(3-4i) = 6-11i-4 = 2-11i$

53. Finding the product: $(2+5i)^2 = (2+5i)(2+5i) = 4+10i+10i-25 = -21+20i$

55. Finding the product: $(1-i)^2 = (1-i)(1-i) = 1-i-i-1 = -2i$

57. Finding the product: $(3-4i)^2 = (3-4i)(3-4i) = 9-12i-12i-16 = -7-24i$

59. Finding the product: $(2+i)(2-i) = 4-i^2 = 4+1 = 5$

61. Finding the product: $(6-2i)(6+2i) = 36 - 4i^2 = 36 + 4 = 40$

63. Finding the product: $(2+3i)(2-3i) = 4 - 9i^2 = 4 + 9 = 13$

65. Finding the product: $(10+8i)(10-8i) = 100 - 64i^2 = 100 + 64 = 164$

67. Simplifying: $(2-5i)^2 + (3+i)^2 = (4 - 10i - 10i - 25) + (9 + 3i + 3i - 1) = (-21 - 20i) + (8 + 6i) = -13 - 14i$

69. Simplifying: $(4+i)(4-i) - (1+2i)^2 = (16 - 4i + 4i + 1) - (1 + 2i + 2i - 4) = (17) - (-3 + 4i) = 20 - 4i$

71. Finding the quotient: $\dfrac{2-3i}{i} = \dfrac{2-3i}{i} \cdot \dfrac{i}{i} = \dfrac{2i+3}{-1} = -3 - 2i$

73. Finding the quotient: $\dfrac{5+2i}{-3i} = \dfrac{5+2i}{-3i} \cdot \dfrac{i}{i} = \dfrac{5i-2}{3} = -\dfrac{2}{3} + \dfrac{5}{3}i$

75. Finding the quotient: $\dfrac{4}{2-3i} = \dfrac{4}{2-3i} \cdot \dfrac{2+3i}{2+3i} = \dfrac{8+12i}{4+9} = \dfrac{8+12i}{13} = \dfrac{8}{13} + \dfrac{12}{13}i$

77. Finding the quotient: $\dfrac{6}{-3+2i} = \dfrac{6}{-3+2i} \cdot \dfrac{-3-2i}{-3-2i} = \dfrac{-18-12i}{9+4} = \dfrac{-18-12i}{13} = -\dfrac{18}{13} - \dfrac{12}{13}i$

79. Finding the quotient: $\dfrac{2+3i}{2-3i} = \dfrac{2+3i}{2-3i} \cdot \dfrac{2+3i}{2+3i} = \dfrac{4+12i-9}{4+9} = \dfrac{-5+12i}{13} = -\dfrac{5}{13} + \dfrac{12}{13}i$

81. Finding the quotient: $\dfrac{5+4i}{3+6i} = \dfrac{5+4i}{3+6i} \cdot \dfrac{3-6i}{3-6i} = \dfrac{15-18i+24}{9+36} = \dfrac{39-18i}{45} = \dfrac{13}{15} - \dfrac{2}{5}i$

83. Dividing to find R: $R = \dfrac{80+20i}{-6+2i} = \dfrac{80+20i}{-6+2i} \cdot \dfrac{-6-2i}{-6-2i} = \dfrac{-480-280i+40}{36+4} = \dfrac{-440-280i}{40} = (-11-7i)$ ohms

85. Writing in terms of i: $\sqrt{-44} = 2i\sqrt{11}$. The correct answer is c.

87. Combining the numbers: $(5-3i) - (-7-4i) = 5 - 3i + 7 + 4i = 12 + i$. The correct answer is a.

89. Solving the equation:
$$\frac{t}{3} - \frac{1}{2} = -1$$
$$6\left(\frac{t}{3} - \frac{1}{2}\right) = 6(-1)$$
$$2t - 3 = -6$$
$$2t = -3$$
$$t = -\frac{3}{2}$$

91. Solving the equation:
$$2 + \frac{5}{y} = \frac{3}{y^2}$$
$$y^2\left(2 + \frac{5}{y}\right) = y^2\left(\frac{3}{y^2}\right)$$
$$2y^2 + 5y = 3$$
$$2y^2 + 5y - 3 = 0$$
$$(2y-1)(y+3) = 0$$
$$y = -3, \frac{1}{2}$$

93. Let x represent the number. The equation is:
$$x + \frac{1}{x} = \frac{41}{20}$$
$$20x\left(x + \frac{1}{x}\right) = 20x\left(\frac{41}{20}\right)$$
$$20x^2 + 20 = 41x$$
$$20x^2 - 41x + 20 = 0$$
$$(5x-4)(4x-5) = 0$$
$$x = \frac{4}{5}, \frac{5}{4}$$
The number is either $\dfrac{5}{4}$ or $\dfrac{4}{5}$.

Chapter 7 Test

1. Simplifying: $-\sqrt{81} = -9$

2. Simplifying: $\sqrt[3]{-125} = -5$

3. Simplifying: $\left(\sqrt{7}\right)^2 = 7$

4. Simplifying: $\left(\sqrt[3]{-15}\right)^3 = -15$

5. Simplifying: $\sqrt{49x^8} = 7x^4$

6. Simplifying: $\sqrt[5]{32x^{10}y^{20}} = 2x^2y^4$

7. Graphing the equation:

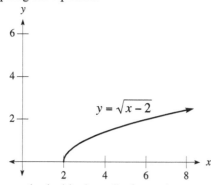

$y = \sqrt{x} - 2$

8. Graphing the equation:

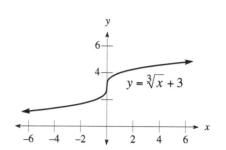

$y = \sqrt[3]{x} + 3$

9. The quantity inside the radical must be non-negative, so:

$$9 - x \geq 0$$
$$-x \geq -9$$
$$x \leq 9$$

The domain is $\{x \mid x \leq 9\} = (-\infty, 9]$.

10. The cube root has no domain restrictions, so the domain is $\{x \mid x \text{ is any real number}\} = (-\infty, \infty)$.

11. Simplifying: $27^{-2/3} = \left(27^{1/3}\right)^{-2} = 3^{-2} = \dfrac{1}{3^2} = \dfrac{1}{9}$

12. Simplifying: $\left(\dfrac{25}{49}\right)^{-1/2} = \left(\dfrac{49}{25}\right)^{1/2} = \dfrac{7}{5}$

13. Simplifying: $a^{3/4} \cdot a^{-1/3} = a^{3/4 - 1/3} = a^{9/12 - 4/12} = a^{5/12}$

14. Simplifying: $\left(x^{3/5}\right)^{5/6} = x^{3/5 \cdot 5/6} = x^{1/2}$

15. Simplifying: $\dfrac{x^{2/3}y^{-3}}{x^{3/4}y^{1/2}} = x^{2/3 - 3/4}y^{-3 - 1/2} = x^{8/12 - 9/12}y^{-6/2 - 1/2} = x^{-1/12}y^{-7/2} = \dfrac{1}{x^{1/12}y^{7/2}}$

16. Simplifying: $\dfrac{\left(36a^8b^4\right)^{1/2}}{\left(27a^9b^6\right)^{1/3}} = \dfrac{6a^4b^2}{3a^3b^2} = 2a$

17. Writing as a rational exponent: $\sqrt[3]{2a} = (2a)^{1/3}$

18. Writing with rational exponents and simplifying: $\sqrt{36x^6y^{18}} = \left(36x^6y^{18}\right)^{1/2} = 6\left(x^6\right)^{1/2}\left(y^{18}\right)^{1/2} = 6x^3y^9$

19. Simplifying: $\sqrt{125x^3y^5} = \sqrt{25x^2y^4 \cdot 5xy} = 5xy^2\sqrt{5xy}$

20. Simplifying: $\sqrt[3]{40x^7y^8} = \sqrt[3]{8x^6y^6 \cdot 5xy^2} = 2x^2y^2\sqrt[3]{5xy^2}$

21. Simplifying: $\sqrt{\dfrac{2}{9}} = \dfrac{\sqrt{2}}{\sqrt{9}} = \dfrac{\sqrt{2}}{3}$

22. Simplifying: $\sqrt{\dfrac{12a^4b^3}{25c^6}} = \dfrac{\sqrt{12a^4b^3}}{\sqrt{25c^6}} = \dfrac{2a^2b\sqrt{3b}}{5c^3}$

23. Combining: $3\sqrt{12} - 4\sqrt{27} = 6\sqrt{3} - 12\sqrt{3} = -6\sqrt{3}$

24. Combining: $\sqrt[3]{24a^3b^3} - 5a\sqrt[3]{3b^3} = 2ab\sqrt[3]{3} - 5ab\sqrt[3]{3} = -3ab\sqrt[3]{3}$

25. Multiplying: $\left(\sqrt{x} + 7\right)\left(\sqrt{x} - 4\right) = x - 4\sqrt{x} + 7\sqrt{x} - 28 = x + 3\sqrt{x} - 28$

26. Multiplying: $\left(3\sqrt{2} - \sqrt{3}\right)^2 = \left(3\sqrt{2} - \sqrt{3}\right)\left(3\sqrt{2} - \sqrt{3}\right) = 18 - 3\sqrt{6} - 3\sqrt{6} + 3 = 21 - 6\sqrt{6}$

27. Rationalizing the denominator: $\sqrt{\dfrac{5}{6}} = \dfrac{\sqrt{5}}{\sqrt{6}} \cdot \dfrac{\sqrt{6}}{\sqrt{6}} = \dfrac{\sqrt{30}}{6}$

28. Rationalizing the denominator: $\sqrt[3]{\dfrac{3x}{4y}} = \dfrac{\sqrt[3]{3x}}{\sqrt[3]{4y}} \cdot \dfrac{\sqrt[3]{2y^2}}{\sqrt[3]{2y^2}} = \dfrac{\sqrt[3]{6xy^2}}{2y}$

29. Rationalizing the denominator: $\dfrac{5}{\sqrt{3}-1} = \dfrac{5}{\sqrt{3}-1} \cdot \dfrac{\sqrt{3}+1}{\sqrt{3}+1} = \dfrac{5\sqrt{3}+5}{3-1} = \dfrac{5+5\sqrt{3}}{2}$

30. Rationalizing the denominator: $\dfrac{\sqrt{x}-\sqrt{2}}{\sqrt{x}+\sqrt{2}} = \dfrac{\sqrt{x}-\sqrt{2}}{\sqrt{x}+\sqrt{2}} \cdot \dfrac{\sqrt{x}-\sqrt{2}}{\sqrt{x}-\sqrt{2}} = \dfrac{x-\sqrt{2x}-\sqrt{2x}+2}{x-2} = \dfrac{x-2\sqrt{2x}+2}{x-2}$

31. Solving the equation:

$$\sqrt{3x+1} = x-3$$
$$\left(\sqrt{3x+1}\right)^2 = (x-3)^2$$
$$3x+1 = x^2 - 6x + 9$$
$$0 = x^2 - 9x + 8$$
$$0 = (x-1)(x-8)$$
$$x = 1, 8$$

The solution is 8 (1 does not check).

32. Solving the equation:

$$\sqrt[3]{2x+7} = -1$$
$$\left(\sqrt[3]{2x+7}\right)^3 = (-1)^3$$
$$2x+7 = -1$$
$$2x = -8$$
$$x = -4$$

33. Solving the equation:

$$\sqrt{x+3} = \sqrt{x+4} - 1$$
$$\left(\sqrt{x+3}\right)^2 = \left(\sqrt{x+4}-1\right)^2$$
$$x+3 = x+4 - 2\sqrt{x+4} + 1$$
$$-2 = -2\sqrt{x+4}$$
$$\sqrt{x+4} = 1$$
$$x+4 = 1$$
$$x = -3$$

34. Setting the real and imaginary parts equal:

$$2x+5 = 6 \qquad\qquad\qquad -(y-3) = -4$$
$$2x = 1 \qquad\qquad\qquad\qquad y - 3 = 4$$
$$x = \dfrac{1}{2} \qquad\qquad\qquad\qquad y = 7$$

35. Performing the operations: $(3+2i)-\left[(7-i)-(4+3i)\right] = (3+2i)-(7-i-4-3i) = (3+2i)-(3-4i) = 3+2i-3+4i = 6i$

36. Performing the operations: $(2-3i)(4+3i) = 8+6i-12i+9 = 17-6i$

37. Performing the operations: $(5-4i)^2 = (5-4i)(5-4i) = 25-20i-20i-16 = 9-40i$

38. Performing the operations: $\dfrac{2-3i}{2+3i} = \dfrac{2-3i}{2+3i} \cdot \dfrac{2-3i}{2-3i} = \dfrac{4-12i-9}{4+9} = \dfrac{-5-12i}{13} = -\dfrac{5}{13} - \dfrac{12}{13}i$

39. Rewriting the exponent: $i^{38} = \left(i^2\right)^{19} = (-1)^{19} = -1$

Chapter 8
Quadratic Equations and Functions

8.1 The Square Root Property and Completing the Square

1. Solving the equation:
$$x^2 = 25$$
$$x = \pm\sqrt{25} = \pm 5$$

3. Solving the equation:
$$a^2 = -9$$
$$a = \pm\sqrt{-9} = \pm 3i$$

5. Solving the equation:
$$y^2 = \frac{3}{4}$$
$$y = \pm\sqrt{\frac{3}{4}} = \pm\frac{\sqrt{3}}{2}$$

7. Solving the equation:
$$x^2 + 12 = 0$$
$$x^2 = -12$$
$$x = \pm\sqrt{-12} = \pm 2i\sqrt{3}$$

9. Solving the equation:
$$4a^2 - 45 = 0$$
$$4a^2 = 45$$
$$a^2 = \frac{45}{4}$$
$$a = \pm\sqrt{\frac{45}{4}} = \pm\frac{3\sqrt{5}}{2}$$

11. Solving the equation:
$$3x^2 + 28 = 0$$
$$3x^2 = -28$$
$$x^2 = -\frac{28}{3}$$
$$x = \sqrt{-\frac{28}{3}} = \frac{\pm 2i\sqrt{7}}{\sqrt{3}}$$
$$x = \frac{\pm 2i\sqrt{7}}{\sqrt{3}} \cdot \frac{\sqrt{3}}{\sqrt{3}} = \frac{\pm 2i\sqrt{21}}{3}$$

13. Solving the equation:
$$(2y-1)^2 = 25$$
$$2y-1 = \pm\sqrt{25} = \pm 5$$
$$2y-1 = -5, 5$$
$$2y = -4, 6$$
$$y = -2, 3$$

15. Solving the equation:
$$(2a+3)^2 = -9$$
$$2a+3 = \pm\sqrt{-9} = \pm 3i$$
$$2a = -3 \pm 3i$$
$$a = -\frac{3}{2} \pm \frac{3}{2}i$$

17. Solving the equation:
$$(5x+2)^2 = -8$$
$$5x+2 = \pm\sqrt{-2} = \pm 2i\sqrt{2}$$
$$5x = -2 \pm 2i\sqrt{2}$$
$$x = -\frac{2}{5} \pm \frac{2\sqrt{2}}{5}i$$

19. Solving the equation:
$$x^2 + 8x + 16 = 27$$
$$(x+4)^2 = 27$$
$$x+4 = \pm\sqrt{27} = \pm 3\sqrt{3}$$
$$x = -4 \pm 3\sqrt{3}$$

21. Solving the equation:

$$4a^2 - 12a + 9 = -4$$
$$(2a - 3)^2 = -4$$
$$2a - 3 = \pm\sqrt{-4} = \pm 2i$$
$$2a = 3 \pm 2i$$
$$a = \frac{3}{2} \pm i$$

23. Completing the square: $x^2 + 12x + 36 = (x + 6)^2$

25. Completing the square: $x^2 - 4x + 4 = (x - 2)^2$

27. Completing the square: $a^2 - 10a + 25 = (a - 5)^2$

29. Completing the square: $x^2 + 5x + \frac{25}{4} = \left(x + \frac{5}{2}\right)^2$

31. Completing the square: $y^2 - 7y + \frac{49}{4} = \left(y - \frac{7}{2}\right)^2$

33. Completing the square: $x^2 + \frac{1}{2}x + \frac{1}{16} = \left(x + \frac{1}{4}\right)^2$

35. Completing the square: $x^2 + \frac{2}{3}x + \frac{1}{9} = \left(x + \frac{1}{3}\right)^2$

37. Solving the equation:

$$x^2 + 4x = 12$$
$$x^2 + 4x + 4 = 12 + 4$$
$$(x + 2)^2 = 16$$
$$x + 2 = \pm\sqrt{16} = \pm 4$$
$$x + 2 = -4, 4$$
$$x = -6, 2$$

39. Solving the equation:

$$x^2 + 12x = -27$$
$$x^2 + 12x + 36 = -27 + 36$$
$$(x + 6)^2 = 9$$
$$x + 6 = \pm\sqrt{9} = \pm 3$$
$$x + 6 = -3, 3$$
$$x = -9, -3$$

41. Solving the equation:

$$a^2 - 2a + 5 = 0$$
$$a^2 - 2a + 1 = -5 + 1$$
$$(a - 1)^2 = -4$$
$$a - 1 = \pm\sqrt{-4} = \pm 2i$$
$$a = 1 \pm 2i$$

43. Solving the equation:

$$y^2 - 8y + 1 = 0$$
$$y^2 - 8y + 16 = -1 + 16$$
$$(y - 4)^2 = 15$$
$$y - 4 = \pm\sqrt{15}$$
$$y = 4 \pm \sqrt{15}$$

45. Solving the equation:

$$x^2 - 5x - 3 = 0$$
$$x^2 - 5x + \frac{25}{4} = 3 + \frac{25}{4}$$
$$\left(x - \frac{5}{2}\right)^2 = \frac{37}{4}$$
$$x - \frac{5}{2} = \pm\frac{\sqrt{37}}{2}$$
$$x = \frac{5 \pm \sqrt{37}}{2}$$

47. Solving the equation:

$$2x^2 - 4x - 8 = 0$$
$$x^2 - 2x - 4 = 0$$
$$x^2 - 2x + 1 = 4 + 1$$
$$(x - 1)^2 = 5$$
$$x - 1 = \pm\sqrt{5}$$
$$x = 1 \pm \sqrt{5}$$

49. Solving the equation:

$$3t^2 - 8t + 1 = 0$$

$$t^2 - \frac{8}{3}t + \frac{1}{3} = 0$$

$$t^2 - \frac{8}{3}t + \frac{16}{9} = -\frac{1}{3} + \frac{16}{9}$$

$$\left(t - \frac{4}{3}\right)^2 = \frac{13}{9}$$

$$t - \frac{4}{3} = \pm\sqrt{\frac{13}{9}} = \pm\frac{\sqrt{13}}{3}$$

$$t = \frac{4 \pm \sqrt{13}}{3}$$

51. Solving the equation:

$$4x^2 - 3x + 5 = 0$$

$$x^2 - \frac{3}{4}x + \frac{5}{4} = 0$$

$$x^2 - \frac{3}{4}x + \frac{9}{64} = -\frac{5}{4} + \frac{9}{64}$$

$$\left(x - \frac{3}{8}\right)^2 = -\frac{71}{64}$$

$$x - \frac{3}{8} = \pm\sqrt{-\frac{71}{64}} = \pm\frac{i\sqrt{71}}{8}$$

$$x = \frac{3}{8} \pm \frac{\sqrt{71}}{8}i$$

53. Solving the equation:

$$3x^2 + 4x - 1 = 0$$

$$x^2 + \frac{4}{3}x - \frac{1}{3} = 0$$

$$x^2 + \frac{4}{3}x + \frac{4}{9} = \frac{1}{3} + \frac{4}{9}$$

$$\left(x + \frac{2}{3}\right)^2 = \frac{7}{9}$$

$$x + \frac{2}{3} = \pm\sqrt{\frac{7}{9}} = \pm\frac{\sqrt{7}}{3}$$

$$x = \frac{-2 \pm \sqrt{7}}{3}$$

55. Solving the equation:

$$2x^2 - 10x = 11$$

$$x^2 - 5x = \frac{11}{2}$$

$$x^2 - 5x + \frac{25}{4} = \frac{11}{2} + \frac{25}{4}$$

$$\left(x - \frac{5}{2}\right)^2 = \frac{47}{4}$$

$$x - \frac{5}{2} = \pm\sqrt{\frac{47}{4}} = \pm\frac{\sqrt{47}}{2}$$

$$x = \frac{5 \pm \sqrt{47}}{2}$$

57. Solving the equation:

$$4x^2 - 10x + 11 = 0$$

$$x^2 - \frac{5}{2}x + \frac{11}{4} = 0$$

$$x^2 - \frac{5}{2}x + \frac{25}{16} = -\frac{11}{4} + \frac{25}{16}$$

$$\left(x - \frac{5}{4}\right)^2 = -\frac{19}{16}$$

$$x - \frac{5}{4} = \pm\sqrt{-\frac{19}{16}} = \pm\frac{i\sqrt{19}}{4}$$

$$x = \frac{5}{4} \pm \frac{\sqrt{19}}{4}i$$

59. **a.** No, it cannot be solved by factoring.

b. Solving the equation:

$$x^2 = -9$$

$$x = \pm\sqrt{-9}$$

$$x = \pm 3i$$

61. **a.** Solving by factoring:

$$x^2 - 6x = 0$$
$$x(x-6) = 0$$
$$x = 0,6$$

b. Solving by completing the square:

$$x^2 - 6x = 0$$
$$x^2 - 6x + 9 = 0 + 9$$
$$(x-3)^2 = 9$$
$$x - 3 = \pm\sqrt{9}$$
$$x - 3 = -3,3$$
$$x = 0,6$$

63. **a.** Solving by factoring:

$$x^2 + 2x = 35$$
$$x^2 + 2x - 35 = 0$$
$$(x+7)(x-5) = 0$$
$$x = -7,5$$

b. Solving by completing the square:

$$x^2 + 2x = 35$$
$$x^2 + 2x + 1 = 35 + 1$$
$$(x+1)^2 = 36$$
$$x + 1 = \pm\sqrt{36}$$
$$x + 1 = -6,6$$
$$x = -7,5$$

65. Substituting: $x^2 - 6x - 7 = \left(-3+\sqrt{2}\right)^2 - 6\left(-3+\sqrt{2}\right) - 7 = 9 - 6\sqrt{2} + 2 + 18 - 6\sqrt{2} - 7 = 22 - 12\sqrt{2}$

No, $x = -3 + \sqrt{2}$ is not a solution to the equation.

67. **a.** Solving the equation:

$$5x - 7 = 0$$
$$5x = 7$$
$$x = \frac{7}{5}$$

b. Solving the equation:

$$5x - 7 = 8$$
$$5x = 15$$
$$x = 3$$

c. Solving the equation:

$$(5x-7)^2 = 8$$
$$5x - 7 = \pm\sqrt{8}$$
$$5x - 7 = \pm 2\sqrt{2}$$
$$5x = 7 \pm 2\sqrt{2}$$
$$x = \frac{7 \pm 2\sqrt{2}}{5}$$

d. Solving the equation:

$$\sqrt{5x-7} = 8$$
$$\left(\sqrt{5x-7}\right)^2 = (8)^2$$
$$5x - 7 = 64$$
$$5x = 71$$
$$x = \frac{71}{5}$$

e. Solving the equation:

$$\frac{5}{2} - \frac{7}{2x} = \frac{4}{x}$$
$$2x\left(\frac{5}{2} - \frac{7}{2x}\right) = 2x\left(\frac{4}{x}\right)$$
$$5x - 7 = 8$$
$$5x = 15$$
$$x = 3$$

69. **a.** Factoring the expression: $(2x-3)^2 - 16 = (2x-3+4)(2x-3-4) = (2x+1)(2x-7)$

b. Simplifying: $(2x-3)^2 - 16 = (2x-3)(2x-3) - 16 = 4x^2 - 12x + 9 - 16 = 4x^2 - 12x - 7$

c. Solving the equation:

$$(2x-3)^2 - 16 = 0$$
$$(2x-3)^2 = 16$$
$$2x - 3 = \pm\sqrt{16} = \pm 4$$
$$2x - 3 = -4,4$$
$$2x = -1,7$$
$$x = -\frac{1}{2}, \frac{7}{2}$$

d. Solving the equation:

$$(2x-3)^2 = -16$$
$$2x - 3 = \pm\sqrt{-16} = \pm 4i$$
$$2x = 3 \pm 4i$$
$$x = \frac{3}{2} \pm 2i$$

71. The diagonal is $\sqrt{2}$ inches.

73. Let x represent the horizontal distance. Using the Pythagorean theorem:
$$x^2 + 120^2 = 790^2$$
$$x^2 + 14400 = 624100$$
$$x^2 = 609700$$
$$x = \sqrt{609700} \approx 781 \text{ feet}$$

75. Solving for r:
$$3456 = 3000(1+r)^2$$
$$(1+r)^2 = 1.152$$
$$1+r = \sqrt{1.152}$$
$$r = \sqrt{1.152} - 1 \approx 0.073$$
The annual interest rate is 7.3%.

77. Let h represent the height the ladder reaches up the building. Using the Pythagorean theorem:
$$7^2 + h^2 = 25^2$$
$$49 + h^2 = 625$$
$$h^2 = 576$$
$$h = \sqrt{576} = 24 \text{ feet}$$

79. Let t represent the required time. The distances for each cyclist are $15t$ and $20t$, so using the Pythagorean theorem:
$$(15t)^2 + (20t)^2 = 70^2$$
$$225t^2 + 400t^2 = 4{,}900$$
$$625t^2 = 4{,}900$$
$$t = \sqrt{\frac{4{,}900}{625}} = \frac{70}{25} = 2.8 \text{ hours}$$

81. Let w represent the width and $2w + 3$ represent the length. Since the area is 25, the equation is:
$$w(2w+3) = 25$$
$$2w^2 + 3w = 25$$
$$w^2 + \frac{3}{2}w = \frac{25}{2}$$
$$w^2 + \frac{3}{2}w + \frac{9}{16} = \frac{25}{2} + \frac{9}{16}$$
$$\left(w + \frac{3}{4}\right)^2 = \frac{209}{16}$$
$$w + \frac{3}{4} = \frac{\sqrt{209}}{4}$$
$$w = \frac{-3 + \sqrt{209}}{4} \approx 2.9 \text{ feet}$$

83. Solving the equation:
$$2x^2 - 9 = 0$$
$$2x^2 = 9$$
$$x^2 = \frac{9}{2}$$
$$x = \pm\sqrt{\frac{9}{2}} = \pm\frac{3}{\sqrt{2}} = \pm\frac{3\sqrt{2}}{2}$$
The correct answer is a.

85. Let d represent the length of the diagonal. Using the Pythagorean theorem:

$$4^2 + 5^2 = d^2$$
$$16 + 25 = d^2$$
$$d^2 = 41$$
$$d = \sqrt{41} \text{ meters}$$

The correct answer is d.

87. Simplifying: $49 - 4(6)2 = 49 - 48 = 1$

89. Simplifying: $25 - 4(4)(-10) = 25 + 160 = 185$

91. Simplifying: $-7 - \dfrac{169}{12} = -\dfrac{84}{12} - \dfrac{169}{12} = -\dfrac{253}{12}$

93. Factoring: $125t^3 + 1 = (5t + 1)(25t^2 - 5t + 1)$

8.2 The Quadratic Formula

1. Using the quadratic formula: $a = \dfrac{4 \pm \sqrt{(-4)^2 - 4(1)(1)}}{2(1)} = \dfrac{4 \pm \sqrt{16 - 4}}{2} = \dfrac{4 \pm \sqrt{12}}{2} = \dfrac{4 \pm 2\sqrt{3}}{2} = 2 \pm \sqrt{3}$

3. Using the quadratic formula: $x = \dfrac{-(-1) \pm \sqrt{(-1)^2 - 4(2)(-5)}}{2(2)} = \dfrac{1 \pm \sqrt{1 + 40}}{4} = \dfrac{1 \pm \sqrt{41}}{4}$

5. Solving the equation:

$$12y^2 - 7y = 10$$
$$12y^2 - 7y - 10 = 0$$

$$y = \frac{-(-7) \pm \sqrt{(-7)^2 - 4(12)(-10)}}{2(12)} = \frac{7 \pm \sqrt{49 + 480}}{24} = \frac{7 \pm \sqrt{529}}{24} = \frac{7 \pm 23}{24} = -\frac{2}{3}, \frac{5}{4}$$

Note that this equation could also be solved by factoring.

7. Solving the equation:

$$2x + 3 = -2x^2$$
$$2x^2 + 2x + 3 = 0$$

$$x = \frac{-2 \pm \sqrt{4 - 24}}{4} = \frac{-2 \pm \sqrt{-20}}{4} = \frac{-2 \pm 2i\sqrt{5}}{4} = -\frac{1}{2} \pm \frac{\sqrt{5}}{2}i$$

9. Using the quadratic formula: $x = \dfrac{-(-28) \pm \sqrt{(-28)^2 - 4(4)(49)}}{2(4)} = \dfrac{28 \pm \sqrt{784 - 784}}{8} = \dfrac{7}{2}$

11. Solving the equation:

$$0.01x^2 + 0.06x - 0.08 = 0$$
$$x^2 + 6x - 8 = 0$$

$$x = \frac{-6 \pm \sqrt{36 + 32}}{2} = \frac{-6 \pm \sqrt{68}}{2} = \frac{-6 \pm 2\sqrt{17}}{2} = -3 \pm \sqrt{17}$$

13. Solving the equation:

$$\frac{1}{6}x^2 - \frac{1}{2}x + \frac{1}{3} = 0$$
$$x^2 - 3x + 2 = 0$$

$$x = \frac{3 \pm \sqrt{9 - 8}}{2} = \frac{3 \pm 1}{2} = 1, 2$$

Note that this equation could also be solved by factoring.

15. Solving the equation:

$$\frac{x^2}{2} + 1 = \frac{2x}{3}$$
$$3x^2 + 6 = 4x$$
$$3x^2 - 4x + 6 = 0$$
$$x = \frac{4 \pm \sqrt{16 - 72}}{6} = \frac{4 \pm \sqrt{-56}}{6} = \frac{4 \pm 2i\sqrt{14}}{6} = \frac{2}{3} \pm \frac{\sqrt{14}}{3}i$$

17. Solving the equation:

$$\frac{2t^2}{3} - t = -\frac{1}{6}$$
$$4t^2 - 6t = -1$$
$$4t^2 - 6t + 1 = 0$$
$$t = \frac{6 \pm \sqrt{36 - 16}}{8} = \frac{6 \pm \sqrt{20}}{8} = \frac{6 \pm 2\sqrt{5}}{8} = \frac{3 \pm \sqrt{5}}{4}$$

19. Solving the equation:

$$\frac{1}{2}r^2 = \frac{1}{6}r - \frac{2}{3}$$
$$3r^2 = r - 4$$
$$3r^2 - r + 4 = 0$$
$$r = \frac{1 \pm \sqrt{1 - 48}}{6} = \frac{1 \pm \sqrt{-47}}{6} = \frac{1}{6} \pm \frac{\sqrt{47}}{6}i$$

21. Solving the equation:

$$(x - 3)(x - 5) = 1$$
$$x^2 - 8x + 15 = 1$$
$$x^2 - 8x + 14 = 0$$
$$x = \frac{8 \pm \sqrt{64 - 56}}{2} = \frac{8 \pm \sqrt{8}}{2} = \frac{8 \pm 2\sqrt{2}}{2} = 4 \pm \sqrt{2}$$

23. Solving the equation:

$$\frac{1}{x+1} - \frac{1}{x} = \frac{1}{2}$$
$$2x(x+1)\left(\frac{1}{x+1} - \frac{1}{x}\right) = 2x(x+1) \cdot \frac{1}{2}$$
$$2x - (2x + 2) = x^2 + x$$
$$2x - 2x - 2 = x^2 + x$$
$$x^2 + x + 2 = 0$$
$$x = \frac{-1 \pm \sqrt{1 - 8}}{2} = \frac{-1 \pm \sqrt{-7}}{2} = -\frac{1}{2} \pm \frac{\sqrt{7}}{2}i$$

25. Solving the equation:

$$\frac{1}{y-1}+\frac{1}{y+1}=1$$

$$(y+1)(y-1)\left(\frac{1}{y-1}+\frac{1}{y+1}\right)=(y+1)(y-1)\cdot 1$$

$$y+1+y-1=y^2-1$$

$$2y=y^2-1$$

$$y^2-2y-1=0$$

$$y=\frac{2\pm\sqrt{4+4}}{2}=\frac{2\pm\sqrt{8}}{2}=\frac{2\pm 2\sqrt{2}}{2}=1\pm\sqrt{2}$$

27. Solving the equation:

$$\frac{1}{x+2}+\frac{1}{x+3}=1$$

$$(x+2)(x+3)\left(\frac{1}{x+2}+\frac{1}{x+3}\right)=(x+2)(x+3)\cdot 1$$

$$x+3+x+2=x^2+5x+6$$

$$2x+5=x^2+5x+6$$

$$x^2+3x+1=0$$

$$x=\frac{-3\pm\sqrt{9-4}}{2}=\frac{-3\pm\sqrt{5}}{2}$$

29. Solving the equation:

$$\frac{6}{r^2-1}-\frac{1}{2}=\frac{1}{r+1}$$

$$2(r+1)(r-1)\left(\frac{6}{(r+1)(r-1)}-\frac{1}{2}\right)=2(r+1)(r-1)\cdot\frac{1}{r+1}$$

$$12-\left(r^2-1\right)=2r-2$$

$$12-r^2+1=2r-2$$

$$r^2+2r-15=0$$

$$(r+5)(r-3)=0$$

$$r=-5,3$$

31. Solving the equation:

$$x^3-8=0$$

$$(x-2)\left(x^2+2x+4\right)=0$$

$$x=2 \quad\text{or}\quad x=\frac{-2\pm\sqrt{4-16}}{2}=\frac{-2\pm\sqrt{-12}}{2}=\frac{-2\pm 2i\sqrt{3}}{2}=-1\pm i\sqrt{3}$$

$$x=2,-1\pm i\sqrt{3}$$

33. Solving the equation:

$$8a^3+27=0$$

$$(2a+3)\left(4a^2-6a+9\right)=0$$

$$a=-\frac{3}{2} \quad\text{or}\quad a=\frac{6\pm\sqrt{36-144}}{8}=\frac{6\pm\sqrt{-108}}{8}=\frac{6\pm 6i\sqrt{3}}{8}=\frac{3\pm 3i\sqrt{3}}{4}$$

$$a=-\frac{3}{2},\frac{3}{4}\pm\frac{3\sqrt{3}}{4}i$$

35. Solving the equation:

$$125t^3 - 1 = 0$$
$$(5t - 1)(25t^2 + 5t + 1) = 0$$

$$t = \frac{1}{5} \quad \text{or} \quad t = \frac{-5 \pm \sqrt{25 - 100}}{50} = \frac{-5 \pm \sqrt{-75}}{50} = \frac{-5 \pm 5i\sqrt{3}}{50} = \frac{-1 \pm i\sqrt{3}}{10}$$

$$t = \frac{1}{5}, -\frac{1}{10} \pm \frac{\sqrt{3}}{10}i$$

37. Solving the equation:

$$2x^3 + 2x^2 + 3x = 0$$
$$x(2x^2 + 2x + 3) = 0$$

$$x = 0 \quad \text{or} \quad x = \frac{-2 \pm \sqrt{4 - 24}}{4} = \frac{-2 \pm \sqrt{-20}}{4} = \frac{-2 \pm 2i\sqrt{5}}{4} = \frac{-1 \pm i\sqrt{5}}{2}$$

$$x = 0, -\frac{1}{2} \pm \frac{\sqrt{5}}{2}i$$

39. Solving the equation:

$$3y^4 = 6y^3 - 6y^2$$
$$3y^4 - 6y^3 + 6y^2 = 0$$
$$3y^2(y^2 - 2y + 2) = 0$$

$$y = 0 \quad \text{or} \quad y = \frac{2 \pm \sqrt{4 - 8}}{2} = \frac{2 \pm \sqrt{-4}}{2} = \frac{2 \pm 2i}{2} = 1 \pm i$$

$$y = 0, 1 \pm i$$

41. Solving the equation:

$$6t^5 + 4t^4 = -2t^3$$
$$6t^5 + 4t^4 + 2t^3 = 0$$
$$2t^3(3t^2 + 2t + 1) = 0$$

$$t = 0 \quad \text{or} \quad t = \frac{-2 \pm \sqrt{4 - 12}}{6} = \frac{-2 \pm \sqrt{-8}}{6} = \frac{-2 \pm 2i\sqrt{2}}{6} = \frac{-1 \pm i\sqrt{2}}{3}$$

$$t = 0, -\frac{1}{3} \pm \frac{\sqrt{2}}{3}i$$

43. The expressions from **a** and **b** are equivalent, since: $\dfrac{6 + 2\sqrt{3}}{4} = \dfrac{2(3 + \sqrt{3})}{4} = \dfrac{3 + \sqrt{3}}{2}$

45. **a.** Solving by factoring:

$$3x^2 - 5x = 0$$
$$x(3x - 5) = 0$$
$$x = 0, \frac{5}{3}$$

b. Using the quadratic formula: $x = \dfrac{5 \pm \sqrt{(-5)^2 - 4(3)(0)}}{2(3)} = \dfrac{5 \pm \sqrt{25 - 0}}{6} = \dfrac{5 \pm 5}{6} = 0, \dfrac{5}{3}$

47. No, it cannot be solved by factoring. Using the quadratic formula:

$$x = \frac{4 \pm \sqrt{(-4)^2 - 4(1)(7)}}{2(1)} = \frac{4 \pm \sqrt{16 - 28}}{2} = \frac{4 \pm \sqrt{-12}}{2} = \frac{4 \pm 2i\sqrt{3}}{2} = 2 \pm i\sqrt{3}$$

49. Substituting: $x^2 + 2x = (-1 + i)^2 + 2(-1 + i) = 1 - 2i + i^2 - 2 + 2i = 1 - 2i - 1 - 2 + 2i = -2$

Yes, $x = -1 + i$ is a solution to the equation.

51. Solving the equation:
$$x^2 + 5x + 6 = 0$$
$$(x+3)(x+2) = 0$$
$$x = -3, -2$$

53. Solving the equation:
$$2y^2 + 10y = 0$$
$$2y(y+5) = 0$$
$$y = -5, 0$$

55. Solving the equation:
$$4a^2 - 27 = 0$$
$$4a^2 = 27$$
$$a^2 = \frac{27}{4}$$
$$a = \pm\sqrt{\frac{27}{4}} = \pm\frac{3\sqrt{3}}{2}$$

57. Solving the equation:
$$y^2 = 5y$$
$$y^2 - 5y = 0$$
$$y(y-5) = 0$$
$$y = 0, 5$$

59. Solving the equation:
$$2x^2 + 5x = 6$$
$$2x^2 + 5x - 6 = 0$$
$$x = \frac{-5 \pm \sqrt{25 - (-48)}}{4} = \frac{-5 \pm \sqrt{73}}{4}$$

61. Solving the equation:
$$100x^2 - 200x + 100 = 0$$
$$100(x^2 - 2x + 1) = 0$$
$$100(x-1)^2 = 0$$
$$x = 1$$

63. Solving the equation:
$$(x+3)^2 + (x-8)(x-1) = 16$$
$$x^2 + 6x + 9 + x^2 - 9x + 8 = 16$$
$$2x^2 - 3x + 1 = 0$$
$$(2x-1)(x-1) = 0$$
$$x = \frac{1}{2}, 1$$

65. Solving the equation:
$$\frac{x^2}{3} - \frac{5x}{6} = \frac{1}{2}$$
$$2x^2 - 5x = 3$$
$$2x^2 - 5x - 3 = 0$$
$$(2x+1)(x-3) = 0$$
$$x = -\frac{1}{2}, 3$$

67. Solving the equation:
$$(19y - 31)^2 - 121 = 0$$
$$(19y - 31)^2 = 121$$
$$19y - 31 = \pm\sqrt{121}$$
$$19y - 31 = -11, 11$$
$$19y = 20, 42$$
$$y = \frac{20}{19}, \frac{42}{19}$$

69. **a.** Solving the equation:

$$(2x+3)(2x-3)=0$$
$$2x=-3,3$$
$$x=-\frac{3}{2},\frac{3}{2}$$

b. Solving the equation:

$$(2x+3)(2x-3)=7$$
$$4x^2-9=7$$
$$4x^2=16$$
$$x^2=4$$
$$x=-2,2$$

c. Solving the equation:

$$(2x+3)^2=7$$
$$2x+3=\pm\sqrt{7}$$
$$2x=-3\pm\sqrt{7}$$
$$x=\frac{-3\pm\sqrt{7}}{2}$$

d. Solving the equation:

$$2x+3=7x^2$$
$$7x^2-2x-3=0$$
$$x=\frac{2\pm\sqrt{4-(-84)}}{14}=\frac{2\pm\sqrt{88}}{14}=\frac{2\pm2\sqrt{22}}{14}=\frac{1\pm\sqrt{22}}{7}$$

71. Let x and $x-2$ represent lengths of the two legs. Using the Pythagorean theorem:

$$x^2+(x-2)^2=12^2$$
$$x^2+x^2-4x+4=144$$
$$2x^2-4x-140=0$$
$$x^2-2x-70=0$$
$$x=\frac{2\pm\sqrt{4-(-280)}}{2}=\frac{2\pm\sqrt{284}}{2}=\frac{2\pm2\sqrt{71}}{1}=1\pm\sqrt{71}\approx-7.4,9.4$$

Since a negative side length is impossible, the legs are 9.4 m and 7.4 m.

73. Let w represent the width and $4w-5$ represent the length. Using the area formula:

$$w(4w-5)=60$$
$$4w^2-5w=60$$
$$4w^2-5w-60=0$$
$$w=\frac{5\pm\sqrt{25-(-960)}}{8}=\frac{5\pm\sqrt{985}}{8}\approx-3.3,4.5$$

Since a negative width is impossible, the width is 4.5 cm and the length is $4(4.5)-5=13$ cm.

75. Using the Pythagorean theorem:

$$(2x+1)^2+(x+6)^2=(4x+3)^2$$
$$4x^2+4x+1+x^2+12x+36=16x^2+24x+9$$
$$5x^2+16x+37=16x^2+24x+9$$
$$11x^2+8x-28=0$$
$$(11x-14)(x+2)=0$$
$$x=\frac{14}{11}\quad(x=-2\text{ is impossible})$$

Therefore the dimensions are:

width: $2\left(\dfrac{14}{11}\right)+1=\dfrac{28}{11}+1=\dfrac{39}{11}$ length: $\dfrac{14}{11}+6=\dfrac{80}{11}$

So the area is given by: $\left(\dfrac{39}{11}\right)\left(\dfrac{80}{11}\right)=\dfrac{3,120}{121}$

77. First write the equation as $2x^2 + x - 5 = 0$. Using the quadratic formula:

$$x = \frac{-1 \pm \sqrt{1^2 - 4(2)(-5)}}{2(2)} = \frac{-1 \pm \sqrt{1 + 40}}{4} = \frac{-1 \pm \sqrt{41}}{4}$$

The correct answer is a.

79. Evaluating $b^2 - 4ac$: $b^2 - 4ac = (-3)^2 - 4(1)(-40) = 9 + 160 = 169$

81. Evaluating $b^2 - 4ac$: $b^2 - 4ac = 12^2 - 4(4)(9) = 144 - 144 = 0$

83. Solving the equation:

$$k^2 - 144 = 0$$
$$(k + 12)(k - 12) = 0$$
$$k = -12, 12$$

85. Multiplying: $(x - 3)(x + 2) = x^2 + 2x - 3x - 6 = x^2 - x - 6$

87. Multiplying: $(x - 3)(x - 3) = x^2 - 3x - 3x + 9 = x^2 - 6x + 9$

8.3 More on Solutions to Quadratic Equations

1. Computing the discriminant: $D = (-6)^2 - 4(1)(5) = 36 - 20 = 16$. The equation will have two rational solutions.

3. First write the equation as $4x^2 - 4x + 1 = 0$. Computing the discriminant: $D = (-4)^2 - 4(4)(1) = 16 - 16 = 0$
The equation will have one rational solution.

5. Computing the discriminant: $D = 1^2 - 4(1)(-1) = 1 + 4 = 5$. The equation will have two irrational solutions.

7. First write the equation as $2y^2 - 3y - 1 = 0$. Computing the discriminant: $D = (-3)^2 - 4(2)(-1) = 9 + 8 = 17$
The equation will have two irrational solutions.

9. Computing the discriminant: $D = 0^2 - 4(1)(-9) = 36$. The equation will have two rational solutions.

11. First write the equation as $5a^2 - 4a - 5 = 0$. Computing the discriminant: $D = (-4)^2 - 4(5)(-5) = 16 + 100 = 116$
The equation will have two irrational solutions.

13. Setting the discriminant equal to 0:

$$(-k)^2 - 4(1)(25) = 0$$
$$k^2 - 100 = 0$$
$$k^2 = 100$$
$$k = \pm 10$$

15. First write the equation as $x^2 - kx + 36 = 0$. Setting the discriminant equal to 0:

$$(-k)^2 - 4(1)(36) = 0$$
$$k^2 - 144 = 0$$
$$k^2 = 144$$
$$k = \pm 12$$

17. Setting the discriminant equal to 0:

$$(-12)^2 - 4(4)(k) = 0$$
$$144 - 16k = 0$$
$$16k = 144$$
$$k = 9$$

19. First write the equation as $kx^2 - 40x - 25 = 0$. Setting the discriminant equal to 0:

$$(-40)^2 - 4(k)(-25) = 0$$
$$1600 + 100k = 0$$
$$100k = -1600$$
$$k = -16$$

21. Setting the discriminant equal to 0:

$$(-k)^2 - 4(3)(2) = 0$$
$$k^2 - 24 = 0$$
$$k^2 = 24$$
$$k = \pm\sqrt{24} = \pm 2\sqrt{6}$$

23. Writing the equation:

$$(x-5)(x-2) = 0$$
$$x^2 - 7x + 10 = 0$$

25. Writing the equation:

$$(t+3)(t-6) = 0$$
$$t^2 - 3t - 18 = 0$$

27. Writing the equation:

$$(y-2)(y+2) = 0$$
$$y^2 - 4 = 0$$

29. Writing the equation:

$$(2x-1)(x-3) = 0$$
$$2x^2 - 7x + 3 = 0$$

31. Writing the equation:

$$(4t+3)(t-3) = 0$$
$$4t^2 - 9t - 9 = 0$$

33. Writing the equation:

$$(x-3)(x+3) = 0$$
$$x^2 - 9 = 0$$

35. Writing the equation:

$$(2a+1)(5a-3) = 0$$
$$10a^2 - a - 3 = 0$$

37. Writing the equation:

$$(3x+2)(3x-2) = 0$$
$$9x^2 - 4 = 0$$

39. Starting with the solutions:

$$x = \pm\sqrt{7}$$
$$x^2 = \left(\pm\sqrt{7}\right)^2$$
$$x^2 = 7$$
$$x^2 - 7 = 0$$

41. Starting with the solutions:

$$x = \pm 5i$$
$$x^2 = \left(\pm 5i\right)^2$$
$$x^2 = -25$$
$$x^2 + 25 = 0$$

43. Starting with the solutions:

$$y = 3 \pm \sqrt{11}$$
$$y - 3 = \pm\sqrt{11}$$
$$(y-3)^2 = \left(\pm\sqrt{11}\right)^2$$
$$y^2 - 6y + 9 = 11$$
$$y^2 - 6y - 2 = 0$$

45. Starting with the solutions:

$$t = -6 \pm \sqrt{2}$$
$$t + 6 = \pm\sqrt{2}$$
$$(t+6)^2 = \left(\pm\sqrt{2}\right)^2$$
$$t^2 + 12t + 36 = 2$$
$$t^2 + 12t + 34 = 0$$

47. Starting with the solutions:

$$x = 1 \pm i$$
$$x - 1 = \pm i$$
$$(x-1)^2 = \left(\pm i\right)^2$$
$$x^2 - 2x + 1 = -1$$
$$x^2 - 2x + 2 = 0$$

49. Starting with the solutions:

$$x = -2 \pm 3i$$
$$x + 2 = \pm 3i$$
$$(x+2)^2 = \left(\pm 3i\right)^2$$
$$x^2 + 4x + 4 = -9$$
$$x^2 + 4x + 13 = 0$$

51. Starting with the solutions:
$$x = 7 \pm i\sqrt{3}$$
$$x - 7 = \pm i\sqrt{3}$$
$$(x-7)^2 = \left(\pm i\sqrt{3}\right)^2$$
$$x^2 - 14x + 49 = -3$$
$$x^2 - 14x + 52 = 0$$

53. Starting with the solutions:
$$x = -3 \pm 5i\sqrt{2}$$
$$x + 3 = \pm 5i\sqrt{2}$$
$$(x+3)^2 = \left(\pm 5i\sqrt{2}\right)^2$$
$$x^2 + 6x + 9 = -50$$
$$x^2 + 6x + 59 = 0$$

55.   **a.**   Finding the equation using the zero-factor property:
$$\left(x - \left(1 - \sqrt{10}\right)\right)\left(x - \left(1 + \sqrt{10}\right)\right) = 0$$
$$\left(x - 1 + \sqrt{10}\right)\left(x - 1 - \sqrt{10}\right) = 0$$
$$(x-1)^2 - \left(\sqrt{10}\right)^2 = 0$$
$$x^2 - 2x + 1 - 10 = 0$$
$$x^2 - 2x - 9 = 0$$

   b.   Finding the equation by squaring each side:
$$x = 1 \pm \sqrt{10}$$
$$x - 1 = \pm \sqrt{10}$$
$$(x-1)^2 = \left(\pm\sqrt{10}\right)^2$$
$$x^2 - 2x + 1 = 10$$
$$x^2 - 2x - 9 = 0$$

57.   **a.**   Finding the equation using the zero-factor property:
$$\left(x - \left(-2 - i\sqrt{2}\right)\right)\left(x - \left(-2 + i\sqrt{2}\right)\right) = 0$$
$$\left(x + 2 + i\sqrt{2}\right)\left(x + 2 - i\sqrt{2}\right) = 0$$
$$(x+2)^2 - \left(i\sqrt{2}\right)^2 = 0$$
$$x^2 + 4x + 4 + 2 = 0$$
$$x^2 + 4x + 6 = 0$$

   b.   Finding the equation by squaring each side:
$$x = -2 \pm i\sqrt{2}$$
$$x + 2 = \pm i\sqrt{2}$$
$$(x+2)^2 = \left(\pm i\sqrt{2}\right)^2$$
$$x^2 + 4x + 4 = -2$$
$$x^2 + 4x + 6 = 0$$

59.   First write the equation as $2x^2 + 5x - 3 = 0$. Computing the discriminant: $D = (5)^2 - 4(2)(-3) = 25 + 24 = 49$
The correct answer is d.

61.   Writing the equation:
$$(3x - 1)(x - 2) = 0$$
$$3x^2 - x - 6x + 2 = 0$$
$$3x^2 - 7x + 2 = 0$$
The correct answer is a.

63.   Simplifying: $(x+3)^2 - 2(x+3) - 8 = x^2 + 6x + 9 - 2x - 6 - 8 = x^2 + 4x - 5$

65.   Simplifying: $(2a - 3)^2 - 9(2a - 3) + 20 = 4a^2 - 12a + 9 - 18a + 27 + 20 = 4a^2 - 30a + 56$

67. Simplifying:

$$2(4a+2)^2 - 3(4a+2) - 20 = 2(16a^2 + 16a + 4) - 3(4a+2) - 20$$
$$= 32a^2 + 32a + 8 - 12a - 6 - 20$$
$$= 32a^2 + 20a - 18$$

69. Solving the equation:

$$x^2 = \frac{1}{4}$$
$$x = \pm\sqrt{\frac{1}{4}} = \pm\frac{1}{2}$$

71. Solving the equation:

$$x^3 = \frac{1}{8}$$
$$8x^3 - 1 = 0$$
$$(2x-1)(4x^2 + 2x + 1) = 0$$
$$x = \frac{1}{2} \quad \text{or} \quad x = \frac{-2 \pm \sqrt{4-16}}{8} = \frac{-2 \pm \sqrt{-12}}{8} = \frac{-2 \pm 2i\sqrt{3}}{8} = \frac{-1 \pm i\sqrt{3}}{4}$$
$$x = \frac{1}{2}, -\frac{1}{4} \pm \frac{\sqrt{3}}{4}i$$

73. Since $\sqrt{x} \geq 0$, this equation has no solution.

75. Solving the equation:

$$\sqrt[3]{x} = -4$$
$$x = (-4)^3 = -64$$

77. Solving the equation:

$$x + 3 = 4$$
$$x = 1$$

79. Solving the equation:

$$y^2 - 2y - 8 = 0$$
$$(y+2)(y-4) = 0$$
$$y = -2, 4$$

81. Solving the equation:

$$4y^2 + 7y - 2 = 0$$
$$(4y-1)(y+2) = 0$$
$$y = -2, \frac{1}{4}$$

8.4 Quadratic Form

1. Solving the equation:

$$(x-3)^2 + 3(x-3) + 2 = 0$$
$$(x-3+2)(x-3+1) = 0$$
$$(x-1)(x-2) = 0$$
$$x = 1, 2$$

3. Solving the equation:

$$(2a-3)^2 - 9(2a-3) = -20$$
$$(2a-3)^2 - 9(2a-3) + 20 = 0$$
$$(2a-3-4)(2a-3-5) = 0$$
$$(2a-7)(2a-8) = 0$$
$$a = \frac{7}{2}, 4$$

5. Solving the equation:

$$x^4 - 6x^2 - 27 = 0$$
$$(x^2-9)(x^2+3) = 0$$
$$x^2 = 9, -3$$
$$x = \pm 3, \pm i\sqrt{3}$$

7. Solving the equation:

$$x^4 + 9x^2 = -20$$
$$x^4 + 9x^2 + 20 = 0$$
$$(x^2+4)(x^2+5) = 0$$
$$x^2 = -4, -5$$
$$x = \pm 2i, \pm i\sqrt{5}$$

9. Solving the equation:

$$6t^4 = -t^2 + 5$$
$$6t^4 + t^2 - 5 = 0$$
$$\left(6t^2 - 5\right)\left(t^2 + 1\right) = 0$$
$$t^2 = \frac{5}{6}, -1$$
$$t = \pm\sqrt{\frac{5}{6}} = \pm\frac{\sqrt{30}}{6}, \pm i$$

11. Solving the equation:

$$9x^4 - 49 = 0$$
$$\left(3x^2 - 7\right)\left(3x^2 + 7\right) = 0$$
$$x^2 = \frac{7}{3}, -\frac{7}{3}$$
$$x = \pm\sqrt{\frac{7}{3}}, \pm\sqrt{-\frac{7}{3}}$$
$$x = \pm\frac{\sqrt{21}}{3}, \pm\frac{i\sqrt{21}}{3}$$

13. Solving the equation:

$$8x^6 + 7x^3 - 1 = 0$$
$$\left(8x^3 - 1\right)\left(x^3 + 1\right) = 0$$
$$(2x-1)\left(4x^2 + 2x + 1\right)(x+1)\left(x^2 - x + 1\right) = 0$$
$$x = -1, \frac{1}{2}$$

Using the quadratic formula:

$$x = \frac{-2 \pm \sqrt{4-16}}{8} = \frac{-2 \pm \sqrt{-12}}{8} = \frac{-2 \pm 2i\sqrt{3}}{8} = \frac{-1 \pm i\sqrt{3}}{4}$$
$$x = \frac{1 \pm \sqrt{1-4}}{2} = \frac{1 \pm \sqrt{-3}}{2} = \frac{1 \pm i\sqrt{3}}{2}$$

15. Solving the equation:

$$x^6 - 28x^3 + 27 = 0$$
$$\left(x^3 - 27\right)\left(x^3 - 1\right) = 0$$
$$(x-3)\left(x^2 + 3x + 9\right)(x-1)\left(x^2 + x + 1\right) = 0$$
$$x = 1, 3$$

Using the quadratic formula:

$$x = \frac{-3 \pm \sqrt{9-36}}{2} = \frac{-3 \pm \sqrt{-27}}{2} = \frac{-3 \pm 3i\sqrt{3}}{2}$$
$$x = \frac{-1 \pm \sqrt{1-4}}{2} = \frac{-1 \pm \sqrt{-3}}{2} = \frac{-1 \pm i\sqrt{3}}{2}$$

17. Solving the equation:

$$t^8 + 81 = 82t^4$$
$$t^8 - 82t^4 + 81 = 0$$
$$\left(t^4 - 1\right)\left(t^4 - 81\right) = 0$$
$$\left(t^2 + 1\right)\left(t^2 - 1\right)\left(t^2 + 9\right)\left(t^2 - 9\right) = 0$$
$$t^2 = 1, 9, -1, -9$$
$$t = \pm 1, \pm 3, \pm i, \pm 3i$$

19. Solving the equation:

$$x^{-2} - 2x^{-1} - 15 = 0$$
$$\left(x^{-1} - 5\right)\left(x^{-1} + 3\right) = 0$$
$$x^{-1} = -3, 5$$
$$x = -\frac{1}{3}, \frac{1}{5}$$

21. Solving the equation:

$$x^{-4} - 14x^{-2} + 45 = 0$$
$$\left(x^{-2} - 9\right)\left(x^{-2} - 5\right) = 0$$
$$x^{-2} = 9, 5$$
$$x^2 = \frac{1}{9}, \frac{1}{5}$$
$$x = \pm\frac{1}{3}, \pm\frac{1}{\sqrt{5}} = \pm\frac{\sqrt{5}}{5}$$

23. Solving the equation:

$$2(x+4)^{-2} + 5(x+4)^{-1} - 12 = 0$$
$$\left[2(x+4)^{-1} - 3\right]\left[(x+4)^{-1} + 4\right] = 0$$
$$(x+4)^{-1} = -4, \frac{3}{2}$$
$$x+4 = -\frac{1}{4}, \frac{2}{3}$$
$$x = -\frac{17}{4}, -\frac{10}{3}$$

25. Solving the equation:

$$2(4a+2)^{-2} = 3(4a+2)^{-1} + 20$$
$$2(4a+2)^{-2} - 3(4a+2)^{-1} - 20 = 0$$
$$\left[2(4a+2)^{-1} + 5\right]\left[(4a+2)^{-1} - 4\right] = 0$$
$$(4a+2)^{-1} = -\frac{5}{2}, 4$$
$$4a+2 = -\frac{2}{5}, \frac{1}{4}$$
$$4a = -\frac{12}{5}, -\frac{7}{4}$$
$$a = -\frac{3}{5}, -\frac{7}{16}$$

27. Solving the equation:

$$x - 7\sqrt{x} + 10 = 0$$
$$\left(\sqrt{x} - 5\right)\left(\sqrt{x} - 2\right) = 0$$
$$\sqrt{x} = 2, 5$$
$$x = 4, 25$$

Both values check in the original equation.

29. Solving the equation:

$$t - 2\sqrt{t} - 15 = 0$$
$$\left(\sqrt{t} - 5\right)\left(\sqrt{t} + 3\right) = 0$$
$$\sqrt{t} = -3, 5$$
$$t = 9, 25$$

Only $t = 25$ checks in the original equation.

31. Solving the equation:

$$(a-2) - 11\sqrt{a-2} + 30 = 0$$
$$\left(\sqrt{a-2} - 6\right)\left(\sqrt{a-2} - 5\right) = 0$$
$$\sqrt{a-2} = 5, 6$$
$$a - 2 = 25, 36$$
$$a = 27, 38$$

33. Solving the equation:

$$(2x+1) - 8\sqrt{2x+1} + 15 = 0$$
$$\left(\sqrt{2x+1} - 3\right)\left(\sqrt{2x+1} - 5\right) = 0$$
$$\sqrt{2x+1} = 3, 5$$
$$2x+1 = 9, 25$$
$$2x = 8, 24$$
$$x = 4, 12$$

35. Solving the equation:

$$6x+11\sqrt{x}=35$$
$$6x+11\sqrt{x}-35=0$$
$$\left(3\sqrt{x}-5\right)\left(2\sqrt{x}+7\right)=0$$
$$\sqrt{x}=\frac{5}{3},-\frac{7}{2}$$
$$x=\frac{25}{9},\frac{49}{4}$$

Only $x=\dfrac{25}{9}$ checks in the original equation.

37. Solving the equation:

$$20x^{2/3}-3=11x^{1/3}$$
$$20x^{2/3}-11x^{1/3}-3=0$$
$$\left(5x^{1/3}+1\right)\left(4x^{1/3}-3\right)=0$$
$$x^{1/3}=-\frac{1}{5},\frac{3}{4}$$
$$x=\left(-\frac{1}{5}\right)^3,\left(\frac{3}{4}\right)^3$$
$$x=-\frac{1}{125},\frac{27}{64}$$

39. Solving the equation:

$$4x^{4/3}-37x^{2/3}+9=0$$
$$\left(4x^{2/3}-1\right)\left(x^{2/3}-9\right)=0$$
$$x^{2/3}=\frac{1}{4},9$$
$$x^{1/3}=\pm\frac{1}{2},\pm3$$
$$x=\left(\pm\frac{1}{2}\right)^3,\left(\pm3\right)^3$$
$$x=\pm\frac{1}{8},\pm27$$

41. Solving the equation:

$$27x^3+19x^{3/2}-8=0$$
$$\left(27x^{3/2}-8\right)\left(x^{3/2}+1\right)=0$$
$$x^{3/2}=-1,\frac{8}{27}$$
$$x^{1/2}=-1,\frac{2}{3}$$
$$x=1,\frac{4}{9}$$

Only $x=\dfrac{4}{9}$ checks in the original equation.

43. Solving the equation:

$$12a^{-1}-8a^{-1/2}+1=0$$
$$\left(6a^{-1/2}-1\right)\left(2a^{-1/2}-1\right)=0$$
$$a^{-1/2}=\frac{1}{6},\frac{1}{2}$$
$$a^{-1}=\frac{1}{36},\frac{1}{4}$$
$$a=4,36$$

45. Using the quadratic formula: $x^2=\dfrac{8\pm\sqrt{64-4}}{2}=\dfrac{8\pm\sqrt{60}}{2}=\dfrac{8\pm2\sqrt{15}}{2}=4\pm\sqrt{15}$

Taking square roots: $x=\pm\sqrt{4\pm\sqrt{15}}$

47. Using the quadratic formula: $x^3=\dfrac{-10\pm\sqrt{100-88}}{2}=\dfrac{-10\pm\sqrt{12}}{2}=\dfrac{-10\pm2\sqrt{3}}{2}=-5\pm\sqrt{3}$

Taking cube roots: $x=\sqrt[3]{-5\pm\sqrt{3}}$

49. Using the quadratic formula: $\sqrt{x}=\dfrac{2\pm\sqrt{4+4}}{2}=\dfrac{2\pm\sqrt{8}}{2}=\dfrac{2\pm2\sqrt{2}}{2}=1\pm\sqrt{2}$

Squaring:

$$x=\left(1+\sqrt{2}\right)^2=1+2\sqrt{2}+2=3+2\sqrt{2} \qquad x=\left(1-\sqrt{2}\right)^2=1-2\sqrt{2}+2=3-2\sqrt{2}$$

Only $x=3+2\sqrt{2}$ checks in the original equation.

51. Solving for t:

$$16t^2 - vt - h = 0$$

$$t = \frac{v \pm \sqrt{v^2 - 4(16)(-h)}}{32} = \frac{v \pm \sqrt{v^2 + 64h}}{32}$$

53. Solving for x:

$$kx^2 + 8x + 4 = 0$$

$$x = \frac{-8 \pm \sqrt{64 - 16k}}{2k} = \frac{-8 \pm 4\sqrt{4 - k}}{2k} = \frac{-4 \pm 2\sqrt{4 - k}}{k}$$

55. Solving for x:

$$x^2 + 2xy + y^2 = 0$$

$$x = \frac{-2y \pm \sqrt{4y^2 - 4y^2}}{2} = \frac{-2y}{2} = -y$$

57. Solving for t (note that $t > 0$):

$$16t^2 - 8t - h = 0$$

$$t = \frac{8 + \sqrt{64 + 64h}}{32} = \frac{8 + 8\sqrt{1 + h}}{32} = \frac{1 + \sqrt{1 + h}}{4}$$

59. Using the quadratic formula: $x^2 = \dfrac{-13 \pm \sqrt{169 + 192}}{8} = \dfrac{-13 \pm \sqrt{361}}{8} = \dfrac{-13 \pm 19}{8} = -4, \dfrac{3}{4}$

Taking square roots: $x = \pm\sqrt{-4} = \pm 2i, x = \pm\sqrt{\dfrac{3}{4}} = \pm\dfrac{\sqrt{3}}{2}$

The correct answer is a.

61. Finding the function values:

$$f(-2) = (-2)^2 = 4$$
$$f(-1) = (-1)^2 = 1$$
$$f(0) = (0)^2 = 0$$
$$f(1) = 1^2 = 1$$
$$f(2) = 2^2 = 4$$

63. Finding the function values:

$$f(-2) = 2(-2)^2 = 8$$
$$f(-1) = 2(-1)^2 = 2$$
$$f(0) = 2(0)^2 = 0$$
$$f(1) = 2(1)^2 = 2$$
$$f(2) = 2(2)^2 = 8$$

65. Finding the function values:

$$f(-2) = -\frac{1}{4}(-2)^2 = -1$$
$$f(-1) = -\frac{1}{4}(-1)^2 = -\frac{1}{4}$$
$$f(0) = -\frac{1}{4}(0)^2 = 0$$
$$f(1) = -\frac{1}{4}(1)^2 = -\frac{1}{4}$$
$$f(2) = -\frac{1}{4}(2)^2 = -1$$

67. Finding the function values:

$$f(-2) = (-2 + 2)^2 = (0)^2 = 0$$
$$f(-1) = (-1 + 2)^2 = (1)^2 = 1$$
$$f(0) = (0 + 2)^2 = (2)^2 = 4$$
$$f(1) = (1 + 2)^2 = (3)^2 = 9$$
$$f(2) = (2 + 2)^2 = (4)^2 = 16$$

69. Finding the function values:

$$f(-2) = (-2)^2 + 2 = 4 + 2 = 6$$
$$f(-1) = (-1)^2 + 2 = 1 + 2 = 3$$
$$f(0) = (0)^2 + 2 = 0 + 2 = 2$$
$$f(1) = 1^2 + 2 = 1 + 2 = 3$$
$$f(2) = 2^2 + 2 = 4 + 2 = 6$$

8.5 Quadratic Functions and Transformations

1. Completing the table:

x	−3	−2	−1	0	1	2	3
$y = 3x^2$	27	12	3	0	3	12	27

3. Completing the table:

x	−3	−2	−1	0	1	2	3
$y = -\dfrac{3}{4}x^2$	$-\dfrac{27}{4}$	−3	$-\dfrac{3}{4}$	0	$-\dfrac{3}{4}$	−3	$-\dfrac{27}{4}$

5. Completing the table:

x	−3	−2	−1	0	1	2	3
$y = (x-3)^2$	36	25	16	9	4	1	0

7. Completing the table:

x	−3	−2	−1	0	1	2	3
$y = x^2 + 3$	12	7	4	3	4	7	12

9. The vertical expansion is 4. The graph opens upward and is narrower than $y = x^2$.

11. The vertical contraction is $\dfrac{2}{3}$ with an x-axis reflection. The graph opens downward and is wider than $y = x^2$.

13. The vertical translation is 4 units upward.
15. The horizontal translation is 1 unit to the right.
17. The horizontal translation is 2 units to the right, and the vertical translation is 5 units upward.
19. The horizontal translation is 6 units to the left, and the vertical translation is 3 units upward.
21. The vertical expansion is 3, the horizontal translation is 5 units to the left, and the vertical translation is 2 units downward.
23. The vertical expansion is 4 with an x-axis reflection, the horizontal translation is 3 units to the right, and the vertical translation is 1 unit upward.

25. Sketching the graphs:

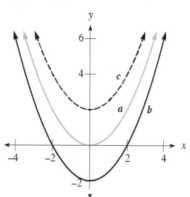

27. Sketching the graphs:

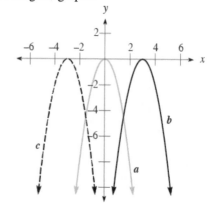

29. Sketching the graph:

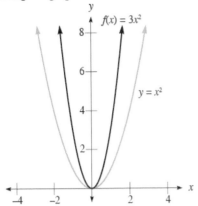

31. Sketching the graph:

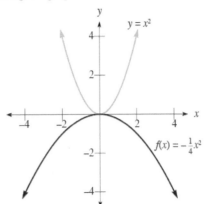

33. Sketching the graph:

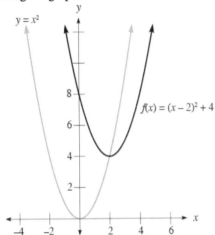

35. Sketching the graph:

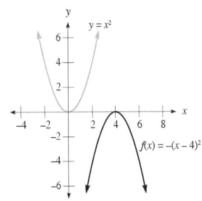

37. Sketching the graph:

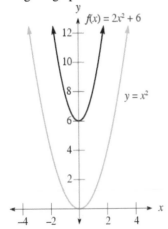

39. Sketching the graph:

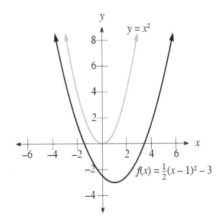

41. Sketching the graph:

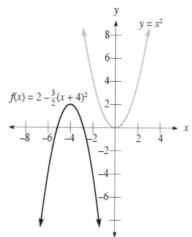

$$f(x) = 2 - \tfrac{3}{2}(x+4)^2$$

$$y = x^2$$

43. The vertex is $(1,3)$, which is the lowest point on the graph. The range is $[3,\infty)$.

45. The vertex is $(-2,4)$, which is the highest point on the graph. The range is $(-\infty,4]$.

47. The vertex is $(2,-4)$, which is the lowest point on the graph. The range is $[-4,\infty)$.

49. The vertex is $(4,-1)$, which is the highest point on the graph. The range is $(-\infty,-1]$.

51. The function is $f(x) = (x-2)^2 - 1$.

53. The function is $f(x) = -(x-2)^2 + 4$.

55. Since $(-2)^2 = 4$, the correct answer is c.

57. The vertex is $(-1,0)$ and there is an x-axis reflection, so the correct answer is c.

59. Evaluating when $x = 1$: $y = 3(1)^2 - 6(1) + 1 = 3 - 6 + 1 = -2$

61. Evaluating: $P(135) = -0.1(135)^2 + 27(135) - 500 = -1,822.5 + 3,645 - 500 = 1,322.5$

63. Solving the equation:
$$0 = a(80)^2 + 70$$
$$0 = 6400a + 70$$
$$6400a = -70$$
$$a = -\frac{7}{640}$$

65. Solving the equation:
$$x^2 - 6x + 5 = 0$$
$$(x-1)(x-5) = 0$$
$$x = 1, 5$$

67. Solving the equation:
$$-x^2 - 2x + 3 = 0$$
$$x^2 + 2x - 3 = 0$$
$$(x+3)(x-1) = 0$$
$$x = -3, 1$$

69. Solving the equation:
$$2x^2 - 6x + 5 = 0$$
$$x = \frac{6 \pm \sqrt{(-6)^2 - 4(2)(5)}}{2(2)} = \frac{6 \pm \sqrt{36-40}}{4} = \frac{6 \pm \sqrt{-4}}{4} = \frac{6 \pm 2i}{4} = \frac{3 \pm i}{2} = \frac{3}{2} \pm \frac{1}{2}i$$

71. Completing the square: $x^2 - 6x + 9 = (x-3)^2$

73. Completing the square: $y^2 + 2y + 1 = (y+1)^2$

8.6 Graphs of Quadratic Functions

1. First complete the square: $f(x) = x^2 - 6x + 5 = (x^2 - 6x + 9) - 9 + 5 = (x - 3)^2 - 4$

   The vertex is $(3,-4)$, which is the lowest point on the graph. The range is $[-4,\infty)$.

3. First complete the square: $f(x) = -x^2 + 2x + 8 = -(x^2 - 2x + 1) + 1 + 8 = -(x - 1)^2 + 9$

   The vertex is $(1,9)$, which is the highest point on the graph. The range is $(-\infty,9]$.

5. First complete the square: $f(x) = -x^2 + 4x + 12 = -(x^2 - 4x + 4) + 4 + 12 = -(x - 2)^2 + 16$

   The vertex is $(2,16)$, which is the highest point on the graph. The range is $(-\infty,16]$.

7. First complete the square: $f(x) = -x^2 - 8x = -(x^2 + 8x + 16) + 16 = -(x + 4)^2 + 16$

   The vertex is $(-4,16)$, which is the highest point on the graph. The range is $(-\infty,16]$.

9. The vertex is $(0,-4)$, which is the lowest point on the graph. The range is $[-4,\infty)$.

11. First complete the square: $f(x) = 3x^2 - 6x + 14 = 3(x^2 - 2x + 1) - 3 + 14 = 3(x - 1)^2 + 11$

    The vertex is $(1,11)$, which is the lowest point on the graph. The range is $[11,\infty)$.

13. First complete the square: $f(x) = -4x^2 - 16x - 17 = -4(x^2 + 4x + 4) + 16 - 17 = -4(x + 2)^2 - 1$

    The vertex is $(-2,-1)$, which is the highest point on the graph. The range is $(-\infty,-1]$.

15. First complete the square: $f(x) = 4x^2 - 4x + 19 = 4\left(x^2 - x + \frac{1}{4}\right) - 1 + 19 = 4\left(x - \frac{1}{2}\right)^2 + 18$

    The vertex is $\left(\frac{1}{2},18\right)$, which is the lowest point on the graph. The range is $[18,\infty)$.

17. First complete the square: $y = x^2 + 2x - 3 = (x^2 + 2x + 1) - 1 - 3 = (x + 1)^2 - 4$

    The x-intercepts are -3 and 1, the y-intercept is -3, and the vertex is $(-1,-4)$. Graphing the parabola:

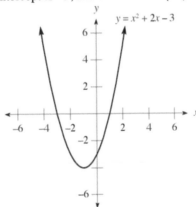

19. First complete the square: $y = -x^2 - 4x + 5 = -\left(x^2 + 4x + 4\right) + 4 + 5 = -\left(x + 2\right)^2 + 9$

The x-intercepts are -5 and 1, the y-intercept is 5, and the vertex is $(-2,9)$. Graphing the parabola:

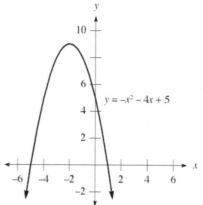

21. The x-intercepts are -1 and 1, the y-intercept is -1, and the vertex is $(0,-1)$. Graphing the parabola:

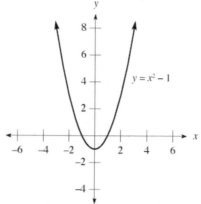

23. The x-intercepts are -3 and 3, the y-intercept is 9, and the vertex is $(0,9)$. Graphing the parabola:

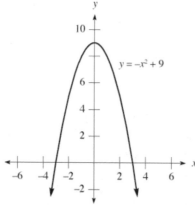

25.   The *x*-intercepts are –3 and 1, the *y*-intercept is –3, and the vertex is (–1,–4). Graphing the parabola:

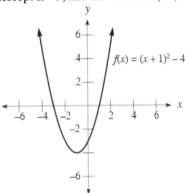

$f(x) = (x+1)^2 - 4$

27.   First complete the square: $y = 2x^2 - 4x - 6 = 2\left(x^2 - 2x + 1\right) - 2 - 6 = 2(x-1)^2 - 8$

The *x*-intercepts are –1 and 3, the *y*-intercept is –6, and the vertex is (1,–8). Graphing the parabola:

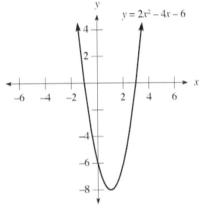

$y = 2x^2 - 4x - 6$

29.   First complete the square: $y = x^2 - 2x - 4 = \left(x^2 - 2x + 1\right) - 1 - 4 = (x-1)^2 - 5$

The *x*-intercepts are $1 \pm \sqrt{5}$, the *y*-intercept is –4, and the vertex is (1,–5). Graphing the parabola:

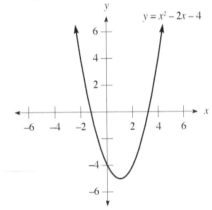

$y = x^2 - 2x - 4$

31. The *x*-intercepts are $3 \pm \sqrt{2}$, the *y*-intercept is –7, and the vertex is (3,2). Graphing the parabola:

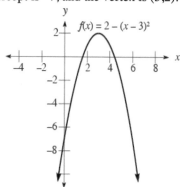

$f(x) = 2 - (x - 3)^2$

33. First complete the square: $y = x^2 - 4x - 4 = \left(x^2 - 4x + 4\right) - 4 - 4 = (x-2)^2 - 8$

The *x*-intercepts are $2 \pm 2\sqrt{2}$, the *y*-intercept is –4, and the vertex is (2,–8). Graphing the parabola:

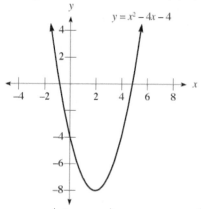

$y = x^2 - 4x - 4$

35. First complete the square: $y = -x^2 + 2x - 5 = -\left(x^2 - 2x + 1\right) + 1 - 5 = -(x-1)^2 - 4$

There are no *x*-intercepts, the *y*-intercept is –5, and the vertex is (1,–4). Graphing the parabola:

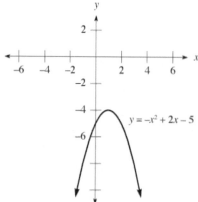

$y = -x^2 + 2x - 5$

37. There are no *x*-intercepts, the *y*-intercept is 1, and the vertex is (0,1). Graphing the parabola:

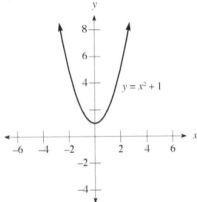

$$y = x^2 + 1$$

39. There are no *x*-intercepts, the *y*-intercept is –3, and the vertex is (0,–3). Graphing the parabola:

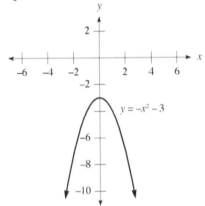

$$y = -x^2 - 3$$

41. First complete the square: $g(x) = 3x^2 + 4x + 1 = 3\left(x^2 + \frac{4}{3}x + \frac{4}{9}\right) + 1 - \frac{4}{3} = 3\left(x + \frac{2}{3}\right)^2 - \frac{1}{3}$

The *x*-intercepts are $-\frac{1}{3}$ and -1, the *y*-intercept is 1, and the vertex is $\left(-\frac{2}{3}, -\frac{1}{3}\right)$. Graphing the parabola:

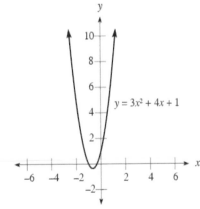

$$y = 3x^2 + 4x + 1$$

43. The *x*-intercepts are $1 \pm \sqrt{3}$, the *y*-intercept is –4, and the vertex is (1,–6). Graphing the parabola:

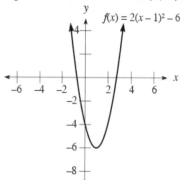

45. There are no *x*-intercepts, the *y*-intercept is –28, and the vertex is (–3,–1). Graphing the parabola:

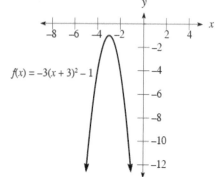

47. First complete the square: $f(x) = x^2 + 3x = \left(x^2 + 3x + \dfrac{9}{4}\right) - \dfrac{9}{4} = \left(x + \dfrac{3}{2}\right)^2 - \dfrac{9}{4}$

The *x*-intercepts are –3 and 0, the *y*-intercept is 0, and the vertex is $\left(-\dfrac{3}{2}, -\dfrac{9}{4}\right)$. Graphing the parabola:

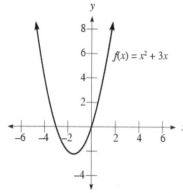

49. First complete the square: $f(x) = -2x^2 + 8x = -2(x^2 - 4x + 4) + 8 = -2(x-2)^2 + 8$

The x-intercepts are 0 and 4, the y-intercept is 0, and the vertex is $(2,8)$. Graphing the parabola:

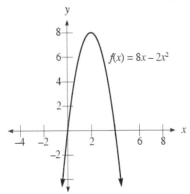

51. First complete the square: $f(x) = 6x^2 - 7x - 3 = 6\left(x^2 - \dfrac{7}{6}x + \dfrac{49}{144}\right) - \dfrac{49}{24} - 3 = 6\left(x - \dfrac{7}{12}\right)^2 - \dfrac{121}{24}$

The x-intercepts are $-\dfrac{1}{3}$ and $\dfrac{3}{2}$, the y-intercept is -3, and the vertex is $\left(\dfrac{7}{12}, -\dfrac{121}{24}\right)$. Graphing the parabola:

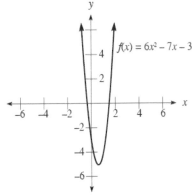

53. First complete the square: $f(x) = -2x^2 - x + 5 = -2\left(x^2 + \dfrac{1}{2}x + \dfrac{1}{16}\right) + \dfrac{1}{8} + 5 = -2\left(x + \dfrac{1}{4}\right)^2 + \dfrac{41}{8}$

The x-intercepts are $\dfrac{-1 \pm \sqrt{41}}{4}$, the y-intercept is 5, and the vertex is $\left(-\dfrac{1}{4}, \dfrac{41}{8}\right)$. Graphing the parabola:

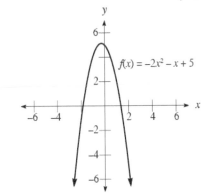

55. First complete the square: $f(x) = 3x^2 - 2x + 3 = 3\left(x^2 - \dfrac{2}{3}x + \dfrac{1}{9}\right) - \dfrac{1}{3} + 3 = 3\left(x - \dfrac{1}{3}\right)^2 + \dfrac{8}{3}$

There are no x-intercepts, the y-intercept is 3, and the vertex is $\left(\dfrac{1}{3}, \dfrac{8}{3}\right)$. Graphing the parabola:

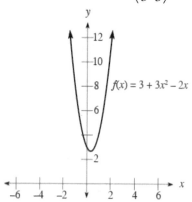

57. Completing the square: $f(x) = x^2 + 4x = \left(x^2 + 4x + 4\right) - 4 = (x+2)^2 - 4$

The vertex is $(-2, -4)$.

59. Completing the square: $f(x) = -x^2 + 2x = -\left(x^2 - 2x + 1\right) + 1 = -(x-1)^2 + 1$

The vertex is $(1, 1)$.

61. Completing the square: $f(x) = 2x^2 - 8x + 13 = 2\left(x^2 - 4x + 4\right) - 8 + 13 = 2(x-2)^2 + 5$

The vertex is $(2, 5)$.

63. Completing the square: $f(x) = -3x^2 - 3x - 2 = -3\left(x^2 + x + \dfrac{1}{4}\right) + \dfrac{3}{4} - 2 = -3\left(x + \dfrac{1}{2}\right)^2 - \dfrac{5}{4}$

The vertex is $\left(-\dfrac{1}{2}, -\dfrac{5}{4}\right)$.

65. Completing the square: $f(x) = 4x^2 + 8x + 4 = 4\left(x^2 + 2x + 1\right) = 4(x+1)^2$

The vertex is $(-1, 0)$.

67. Finding the x-intercepts:
$$a(x-h)^2 + k = 0$$
$$a(x-h)^2 = -k$$
$$(x-h)^2 = -\dfrac{k}{a}$$
$$x - h = \sqrt{-\dfrac{k}{a}}$$
$$x = h + \sqrt{-\dfrac{k}{a}}$$

69. Completing the table:

t	0	$\dfrac{1}{2}$	1	$\dfrac{3}{2}$	2
$h(t)$	0	12	16	12	0

Sketching the graph:

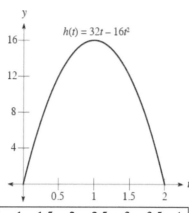

$h(t) = 32t - 16t^2$

71. Completing the table:

t	0	0.5	1	1.5	2	2.5	3	3.5	4
$h(t)$	0	28	48	60	64	60	48	28	0

Sketching the graph:

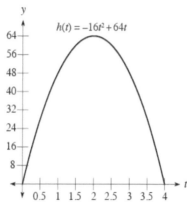

$h(t) = -16t^2 + 64t$

73. Completing the square: $f(x) = 2x^2 + 4x - 1 = 2\left(x^2 + 2x + 1\right) - 2 - 1 = 2(x+1)^2 - 3$

The vertex is $(-1, -3)$. The correct answer is c.

75. Completing the square: $f(x) = -x^2 + 4x - 5 = -\left(x^2 - 4x + 4\right) + 4 - 5 = -(x-2)^2 - 1$

The vertex is $(2, -1)$ and the parabola is pointed down. The correct answer is d.

77. Evaluating the function for $t = 1$ and $t = 3$:

$$f(1) = -16(1)^2 + 112(1) = -16 + 112 = 96$$
$$f(3) = -16(3)^2 + 112(3) = -144 + 336 = 192$$

79. Solving the equation:

$$-16x^2 + 112x = 0$$
$$-16x(x - 7) = 0$$
$$x = 0, 7$$

81. Solving the equation:

$$-16x^2 + 112x = 160$$
$$-16x^2 + 112x - 160 = 0$$
$$-16\left(x^2 - 7x + 10\right) = 0$$
$$-16(x - 2)(x - 5) = 0$$
$$x = 2, 5$$

83. Solving the equation:

$$96 + 80t - 16t^2 = 160$$
$$-16t^2 + 80t - 64 = 0$$
$$-16\left(t^2 - 5t + 4\right) = 0$$
$$-16\left(t - 1\right)\left(t - 4\right) = 0$$
$$t = 1, 4$$

85. Completing the square: $f(x) = -300x^2 + 900x = -300\left(x^2 - 3x + \dfrac{9}{4}\right) + 675 = -300\left(x - \dfrac{3}{2}\right)^2 + 675$

The vertex is $\left(\dfrac{3}{2}, 675\right)$.

8.7 Applications of Quadratic Functions

1. Substituting $p = 1.5$: $R = (900 - 300 \cdot 1.5)(1.5) = (450)(1.5) = 675$

3. **a.** Substituting $x = 100$: $P = -0.1(100)^2 + 27(100) + 1{,}700 = -1{,}000 + 2{,}700 + 1{,}700 = 3{,}400$

    b. Substituting $x = 170$: $P = -0.1(170)^2 + 27(170) - 1{,}700 = -2{,}890 + 4{,}590 + 1{,}700 = 3{,}400$

5. **a.** Substituting $t = \dfrac{1}{4}$: $h = 16 + 32\left(\dfrac{1}{4}\right) - 16\left(\dfrac{1}{4}\right)^2 = 16 + 8 - 1 = 23$

    b. Substituting $t = \dfrac{7}{4}$: $h = 16 + 32\left(\dfrac{7}{4}\right) - 16\left(\dfrac{7}{4}\right)^2 = 16 + 56 - 49 = 23$

7. **a.** Sketching the graph:

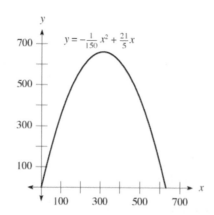

    b. Finding the x-intercepts:

$$-\frac{1}{150}x^2 + \frac{21}{5}x = 0$$
$$-\frac{1}{150}x(x - 630) = 0$$
$$x = 0, 630$$

The width is 630 feet.

9. Substituting $h = 192$:
$$192 = 96 + 80t - 16t^2$$
$$0 = -16t^2 + 80t - 96$$
$$0 = -16\left(t^2 - 5t + 6\right)$$
$$0 = -16(t-2)(t-3)$$
$$t = 2, 3$$
The bullet will be 192 feet in the air after 2 sec and 3 sec.

11. Substituting $h = 0$:
$$0 = 32t - 16t^2$$
$$0 = -16t^2 + 32t$$
$$0 = -16t(t-2)$$
$$t = 0, 2$$
The object will hit the ground after 0 sec and 2 sec.

13. Substituting $h = 32$:
$$16 + 32t - 16t^2 = 32$$
$$16t^2 - 32t + 16 = 0$$
$$16\left(t^2 - 2t + 1\right) = 0$$
$$16(t-1)^2 = 0$$
$$t = 1$$
The object will reach a height of 32 feet after 1 second.

15. Substituting $R = \$7,000$:
$$R = xp$$
$$7,000 = (1,700 - 100p)p$$
$$7,000 = 1,700p - 100p^2$$
$$0 = -100p^2 + 1,700p - 7,000$$
$$0 = -100\left(p^2 - 17p + 70\right)$$
$$0 = -100(p-7)(p-10)$$
$$p = 7, 10$$
The calculators should be sold for either \$7 or \$10.

17. Substituting $R = \$650$:
$$650 = 11.5x - 0.05x^2$$
$$0.05x^2 - 11.5x + 650 = 0$$
$$0.05\left(x^2 - 230x + 13,000\right) = 0$$
$$0.05(x-100)(x-130) = 0$$
$$x = 100, 130$$
They must sell either 100 or 130 DVDs to receive \$650 in revenue.

19. Since profit is revenue minus the cost, the equation is:
$$100x - 0.5x^2 - (60x + 300) = 300$$
$$100x - 0.5x^2 - 60x - 300 = 300$$
$$-0.5x^2 + 40x - 600 = 0$$
$$x^2 - 80x + 1,200 = 0$$
$$(x-20)(x-60) = 0$$
$$x = 20, 60$$
The weekly profit is \$300 if 20 items or 60 items are sold.

21. First complete the square:

$$P(x) = -0.002x^2 + 3.5x - 800 = -0.002\left(x^2 - 1750x + 765{,}625\right) + 1{,}531.25 - 800 = -0.002\left(x - 875\right)^2 + 731.25$$

It must sell 875 patterns to obtain a maximum profit of $731.25.

23. The ball is in her hand at times 0 sec and 2 sec.

Completing the square: $h(t) = -16t^2 + 32t = -16\left(t^2 - 2t + 1\right) + 16 = -16\left(t - 1\right)^2 + 16$

The maximum height of the ball is 16 feet.

25. Completing the square: $R = xp = 1200p - 100p^2 = -100\left(p^2 - 12p + 36\right) + 3600 = -100\left(p - 6\right)^2 + 3600$

The price is $6.00 and the maximum revenue is $3,600. Sketching the graph:

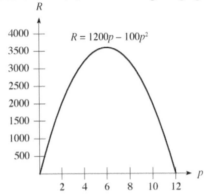

27. Completing the square: $R = xp = 1700p - 100p^2 = -100\left(p^2 - 17p + 72.25\right) + 7225 = -100\left(p - 8.5\right)^2 + 7225$

The price is $8.50 and the maximum revenue is $7,225. Sketching the graph:

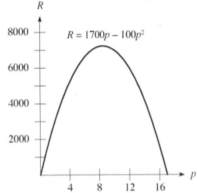

29. Completing the square on the income:

$$
\begin{aligned}
y &= \left(10{,}000 - 200x\right)\left(100 + 10x\right) \\
&= 2{,}000\left(50 - x\right)\left(10 + x\right) \\
&= 2{,}000\left(-x^2 + 40x + 500\right) \\
&= -2{,}000\left(x^2 - 40x\right) + 1{,}000{,}000 \\
&= -2{,}000\left(x^2 - 40x + 400\right) + 800{,}000 + 1{,}000{,}000 \\
&= -2{,}000\left(x - 20\right)^2 + 1{,}800{,}000
\end{aligned}
$$

The union should have 20 increases of $10, so their new dues should be $100 + 20($10) = $300, and their income will be $1,800,000.

31. Let x represent the number of $2 increases in price. Completing the square on the income:

$$
\begin{aligned}
y &= (40 - 2x)(20 + 2x) \\
&= -4(x - 20)(x + 10) \\
&= -4(x^2 - 10x - 200) \\
&= -4(x^2 - 10x) + 800 \\
&= -4(x^2 - 10x + 25) + 100 + 800 \\
&= -4(x - 5)^2 + 900
\end{aligned}
$$

The business should have 5 increases of $2, so they should charge $20 + 5($2) = $30, and their income will be $900.

33. The vertex of the parabola is (90,60), so the parabola has the form $y = a(x - 90)^2 + 60$. Since (180,0) is a point on the parabola, we can substitute to find a:

$$
\begin{aligned}
0 &= a(180 - 90)^2 + 60 \\
0 &= 8,100a + 60 \\
-8,100a &= 60 \\
a &= -\frac{1}{135}
\end{aligned}
$$

So the equation is $y = -\dfrac{1}{135}(x - 90)^2 + 60$. Sketching the graph:

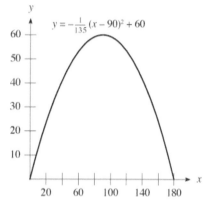

35. The vertex of the parabola is (315,630), so the parabola has the form $y = a(x - 315)^2 + 630$. Since (630,0) is a point on the parabola, we can substitute to find a:

$$
\begin{aligned}
0 &= a(630 - 315)^2 + 630 \\
0 &= 99,225a + 630 \\
-99,225a &= 630 \\
a &= -\frac{2}{315}
\end{aligned}
$$

So the equation is $y = -\dfrac{2}{315}(x - 315)^2 + 630$.

37. Write the general form of the function as $f(x) = ax^2 + bx + c$. Substituting each point into the equation:

$$-5 = a(-4)^2 + b(-4) + c$$
$$-8 = a(-1)^2 + b(-1) + c$$
$$7 = a(2)^2 + b(2) + c$$

These equations simplify to:

$$16a - 4b + c = -5$$
$$a - b + c = -8$$
$$4a + 2b + c = 7$$

Subtracting equation 2 from equation 1, and equation 3 from equation 1 results in the system:

$$15a - 3b = 3$$
$$12a - 6b = -12$$

These simplify to the system:

$$5a - b = 1$$
$$2a - b = -2$$

Subtracting equation 2 from equation 1:

$$3a = 3$$
$$a = 1$$

Substituting to find b:

$$2(1) - b = -2$$
$$-b = -4$$
$$b = 4$$

Substituting to find c:

$$4(1) + 2(4) + c = 7$$
$$12 + c = 7$$
$$c = -5$$

The equation of the function is $f(x) = x^2 + 4x - 5$.

39. The height function is given by $h(t) = -16t^2 + 44t + 6$. Substituting $h = 0$:

$$-16t^2 + 44t + 6 = 0$$
$$8t^2 - 22t - 3 = 0$$

$$t = \frac{22 \pm \sqrt{484 + 96}}{16} = \frac{22 \pm \sqrt{580}}{16} = \frac{22 \pm 2\sqrt{145}}{16} = \frac{11 \pm \sqrt{145}}{8} \approx -0.1, 2.9$$

Since the time must be positive, $t \approx 2.9$ seconds. The correct answer is b.

41. Completing the square: $h(t) = -16t^2 + 44t + 6 = -16\left(t^2 - \frac{11}{4}t + \frac{121}{64}\right) + \frac{121}{4} + 6 = -16\left(t - \frac{11}{8}\right)^2 + \frac{145}{4}$

The maximum height of the baseball is $\frac{145}{4} = 36.25 \text{ feet}$. The correct answer is a.

43. Solving the equation:

$$x^2 - 2x - 8 = 0$$
$$(x - 4)(x + 2) = 0$$
$$x = -2, 4$$

45. Solving the equation:

$$6x^2 - x = 2$$
$$6x^2 - x - 2 = 0$$
$$(2x + 1)(3x - 2) = 0$$
$$x = -\frac{1}{2}, \frac{2}{3}$$

47. Solving the equation:

$$x^2 - 6x + 9 = 0$$
$$(x - 3)^2 = 0$$
$$x = 3$$

8.8 Quadratic and Rational Inequalities

1. Factoring the inequality:
$$x^2 + x - 6 > 0$$
$$(x+3)(x-2) > 0$$
Forming the sign chart:

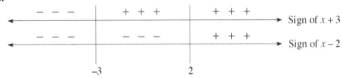

The solution set is $x < -3$ or $x > 2$. Graphing the solution set:

3. Factoring the inequality:
$$x^2 - x - 12 \le 0$$
$$(x+3)(x-4) \le 0$$
Forming the sign chart:

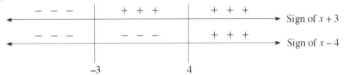

The solution set is $-3 \le x \le 4$. Graphing the solution set:

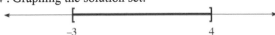

5. Factoring the inequality:
$$x^2 + 5x \ge -6$$
$$x^2 + 5x + 6 \ge 0$$
$$(x+2)(x+3) \ge 0$$
Forming the sign chart:

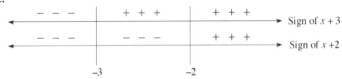

The solution set is $x \le -3$ or $x \ge -2$. Graphing the solution set:

7. Factoring the inequality:
$$6x^2 < 5x - 1$$
$$6x^2 - 5x + 1 < 0$$
$$(3x-1)(2x-1) < 0$$
Forming the sign chart:

The solution set is $\frac{1}{3} < x < \frac{1}{2}$. Graphing the solution set:

9. Factoring the inequality:
$$x^2 - 9 < 0$$
$$(x + 3)(x - 3) < 0$$

Forming the sign chart:

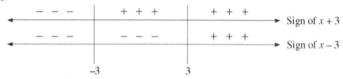

The solution set is $-3 < x < 3$. Graphing the solution set:

11. Factoring the inequality:
$$4x^2 - 9 \geq 0$$
$$(2x + 3)(2x - 3) \geq 0$$

Forming the sign chart:

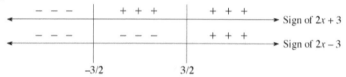

The solution set is $x \leq -\frac{3}{2}$ or $x \geq \frac{3}{2}$. Graphing the solution set:

13. Factoring the inequality:
$$2x^2 - x - 3 < 0$$
$$(2x - 3)(x + 1) < 0$$

Forming the sign chart:

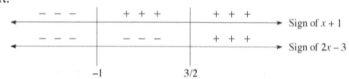

The solution set is $-1 < x < \frac{3}{2}$. Graphing the solution set:

15. Factoring the inequality:
$$x^2 - 4x + 4 \geq 0$$
$$(x - 2)^2 \geq 0$$

Since this inequality is always true, the solution set is all real numbers. Graphing the solution set:

17. Factoring the inequality:

$$x^2 - 10x + 25 < 0$$
$$(x - 5)^2 < 0$$

Since this inequality is never true, there is no solution.

19. Forming the sign chart:

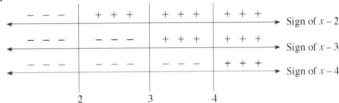

The solution set is $2 < x < 3$ or $x > 4$. Graphing the solution set:

21. Forming the sign chart:

The solution set is $x \leq -3$ or $-2 \leq x \leq -1$. Graphing the solution set:

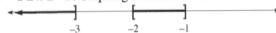

23. Forming the sign chart:

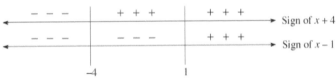

The solution set is $-4 < x \leq 1$. Graphing the solution set:

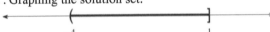

25. Write the inequality as $\dfrac{3x - 8}{x + 6} < 0$. Forming the sign chart:

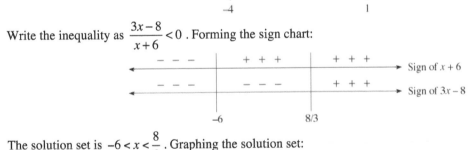

The solution set is $-6 < x < \dfrac{8}{3}$. Graphing the solution set:

27. Write the inequality as $\dfrac{4+x-6}{x-6}<0$, or $\dfrac{x-2}{x-6}<0$. Forming the sign chart:

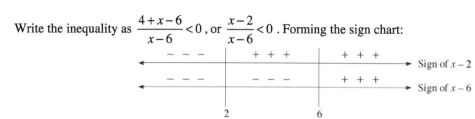

The solution set is $x<2$ or $x>6$. Graphing the solution set:

29. Forming the sign chart:

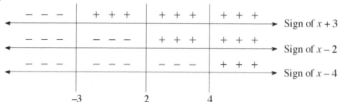

The solution set is $x<-3$ or $2<x<4$. Graphing the solution set:

31. Simplify the inequality:

$$\frac{2}{x-4}-\frac{1}{x-3}<0$$

$$\frac{2(x-3)-1(x-4)}{(x-4)(x-3)}<0$$

$$\frac{2x-6-x+4}{(x-4)(x-3)}<0$$

$$\frac{x-2}{(x-4)(x-3)}<0$$

Forming the sign chart:

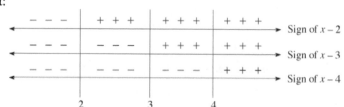

The solution set is $2<x<3$ or $x>4$. Graphing the solution set:

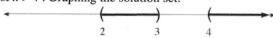

33. Simplify the inequality:

$$\frac{x+7}{2x+12}+\frac{6}{x^2-36}\le 0$$

$$\frac{x+7}{2(x+6)}+\frac{6}{(x+6)(x-6)}\le 0$$

$$\frac{(x+7)(x-6)+6\cdot 2}{2(x+6)(x-6)}\le 0$$

$$\frac{x^2+x-42+12}{2(x+6)(x-6)}\le 0$$

$$\frac{x^2+x-30}{2(x+6)(x-6)}\le 0$$

$$\frac{(x+6)(x-5)}{2(x+6)(x-6)}\le 0$$

$$\frac{x-5}{2(x-6)}\le 0$$

Forming the sign chart:

The solution set is $5\le x<6$. Graphing the solution set:

35. **a.** The solution set is $-2<x<2$. In interval notation, this is $(-2,2)$.

    b. The solution set is $x<-2$ or $x>2$. In interval notation, this is $(-\infty,-2)\cup(2,\infty)$.

    c. The solution set is $x=-2,2$.

37. **a.** The solution set is $-2<x<5$. In interval notation, this is $(-2,5)$.

    b. The solution set is $x<-2$ or $x>5$. In interval notation, this is $(-\infty,-2)\cup(5,\infty)$.

    c. The solution set is $x=-2,5$.

39. **a.** The solution set is $x<-1$ or $1<x<3$. In interval notation, this is $(-\infty,-1)\cup(1,3)$.

    b. The solution set is $-1<x<1$ or $x>3$. In interval notation, this is $(-1,1)\cup(3,\infty)$.

    c. The solution set is $x=-1,1,3$.

41. Let w represent the width and $2w+3$ represent the length. Using the area formula:

$$w(2w+3)\ge 44$$

$$2w^2+3w\ge 44$$

$$2w^2+3w-44\ge 0$$

$$(2w+11)(w-4)\ge 0$$

Forming the sign chart:

The width is at least 4 inches.

43. Solving the inequality:
$$1300p - 100p^2 \geq 4000$$
$$-100p^2 + 1300p - 4000 \geq 0$$
$$p^2 - 13p + 40 \leq 0$$
$$(p-8)(p-5) \leq 0$$
Forming the sign chart:

She should charge at least \$5 but no more than \$8 per radio.

45. Factoring the inequality:
$$2x^2 - 3x - 20 < 0$$
$$(2x+5)(x-4) < 0$$
Forming the sign chart:

The solution set is $-\dfrac{5}{2} < x < 4$. The correct answer is d.

47. Using a calculator: $\dfrac{50,000}{32,000} = 1.5625$

49. Using a calculator: $\dfrac{1}{2}\left(\dfrac{4.5926}{1.3876} - 2\right) \approx 0.6549$

51. Solving the equation:
$$2\sqrt{3t-1} = 2$$
$$\sqrt{3t-1} = 1$$
$$\left(\sqrt{3t-1}\right)^2 = (1)^2$$
$$3t - 1 = 1$$
$$3t = 2$$
$$t = \dfrac{2}{3}$$

The solution is $\dfrac{2}{3}$.

53. Solving the equation:
$$\sqrt{x+3} = x - 3$$
$$\left(\sqrt{x+3}\right)^2 = (x-3)^2$$
$$x + 3 = x^2 - 6x + 9$$
$$0 = x^2 - 7x + 6$$
$$0 = (x-6)(x-1)$$
$$x = 1, 6 \qquad (x = 1 \text{ does not check})$$

The solution is 6.

55. Graphing the equation:

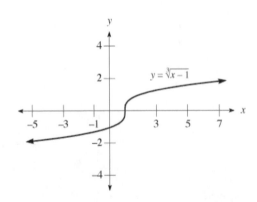

Chapter 8 Test

1. Solving the equation:

$$(2x+4)^2 = 25$$
$$2x+4 = \pm 5$$
$$2x+4 = -5, 5$$
$$2x = -9, 1$$
$$x = -\frac{9}{2}, \frac{1}{2}$$

2. Solving the equation:

$$(2x-6)^2 = -8$$
$$2x-6 = \pm\sqrt{-8}$$
$$2x-6 = \pm 2i\sqrt{2}$$
$$2x = 6 \pm 2i\sqrt{2}$$
$$x = 3 \pm i\sqrt{2}$$

3. Solving the equation:

$$y^2 - 10y + 25 = -4$$
$$(y-5)^2 = -4$$
$$y-5 = \pm\sqrt{-4}$$
$$y-5 = \pm 2i$$
$$y = 5 \pm 2i$$

4. Solving the equation:

$$(y+1)(y-3) = -6$$
$$y^2 - 2y - 3 = -6$$
$$y^2 - 2y + 3 = 0$$
$$y = \frac{2 \pm \sqrt{4-12}}{2} = \frac{2 \pm \sqrt{-8}}{2} = \frac{2 \pm 2i\sqrt{2}}{2} = 1 \pm i\sqrt{2}$$

5. Solving the equation:

$$8t^3 - 125 = 0$$
$$(2t-5)(4t^2 + 10t + 25) = 0$$
$$t = \frac{5}{2}, \frac{-10 \pm \sqrt{100-400}}{8} = \frac{-10 \pm \sqrt{-300}}{8} = \frac{-10 \pm 10i\sqrt{3}}{8} = -\frac{5}{4} \pm \frac{5i\sqrt{3}}{4}$$

6. Solving the equation:

$$\frac{1}{a+2} - \frac{1}{3} = \frac{1}{a}$$
$$3a(a+2)\left(\frac{1}{a+2} - \frac{1}{3}\right) = 3a(a+2)\left(\frac{1}{a}\right)$$
$$3a - a(a+2) = 3(a+2)$$
$$3a - a^2 - 2a = 3a + 6$$
$$-a^2 - 2a - 6 = 0$$
$$a^2 + 2a + 6 = 0$$
$$a = \frac{-2 \pm \sqrt{4-24}}{2} = \frac{-2 \pm \sqrt{-20}}{2} = \frac{-2 \pm 2i\sqrt{5}}{2} = -1 \pm i\sqrt{5}$$

7. Solving for r:

$$64(1+r)^2 = A$$
$$(1+r)^2 = \frac{A}{64}$$
$$1+r = \pm\frac{\sqrt{A}}{8}$$
$$r = -1 \pm \frac{\sqrt{A}}{8}$$

8. Solving by completing the square:

$$x^2 - 4x = -2$$
$$x^2 - 4x + 4 = -2 + 4$$
$$(x-2)^2 = 2$$
$$x - 2 = \pm\sqrt{2}$$
$$x = 2 \pm \sqrt{2}$$

9. First write the equation as $kx^2 - 12x + 4 = 0$. Setting the discriminant equal to 0:

$$(-12)^2 - 4(k)(4) = 0$$
$$144 - 16k = 0$$
$$-16k = -144$$
$$k = 9$$

10. First write the equation as $2x^2 - 5x - 7 = 0$. Finding the discriminant: $D = (-5)^2 - 4(2)(-7) = 25 + 56 = 81$

Since the discriminant is a perfect square $\left(9^2 = 81\right)$, the equation has two rational solutions.

11. Finding the equation:

$$(x-5)(3x+2) = 0$$
$$3x^2 - 13x - 10 = 0$$

12. Finding the equation:

$$x = \pm 2i$$
$$x^2 = -4$$
$$x^2 + 4 = 0$$

13. Solving the equation:

$$4x^4 - 7x^2 - 2 = 0$$
$$\left(x^2 - 2\right)\left(4x^2 + 1\right) = 0$$
$$x^2 = 2, -\frac{1}{4}$$
$$x = \pm\sqrt{2}, \pm\frac{1}{2}i$$

14. Solving the equation:

$$(2t+1)^2 - 5(2t+1) + 6 = 0$$
$$4t^2 + 4t + 1 - 10t - 5 + 6 = 0$$
$$4t^2 - 6t + 2 = 0$$
$$2t^2 - 3t + 1 = 0$$
$$(2t-1)(t-1) = 0$$
$$t = \frac{1}{2}, 1$$

15. Solving the equation:

$$2t - 7\sqrt{t} + 3 = 0$$
$$\left(2\sqrt{t} - 1\right)\left(\sqrt{t} - 3\right) = 0$$
$$\sqrt{t} = \frac{1}{2}, 3$$
$$t = \frac{1}{4}, 9$$

Both values check in the original equation.

16. Solving for t:

$$16t^2 - 14t - h = 0$$

$$t = \frac{14 + \sqrt{196 - 4(16)(-h)}}{32} = \frac{14 + \sqrt{196 + 64h}}{32} = \frac{14 + 2\sqrt{49 + 16h}}{32} = \frac{7 + \sqrt{49 + 16h}}{16}$$

Note that only the positive answer was given here since t represents time, thus $t > 0$.

17. The vertex is $(-2, 3)$, the x-intercepts are $-2 \pm \sqrt{3}$, and the y-intercept is -1. Graphing the parabola:

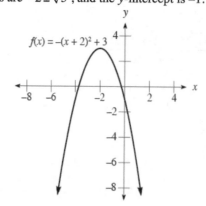

18. The vertex is $(1,-3)$, the x-intercepts are $1 \pm \dfrac{\sqrt{6}}{2}$, and the y-intercept is -1. Graphing the parabola:

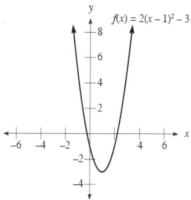

19. Completing the square: $f(x) = x^2 - 2x - 3 = \left(x^2 - 2x + 1\right) - 1 - 3 = (x-1)^2 - 4$

The vertex is $(1,-4)$, the x-intercepts are -1 and 3, and the y-intercept is -3. Graphing the parabola:

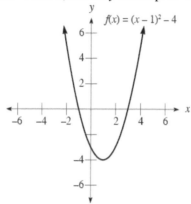

20. Completing the square: $f(x) = -x^2 + 2x + 8 = -\left(x^2 - 2x + 1\right) + 1 + 8 = -(x-1)^2 + 9$

The vertex is $(1,9)$, the x-intercepts are -2 and 4, and the y-intercept is 8. Graphing the parabola:

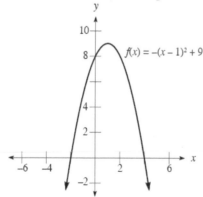

21. Solving the equation:

$$32t - 16t^2 = 12$$
$$-16t^2 + 32t - 12 = 0$$
$$4t^2 - 8t + 3 = 0$$
$$(2t - 1)(2t - 3) = 0$$
$$t = \frac{1}{2}, \frac{3}{2}$$

The object will be 12 feet above the ground after $\frac{1}{2}$ sec or $\frac{3}{2}$ sec.

22. Finding when the profit is equal to $200:

$$\left(25x - 0.2x^2\right) - \left(2x + 100\right) = 200$$
$$25x - 0.2x^2 - 2x - 100 = 200$$
$$-0.2x^2 + 23x - 300 = 0$$
$$-0.2\left(x^2 - 115x + 1{,}500\right) = 0$$
$$-0.2(x - 15)(x - 100) = 0$$
$$x = 15, 100$$

The company must sell 15 or 100 coffee cups to make a profit of $200.

23. Finding the profit function: $P(x) = R(x) - C(x) = \left(25x - 0.1x^2\right) - (5x + 100) = -0.1x^2 + 20x - 100$

Completing the square: $P(x) = -0.1x^2 + 20x - 100 = -0.1\left(x^2 - 200x + 10{,}000\right) + 1{,}000 - 100 = -0.1(x - 100)^2 + 900$

The maximum weekly profit is $900, obtained by selling 100 items per week.

24. Factoring the inequality:

$$x^2 - x - 6 \leq 0$$
$$(x + 2)(x - 3) \leq 0$$

Forming a sign chart:

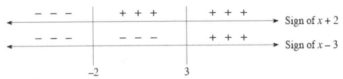

The solution set is $-2 \leq x \leq 3$. Graphing the solution set:

25. Factoring the inequality:

$$2x^2 + 5x > 3$$
$$2x^2 + 5x - 3 > 0$$
$$(2x - 1)(x + 3) > 0$$

Forming a sign chart:

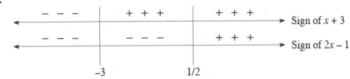

The solution set is $x < -3$ or $x > \frac{1}{2}$. Graphing the solution set:

Chapter 9
Exponential and Logarithmic Functions

9.1 Exponential Functions

1. Evaluating: $g(0) = \left(\dfrac{1}{2}\right)^0 = 1$

3. Evaluating: $g(-1) = \left(\dfrac{1}{2}\right)^{-1} = 2$

5. Evaluating: $f(-3) = 3^{-3} = \dfrac{1}{27}$

7. Evaluating: $f(2) + g(-2) = 3^2 + \left(\dfrac{1}{2}\right)^{-2} = 9 + 4 = 13$

9. Evaluating: $f(-1) + g(1) = 4^{-1} + \left(\dfrac{1}{3}\right)^1 = \dfrac{1}{4} + \dfrac{1}{3} = \dfrac{3}{12} + \dfrac{4}{12} = \dfrac{7}{12}$

11. Evaluating: $\dfrac{f(-2)}{g(1)} = \dfrac{4^{-2}}{\left(\dfrac{1}{3}\right)^1} = \dfrac{1}{16} \div \dfrac{1}{3} = \dfrac{3}{16}$

13. Approximating the value: $f\left(\dfrac{1}{3}\right) = 2^{1/3} \approx 1.26$

15. Approximating the value: $f(-\sqrt{7}) = 2^{-\sqrt{7}} \approx 0.16$

17. Approximating the value: $f(3) = e^3 \approx 20.09$

19. Approximating the value: $f(-0.5) = e^{-0.5} \approx 0.61$

21. Approximating the value: $f\left(\dfrac{1}{5}\right) = e^{1/5} \approx 1.22$

23. Approximating the value: $f(\pi) = e^{\pi} \approx 23.14$

25. Graphing the function:

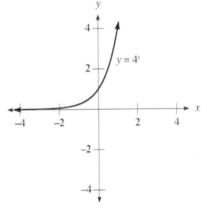

27. Graphing the function:

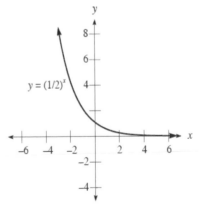

29. Graphing the function:

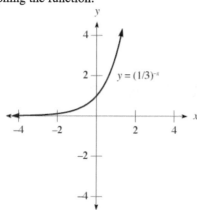

31. Graphing the function:

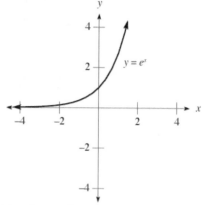

33. The horizontal asymptote is $y = 0$ and the range is $\{y \mid y > 0\}$. Sketching the graph:

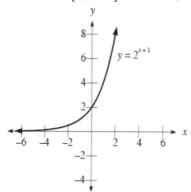

35. The horizontal asymptote is $y = 2$ and the range is $\{y \mid y > 2\}$. Sketching the graph:

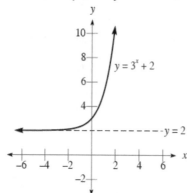

37. The horizontal asymptote is $y = 0$ and the range is $\{y \mid y < 0\}$. Sketching the graph:

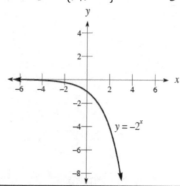

39. The horizontal asymptote is $y = 0$ and the range is $\{y \mid y > 0\}$. Sketching the graph:

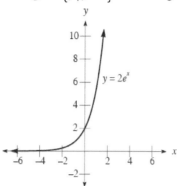

41. The horizontal asymptote is $y = 4$ and the range is $\{y \mid y < 4\}$. Sketching the graph:

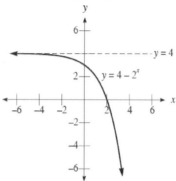

43. The horizontal asymptote is $y = 2$ and the range is $\{y \mid y > 2\}$. Sketching the graph:

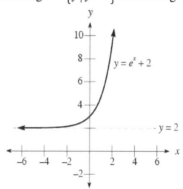

45. Graphing the functions:

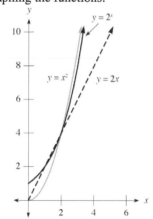

47. Graphing the functions:

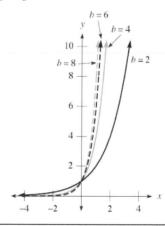

49. The equation is: $h(n) = 6\left(\dfrac{2}{3}\right)^n$. Substituting $n = 5$: $h(5) = 6\left(\dfrac{2}{3}\right)^5 \approx 0.79$ feet

51. For 2000, substitute $t = 0$: $p(0) = 17.6(1.25)^0 = \$17.60$ per pound

For 2010, substitute $t = 10$: $p(10) = 17.6(1.25)^{10} \approx \$163.91$ per pound

For 2025, substitute $t = 25$: $p(25) = 17.6(1.25)^{25} \approx \$4,658.68$ per pound

53. Finding the function values:

$$f(1) = 50 \cdot 4^1 = 200 \text{ bacteria}$$
$$f(2) = 50 \cdot 4^2 = 800 \text{ bacteria}$$
$$f(3) = 50 \cdot 4^3 = 3,200 \text{ bacteria}$$

55. **a.** Evaluating when $t = 40$: $C(40) = 0.10e^{0.0576(40)} \approx \$1.00$

b. Evaluating when $t = 55$: $C(55) = 0.10e^{0.0576(55)} \approx \$2.38$

c. Evaluating when $t = 90$: $C(90) = 0.10e^{0.0576(90)} \approx \$17.84$

57. **a.** The equation is $A(t) = 1,200\left(1 + \dfrac{0.06}{4}\right)^{4t}$.

b. Substitute $t = 8$: $A(8) = 1,200\left(1 + \dfrac{0.06}{4}\right)^{32} \approx \$1,932.39$

c. Substitute $t = 8$ into the compound interest formula: $A(8) = 1,200e^{0.06 \times 8} \approx \$1,939.29$

59. **a.** The value is $A(5) = 10,000\left(1 + \dfrac{0.015}{4}\right)^{4 \cdot 5} \approx \$10,777.33$.

b. The value is $A(5) = 10,000\left(1 + \dfrac{0.015}{12}\right)^{12 \cdot 5} \approx \$10,778.34$.

c. The value is $A(5) = 10,000e^{0.015 \cdot 5} \approx \$10,778.84$.

61. Evaluating the two options:

$$A(4) = 2,500\left(1 + \dfrac{0.014}{4}\right)^{4 \cdot 4} \approx \$2,643.74$$
$$B(4) = 2,500e^{0.0135 \cdot 4} \approx \$2,638.71$$

The first bank (1.4% interest compounded quarterly) is the better deal.

63. Graphing the function:

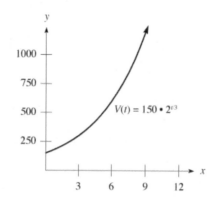

$$V(t) = 150 \cdot 2^{t/3}$$

65. **a.** Using the model: $B(36) = 0.798 \cdot 1.164^{36} \approx 188.9$ million bankruptcies

b. Sketching the graph:

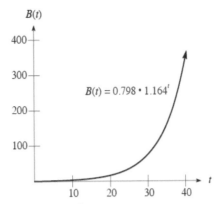

$B(t) = 0.798 \cdot 1.164^t$

67. **a.** Substitute $t = 3.5$: $V(5) = 450{,}000(1 - 0.30)^5 \approx \$129{,}138.48$

b. The domain is $\{t \mid 0 \le t \le 6\}$.

c. Sketching the graph:

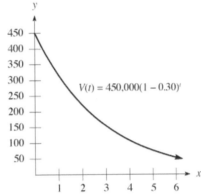

$V(t) = 450{,}000(1 - 0.30)^t$

d. The range is $\{V(t) \mid 52{,}942.05 \le V(t) \le 450{,}000\}$.

e. From the graph, the crane will be worth \$85,000 after approximately 4.7 years, or 4 years 8 months.

69. It appears to approach e. Completing the table:

x	$(1+x)^{1/x}$
1	2
0.5	2.25
0.1	2.5937
0.01	2.7048
0.001	2.7169
0.0001	2.7181
0.00001	2.7183

71. Evaluating the function: $f(-2) = \left(\dfrac{1}{2}\right)^{-2} = 4$. The correct answer is c.

73. The value is $A(8) = 600\left(1 + \dfrac{0.035}{12}\right)^{12 \cdot 8} \approx \$793.55$. The correct answer is d.

75. Solving for y:
$$x = 2y - 3$$
$$2y = x + 3$$
$$y = \frac{x+3}{2}$$

77. Solving for y:
$$x = y^2 - 2$$
$$y^2 = x + 2$$
$$y = \pm\sqrt{x+2}$$

79. Solving for y:
$$x = \frac{y-4}{y-2}$$
$$x(y-2) = y - 4$$
$$xy - 2x = y - 4$$
$$xy - y = 2x - 4$$
$$y(x-1) = 2x - 4$$
$$y = \frac{2x-4}{x-1}$$

81. Solving for y:
$$x = \sqrt{y-3}$$
$$x^2 = y - 3$$
$$y = x^2 + 3$$

9.2 The Inverse of a Function

1. The inverse is $\{(0,1),(1,2),(2,3),(3,4)\}$. Yes, the inverse does represent a function.

3. The inverse is $\{(3,-4),(-1,-2),(3,1),(-2,3)\}$. No, the inverse does not represent a function.

5. The inverse is $\{(4,-3),(4,0),(4,3)\}$. No, the inverse does not represent a function.

7. Finding the inverse:
$$2y - 1 = x$$
$$2y = x + 1$$
$$y = \frac{x+1}{2}$$

The inverse is $y = \frac{x+1}{2}$. Graphing each curve:

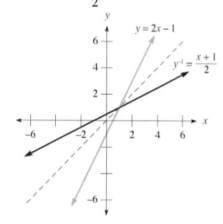

9. Finding the inverse:
$$y^2 - 3 = x$$
$$y^2 = x + 3$$
$$y = \pm\sqrt{x+3}$$

The inverse is $y = \pm\sqrt{x+3}$. Graphing each curve:

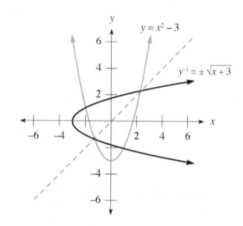

11. Finding the inverse:

$$y^2 - 2y - 3 = x$$
$$y^2 - 2y + 1 = x + 3 + 1$$
$$(y-1)^2 = x + 4$$
$$y - 1 = \pm\sqrt{x+4}$$
$$y = 1 \pm \sqrt{x+4}$$

The inverse is $y = 1 \pm \sqrt{x+4}$. Graphing each curve:

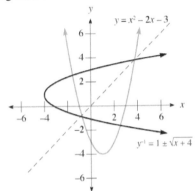

13. The inverse is $x = 3^y$. Graphing each curve:

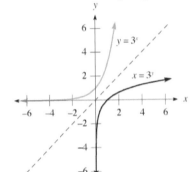

15. The inverse is $x = 4$. Graphing each curve:

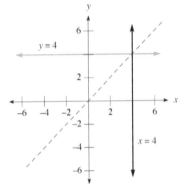

17. Finding the inverse:

$$\frac{1}{2}y^3 = x$$
$$y^3 = 2x$$
$$y = \sqrt[3]{2x}$$

The inverse is $y = \sqrt[3]{2x}$. Graphing each curve:

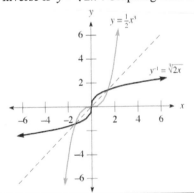

19. Finding the inverse:

$$\frac{1}{2}y + 2 = x$$
$$y + 4 = 2x$$
$$y = 2x - 4$$

The inverse is $y = 2x - 4$. Graphing each curve:

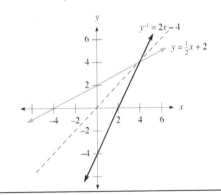

21. Finding the inverse:

$$\sqrt{y+2} = x$$
$$y+2 = x^2$$
$$y = x^2 - 2$$

The inverse is $y = x^2 - 2, x \geq 0$. Graphing each curve:

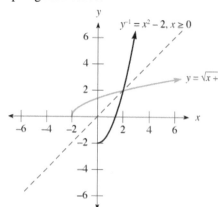

23. Yes, this function is one-to-one.

25. Yes, this function is one-to-one.

27. No, this function is not one-to-one.

29. Yes, this function is one-to-one.

31. No, this function is not one-to-one.

33. No, there are two x-values paired with the same y-value.

35. Yes, each y-value is paired with only one x-value.

37. Let $y = f(x)$. Switch x and y and solve for y:

$$3y - 1 = x$$
$$3y = x + 1$$
$$y = \frac{x+1}{3}$$

The inverse is $f^{-1}(x) = \frac{x+1}{3}$.

39. Let $y = f(x)$. Switch x and y and solve for y:

$$y^3 = x$$
$$y = \sqrt[3]{x}$$

The inverse is $f^{-1}(x) = \sqrt[3]{x}$.

41. Let $y = f(x)$. Switch x and y and solve for y:

$$\frac{y-3}{y-1} = x$$
$$y - 3 = xy - x$$
$$y - xy = 3 - x$$
$$y(1-x) = 3 - x$$
$$y = \frac{3-x}{1-x} = \frac{x-3}{x-1}$$

The inverse is $f^{-1}(x) = \frac{x-3}{x-1}$.

43. Let $y = f(x)$. Switch x and y and solve for y:

$$\frac{y-3}{4} = x$$
$$y - 3 = 4x$$
$$y = 4x + 3$$

The inverse is $f^{-1}(x) = 4x + 3$.

45. Let $y = f(x)$. Switch x and y and solve for y:

$$\frac{1}{2}y - 3 = x$$
$$y - 6 = 2x$$
$$y = 2x + 6$$

The inverse is $f^{-1}(x) = 2x + 6$.

47. Let $y = f(x)$. Switch x and y and solve for y:

$$\frac{2}{3}y - 3 = x$$
$$2y - 9 = 3x$$
$$2y = 3x + 9$$
$$y = \frac{3}{2}x + \frac{9}{2}$$

The inverse is $f^{-1}(x) = \frac{3}{2}x + \frac{9}{2}$.

49. Let $y = f(x)$. Switch x and y and solve for y:

$$y^3 - 4 = x$$
$$y^3 = x + 4$$
$$y = \sqrt[3]{x+4}$$

The inverse is $f^{-1}(x) = \sqrt[3]{x+4}$.

51. Let $y = f(x)$. Switch x and y and solve for y:

$$\frac{4y-3}{2y+1} = x$$
$$4y - 3 = 2xy + x$$
$$4y - 2xy = x + 3$$
$$y(4 - 2x) = x + 3$$
$$y = \frac{x+3}{4-2x}$$

The inverse is $f^{-1}(x) = \frac{x+3}{4-2x}$.

53. Let $y = f(x)$. Switch x and y and solve for y:

$$\frac{2y+1}{3y+1} = x$$
$$2y + 1 = 3xy + x$$
$$2y - 3xy = x - 1$$
$$y(2 - 3x) = x - 1$$
$$y = \frac{x-1}{2-3x} = \frac{1-x}{3x-2}$$

The inverse is $f^{-1}(x) = \frac{1-x}{3x-2}$.

55. **a.** Evaluating the function: $f(2) = 3(2) - 2 = 6 - 2 = 4$

   b. Evaluating the function: $f^{-1}(2) = \frac{2+2}{3} = \frac{4}{3}$

   c. Evaluating the function: $f\left(f^{-1}(2)\right) = f\left(\frac{4}{3}\right) = 3\left(\frac{4}{3}\right) - 2 = 4 - 2 = 2$

   d. Evaluating the function: $f^{-1}\left(f(2)\right) = f^{-1}(4) = \frac{4+2}{3} = \frac{6}{3} = 2$

   e. Evaluating the function: $f\left(f^{-1}(x)\right) = f\left(\frac{x+2}{3}\right) = 3\left(\frac{x+2}{3}\right) - 2 = x + 2 - 2 = x$

   f. Evaluating the function: $f^{-1}\left(f(x)\right) = f^{-1}(3x-2) = \frac{3x-2+2}{3} = \frac{3x}{3} = x$

57. Let $y = f(x)$. Switch x and y and solve for y:

$$\frac{1}{y} = x$$
$$y = \frac{1}{x}$$

The inverse is $f^{-1}(x) = \frac{1}{x}$.

59. Sketching the inverse by reflecting along $y = x$:

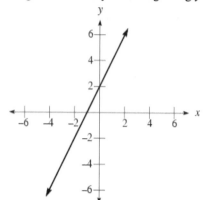

61. Sketching the inverse by reflecting along $y = x$:

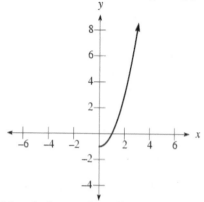

63. Sketching the inverse by reflecting along $y = x$:

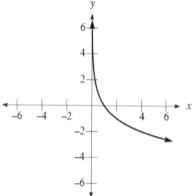

65. Sketching the inverse by reflecting along $y = x$:

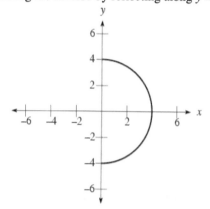

67. Verifying the inverses:

$$f\left(g(x)\right) = f\left(\frac{x-4}{3}\right) = 3\left(\frac{x-4}{3}\right) + 4 = x - 4 + 4 = x$$

$$g\left(f(x)\right) = g(3x+4) = \frac{3x+4-4}{3} = \frac{3x}{3} = x$$

69. Verifying the inverses:

$$f\left(g(x)\right) = f\left(x^2 - 4\right) = \sqrt{x^2 - 4 + 4} = \sqrt{x^2} = x$$

$$g\left(f(x)\right) = g\left(\sqrt{x+4}\right) = \left(\sqrt{x+4}\right)^2 - 4 = x + 4 - 4 = x$$

71. Verifying the inverses:

$$f\left(g(x)\right) = f\left(\frac{1-x}{x}\right) = \frac{1}{\frac{1-x}{x} + 1} \cdot \frac{x}{x} = \frac{x}{1-x+x} = x$$

$$g\left(f(x)\right) = g\left(\frac{1}{x+1}\right) = \frac{1 - \frac{1}{x+1}}{\frac{1}{x+1}} \cdot \frac{x+1}{x+1} = \frac{x+1-1}{1} = x$$

73. The inverse is $f^{-1}(x) = 7(x+2) = 7x + 14$.

75. **a.** The value is –3.   **b.** The value is –6.
     c. The value is 2.   **d.** The value is 3.
     e. The value is –2.   **f.** The value is 3.
     g. They are inverses of each other.

77. **a.** Substituting $t = 30$: $s(30) = 16(30) + 249.4 = \$729.4$ billion

b. Finding the inverse:
$$s = 16t + 249.4$$
$$16t = s - 249.4$$
$$t(s) = \frac{s - 249.4}{16}$$
$$s^{-1}(t) = \frac{t - 249.4}{16}$$

c. Substitute $s = 1{,}000$: $s^{-2}(1{,}000) = \frac{1{,}000 - 249.4}{16} \approx 46$.

The payments will reach \$1 trillion during the year $1990 + 46 = 2036$.

79. **a.** Substituting $m = 4520$: $f = \frac{22(4520)}{15} \approx 6{,}629$ feet per second

b. Finding the inverse:
$$f = \frac{22m}{15}$$
$$15f = 22m$$
$$m(f) = \frac{15f}{22}$$

c. Substituting $f = 2$: $m(2) = \frac{15(2)}{22} \approx 1.36$ mph

81. Since the inverse switches the x and y values, the correct answer is b.

83. Finding the inverse:
$$4y + 12 = x$$
$$4y = x - 12$$
$$y = \frac{x - 12}{4} = \frac{1}{4}x - 3$$

So $f^{-1}(x) = \frac{1}{4}x - 3$. The correct answer is a.

85. The correct answer is a.

87. Simplifying: $2^3 = 8$

89. Solving the equation:
$$3 = 5x$$
$$x = \frac{3}{5}$$

91. Solving the equation:
$$12 = x^2$$
$$x = \pm\sqrt{12} = \pm 2\sqrt{3}$$

93. Completing the statement: $27 = 3^3$

95. Completing the statement: $1{,}000 = 10^3$

97. Completing the statement: $81 = 9^2$

99. Completing the statement: $1 = 5^0$

9.3 Logarithms and Logarithmic Functions

1. Writing in logarithmic form: $\log_2 16 = 4$

3. Writing in logarithmic form: $\log_5 125 = 3$

5. Writing in logarithmic form: $\log_{10} 0.01 = -2$

7. Writing in logarithmic form: $\log_2 \dfrac{1}{32} = -5$

9. Writing in logarithmic form: $\log_{1/2} 8 = -3$

11. Writing in logarithmic form: $\log_3 27 = 3$

13. Writing in exponential form: $10^2 = 100$

15. Writing in exponential form: $2^6 = 64$

17. Writing in exponential form: $8^0 = 1$

19. Writing in exponential form: $10^{-3} = 0.001$

21. Writing in exponential form: $6^2 = 36$

23. Writing in exponential form: $5^{-2} = \dfrac{1}{25}$

25. Simplifying the logarithm:
$$x = \log_2 16$$
$$2^x = 16$$
$$x = 4$$

27. Simplifying the logarithm:
$$x = \log_{10} 1,000$$
$$10^x = 1,000$$
$$x = 3$$

29. Simplifying the logarithm:
$$x = \log_3 3$$
$$3^x = 3$$
$$x = 1$$

31. Simplifying the logarithm:
$$x = \log_5 1$$
$$5^x = 1$$
$$x = 0$$

33. Simplifying the logarithm:
$$x = \log_8 \frac{1}{8}$$
$$8^x = \frac{1}{8}$$
$$x = -1$$

35. Simplifying the logarithm:
$$x = \log_4 \frac{1}{16}$$
$$4^x = \frac{1}{16}$$
$$x = -2$$

37. Simplifying the logarithm:
$$x = \log_{10} 0.01$$
$$10^x = 0.01$$
$$x = -2$$

39. Simplifying the logarithm:
$$x = \log_{16} 4$$
$$16^x = 4$$
$$4^{2x} = 4^1$$
$$2x = 1$$
$$x = \frac{1}{2}$$

41. Simplifying the logarithm:
$$x = \log_{64} 4$$
$$64^x = 4$$
$$4^{3x} = 4^1$$
$$3x = 1$$
$$x = \frac{1}{3}$$

43. Simplifying the logarithm:
$$x = \log_{25} 125$$
$$25^x = 125$$
$$5^{2x} = 5^3$$
$$2x = 3$$
$$x = \frac{3}{2}$$

45. Simplifying the logarithm:
$$x = \log_4 8$$
$$4^x = 8$$
$$2^{2x} = 2^3$$
$$2x = 3$$
$$x = \frac{3}{2}$$

47. Simplifying the logarithm:
$$x = \log_{32} 16$$
$$32^x = 16$$
$$2^{5x} = 2^4$$
$$5x = 4$$
$$x = \frac{4}{5}$$

49. Sketching the graph:

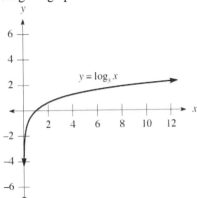

51. Sketching the graph:

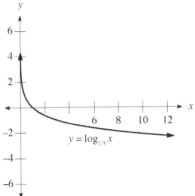

53. Sketching the graph:

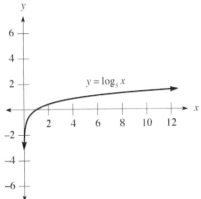

55. Sketching the graph:

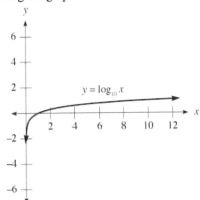

57. The inverse function is $f^{-1}(x) = 4^x$.

59. The inverse function is $f^{-1}(x) = \log_{1/8} x$.

61. The quantity inside the logarithm must be positive, so the domain is $\{x \mid x > 0\} = (0, \infty)$.

63. The quantity inside the logarithm must be positive:

$$x + 6 > 0$$
$$x > -6$$

The domain is $\{x \mid x > -6\} = (-6, \infty)$.

65. The quantity inside the logarithm must be positive:

$$1 - x > 0$$
$$-x > -1$$
$$x < 1$$

The domain is $\{x \mid x < 1\} = (-\infty, 1)$.

67. The quantity inside the logarithm must be positive:

$$2x + 3 > 0$$
$$2x > -3$$
$$x > -\frac{3}{2}$$

The domain is $\left\{ x \mid x > -\frac{3}{2} \right\} = \left(-\frac{3}{2}, \infty \right)$.

69. The vertical asymptote is $x = 3$. Sketching the graph:

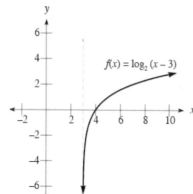

71. The vertical asymptote is $x = 0$. Sketching the graph:

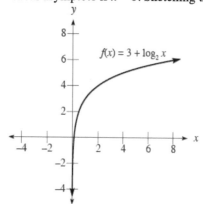

73. The vertical asymptote is $x = 0$. Sketching the graph:

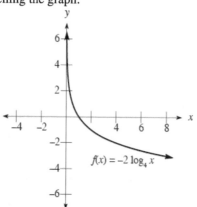

75. The function is $f(x) = 3^x$.

77. The function is $f(x) = \log_{1/3} x$.

79. Completing the table:

Prefix	Multiplying Factor	$\log_{10}$ (Multiplying Factor)
Nano	0.000000001	−9
Micro	0.000001	−6
Deci	0.1	−1
Giga	1,000,000,000	9
Peta	1,000,000,000,000,000	15

81. Using the relationship $M = \log_{10} T$:

$$M = \log_{10} 100$$
$$10^M = 100$$
$$M = 2$$

83. It is 10^8 times as large.

85. Since $M = 6$, there are 120 earthquakes.

87. Writing in logarithmic form: $\log_5 100 = x$. The correct answer is a.

89. Simplifying the logarithm:

$$x = \log_6 \frac{1}{36}$$
$$6^x = \frac{1}{36}$$
$$x = -2$$

The correct answer is a.

91. Simplifying: $8^{2/3} = \left(8^{1/3}\right)^2 = \left(\sqrt[3]{8}\right)^2 = 2^2 = 4$

93. Solving the equation:

$$(x+2)(x) = 2^3$$
$$x^2 + 2x = 8$$
$$x^2 + 2x - 8 = 0$$
$$(x+4)(x-2) = 0$$
$$x = -4, 2$$

95. Solving the equation:

$$\frac{x-2}{x+1} = 9$$
$$x - 2 = 9(x+1)$$
$$x - 2 = 9x + 9$$
$$-8x = 11$$
$$x = -\frac{11}{8}$$

97. Writing in exponential form: $2^3 = (x+2)(x)$

99. Writing in exponential form: $3^4 = \dfrac{x-2}{x+1}$

9.4 Properties of Logarithms

1. Evaluating using properties of logarithms: $\log_{17} 1 = \log_{17}\left(17^0\right) = 0$

3. Evaluating using properties of logarithms: $4\log_9 9 = 4\log_9\left(9^1\right) = 4 \cdot 1 = 4$

5. Evaluating using properties of logarithms: $8^{\log_8 3} = 3$

7. Evaluating using properties of logarithms: $\log_2 2^{\sqrt{2}} = \sqrt{2}$

9. Evaluating using properties of logarithms: $3\log_7 7^4 = 3 \cdot 4 = 12$

11. Evaluating using properties of logarithms: $6^{2\log_6 9} = 6^{\log_6 9^2} = 9^2 = 81$

13. Evaluating using properties of logarithms: $\log_9 81^2 = \log_9\left(9^2\right)^2 = \log_9 9^4 = 4$

15. Evaluating using properties of logarithms: $\log_3\left(\log_2 8\right) = \log_3\left(\log_2 2^3\right) = \log_3 3 = \log_3 3^1 = 1$

17. Evaluating using properties of logarithms: $\log_{1/2}\left(\log_3 81\right) = \log_{1/2}\left(\log_3 3^4\right) = \log_{1/2} 4 = \log_{1/2}\left(\frac{1}{2}\right)^{-2} = -2$

19. Evaluating using properties of logarithms: $\log_3\left(\log_6 6\right) = \log_3\left(\log_6 6^1\right) = \log_3 1 = \log_3 3^0 = 0$

21. Evaluating using properties of logarithms:

$$\log_4\left(\log_2\left(\log_2 16\right)\right) = \log_4\left(\log_2\left(\log_2 2^4\right)\right) = \log_4\left(\log_2 4\right) = \log_4\left(\log_2 2^2\right) = \log_4 2 = \log_4 4^{1/2} = \frac{1}{2}$$

23. Using properties of logarithms: $\log_3 4x = \log_3 4 + \log_3 x$

25. Using properties of logarithms: $\log_6 \dfrac{5}{x} = \log_6 5 - \log_6 x$

27. Using properties of logarithms: $\log_2 y^5 = 5\log_2 y$

29. Using properties of logarithms: $\log_9 \sqrt[3]{z} = \log_9 z^{1/3} = \dfrac{1}{3}\log_9 z$

31. Using properties of logarithms: $\log_6 x^2 y^4 = \log_6 x^2 + \log_6 y^4 = 2\log_6 x + 4\log_6 y$

33. Using properties of logarithms: $\log_5\left(\sqrt{x} \cdot y^4\right) = \log_5 x^{1/2} + \log_5 y^4 = \dfrac{1}{2}\log_5 x + 4\log_5 y$

35. Using properties of logarithms: $\log_b \dfrac{xy}{z} = \log_b xy - \log_b z = \log_b x + \log_b y - \log_b z$

37. Using properties of logarithms: $\log_{10} \dfrac{4}{xy} = \log_{10} 4 - \log_{10} xy = \log_{10} 4 - \log_{10} x - \log_{10} y$

39. Using properties of logarithms: $\log_{10} \dfrac{x^2 y}{\sqrt{z}} = \log_{10} x^2 + \log_{10} y - \log_{10} z^{1/2} = 2\log_{10} x + \log_{10} y - \dfrac{1}{2}\log_{10} z$

41. Using properties of logarithms: $\log_{10} \dfrac{x^3\sqrt{y}}{z^4} = \log_{10} x^3 + \log_{10} y^{1/2} - \log_{10} z^4 = 3\log_{10} x + \dfrac{1}{2}\log_{10} y - 4\log_{10} z$

43. Using properties of logarithms: $\log_b \sqrt[3]{\dfrac{x^2 y}{z^4}} = \log_b \dfrac{x^{2/3} y^{1/3}}{z^{4/3}} = \log_b x^{2/3} + \log_b y^{1/3} - \log_b z^{4/3} = \dfrac{2}{3}\log_b x + \dfrac{1}{3}\log_b y - \dfrac{4}{3}\log_b z$

45. Using properties of logarithms: $\log_3 \sqrt[3]{\dfrac{x^2 y}{z^6}} = \log_3 \dfrac{x^{2/3} y^{1/3}}{z^2} = \log_3 x^{2/3} + \log_3 y^{1/3} - \log_3 z^2 = \dfrac{2}{3}\log_3 x + \dfrac{1}{3}\log_3 y - 2\log_3 z$

47. Using properties of logarithms:
$$\log_a \dfrac{4x^5}{9a^2} = \log_a 4x^5 - \log_a 9a^2 = \log_a 2^2 + \log_a x^5 - \log_a 3^2 - \log_a a^2 = 2\log_a 2 + 5\log_a x - 2\log_a 3 - 2$$

49. Using properties of logarithms: $\log_4 x^2 (x+2) = \log_4 x^2 + \log_4 (x+2) = 2\log_4 x + \log_4 (x+2)$

51. Using properties of logarithms: $\log_b \left(5b^7\right) = \log_b 5 + \log_b b^7 = \log_b 5 + 7$

53. Using properties of logarithms: $\log_8 \left(8x^9\right) = \log_8 8 + \log_8 x^9 = 1 + 9\log_8 x$

55. Using properties of logarithms: $\log_2 8(x-1)^5 = \log_2 8 + \log_2 (x-1)^5 = \log_2 2^3 + \log_2 (x-1)^5 = 3 + 5\log_2 (x-1)$

57. Using properties of logarithms:
$$\log_6 \dfrac{x^2 z^3}{\sqrt{x+z}} = \log_6 \left(x^2 z^3\right) - \log_6 \sqrt{x+z} = \log_6 x^2 + \log_6 z^3 - \log_6 (x+z)^{1/2} = 2\log_6 x + 3\log_6 z - \dfrac{1}{2}\log_6 (x+z)$$

59. Using properties of logarithms: $\log_9 \sqrt{\dfrac{x+3}{x-3}} = \log_9 \left(\dfrac{x+3}{x-3}\right)^{1/2} = \dfrac{1}{2}\log_9 \left(\dfrac{x+3}{x-3}\right) = \dfrac{1}{2}\log_9 (x+3) - \dfrac{1}{2}\log_9 (x-3)$

61. Using properties of logarithms: $\log_6 3 + \log_6 12 = \log_6 (3\cdot 12) = \log_6 36 = \log_6 6^2 = 2$

63. Using properties of logarithms: $\log_5 50 - \log_5 2 = \log_5 \dfrac{50}{2} = \log_5 25 = \log_5 5^2 = 2$

65. Using properties of logarithms:
$$\log_4 100 - 2\log_4 5 = \log_4 100 - \log_4 5^2 = \log_4 100 - \log_4 25 = \log_4 \dfrac{100}{25} = \log_4 4 = \log_4 4^1 = 1$$

67. Writing as a single logarithm: $\log_b x + \log_b z = \log_b xz$

69. Writing as a single logarithm: $2\log_3 x - 3\log_3 y = \log_3 x^2 - \log_3 y^3 = \log_3 \dfrac{x^2}{y^3}$

71. Writing as a single logarithm: $\dfrac{1}{2}\log_{10} x + \dfrac{1}{3}\log_{10} y = \log_{10} x^{1/2} + \log_{10} y^{1/3} = \log_{10}\left(\sqrt{x}\sqrt[3]{y}\right)$

73. Writing as a single logarithm: $3\log_2 x + \dfrac{1}{2}\log_2 y - \log_2 z = \log_2 x^3 + \log_2 y^{1/2} - \log_2 z = \log_2\left(\dfrac{x^3\sqrt{y}}{z}\right)$

75. Writing as a single logarithm: $\dfrac{1}{2}\log_2 x - 3\log_2 y - 4\log_2 z = \log_2 x^{1/2} - \log_2 y^3 - \log_2 z^4 = \log_2\left(\dfrac{\sqrt{x}}{y^3 z^4}\right)$

77. Writing as a single logarithm: $\dfrac{3}{2}\log_{10} x - \dfrac{3}{4}\log_{10} y - \dfrac{4}{5}\log_{10} z = \log_{10} x^{3/2} - \log_{10} y^{3/4} - \log_{10} z^{4/5} = \log_{10}\left(\dfrac{x^{3/2}}{y^{3/4} z^{4/5}}\right)$

79. Writing as a single logarithm: $\dfrac{1}{2}\log_5 x + \dfrac{2}{3}\log_5 y - 4\log_5 z = \log_5 x^{1/2} + \log_5 y^{2/3} - \log_5 z^4 = \log_5\left(\dfrac{\sqrt{x}\cdot\sqrt[3]{y^2}}{z^4}\right)$

81. Writing as a single logarithm: $2\log_b x + 3\log_b (x-10) = \log_b x^2 + \log_b (x-10)^3 = \log_b\left(x^2 (x-10)^3\right)$

83. Writing as a single logarithm: $4\log_6 x + 5\log_6 z - 2\log_6 (y+z) = \log_6 x^4 + \log_6 z^5 - \log_6 (y+z)^2 = \log_6 \dfrac{x^4 z^5}{(y+z)^2}$

85. Writing as a single logarithm:

$$\log_3\left(x^2-16\right)-2\log_3\left(x+4\right)=\log_3\left(x^2-16\right)-\log_3\left(x+4\right)^2=\log_3\frac{(x+4)(x-4)}{(x+4)^2}=\log_3\left(\frac{x-4}{x+4}\right)$$

87. Rewriting the formula:

$$D=10\log_{10}\left(\frac{I}{I_0}\right)$$

$$D=10\left(\log_{10}I-\log_{10}I_0\right)$$

89. **a.** Finding the value: $\log_{10}40=\log_{10}\left(8\cdot5\right)=\log_{10}8+\log_{10}5=0.903+0.699=1.602$

   b. Finding the value: $\log_{10}320=\log_{10}\left(8^2\cdot5\right)=\log_{10}8^2+\log_{10}5=2\log_{10}8+\log_{10}5=2(0.903)+0.699=2.505$

   c. Finding the value:

$$\log_{10}1600=\log_{10}\left(8^2\cdot5^2\right)=\log_{10}8^2+\log_{10}5^2=2\log_{10}8+2\log_{10}5=2(0.903)+2(0.699)=3.204$$

91. Rewriting the equation: $\text{pH}=6.1+\log_{10}\left(\frac{x}{y}\right)=6.1+\log_{10}x-\log_{10}y$

93. Solving for N: $N=\log_{10}\dfrac{100}{1}=\log_{10}10^2=2$

95. Using properties of logarithms: $\log_{10}\dfrac{xy}{z^3}=\log_{10}\left(xy\right)-\log_{10}z^3=\log_{10}x+\log_{10}y-3\log_{10}z$. The correct answer is a.

97. Simplifying: $5^0=1$

99. Simplifying: $\log_3 3=\log_3 3^1=1$

101. Simplifying: $\log_b b^4=4$

9.5 Common Logarithms, Natural Logarithms, and Change of Base

1. Evaluating the logarithm: $\log 1=\log 10^0=0$

3. Evaluating the logarithm: $\ln e=\ln e^1=1$

5. Evaluating the logarithm: $\log 10,000=\log 10^4=4$

7. Evaluating the logarithm: $\ln e^5=5$

9. Evaluating the logarithm: $\log\sqrt{1000}=\log 10^{3/2}=\dfrac{3}{2}$

11. Evaluating the logarithm: $\ln\dfrac{1}{e^3}=\log e^{-3}=-3$

13. Approximating the logarithm: $\log 378\approx2.5775$

15. Approximating the logarithm: $\ln 345\approx5.8435$

17. Approximating the logarithm: $\log 0.4260\approx-0.3706$

19. Approximating the logarithm: $\ln 0.345\approx-1.0642$

21. Simplifying the logarithm: $\ln e^x=x$

23. Simplifying the logarithm: $\log 10^x=x$

25. Simplifying the logarithm: $10^{\log 3x}=3x$

27. Simplifying the logarithm: $e^{4\ln x}=e^{\ln x^4}=x^4$

29. Using properties of logarithms: $\ln 10e^{3t}=\ln 10+\ln e^{3t}=3t+\ln 10$

31. Using properties of logarithms: $\ln Ae^{-2t}=\ln A+\ln e^{-2t}=-2t+\ln A$

33. Using properties of logarithms: $\log\left[100\left(1.01\right)^{3t}\right]=\log 10^2+\log 1.01^{3t}=2+3t\log 1.01$

35. Using properties of logarithms: $\ln\left(Pe^{rt}\right)=\ln P+\ln e^{rt}=\ln P+rt$

37. Using properties of logarithms: $-\log\left(4.2\times10^{-3}\right)=-\log 4.2-\log 10^{-3}=3-\log 4.2$

39. Using properties of logarithms: $\log x+\log\left(x-2\right)=\log x(x-2)$

41. Using properties of logarithms: $\ln\left(x+1\right)-\ln\left(x+4\right)=\ln\dfrac{x+1}{x+4}$

43. Using properties of logarithms: $2\log x-5\log y=\log x^2-\log y^5=\log\dfrac{x^2}{y^5}$

45. Evaluating the logarithm: $\ln 15=\ln\left(3\cdot5\right)=\ln 3+\ln 5=1.0986+1.6094=2.7080$

47. Evaluating the logarithm: $\ln\dfrac{1}{3} = \ln 3^{-1} = -\ln 3 = -1.0986$

49. Evaluating the logarithm: $\ln 9 = \ln 3^2 = 2\ln 3 = 2(1.0986) = 2.1972$

51. Evaluating the logarithm: $\ln 16 = \ln 2^4 = 4\ln 2 = 4(0.6931) = 2.7724$

53. Sketching the graph:

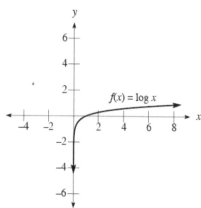

55. Evaluating the logarithm: $\log_8 16 = \dfrac{\log 16}{\log 8} = \dfrac{\log 2^4}{\log 2^3} = \dfrac{4}{3}$ **57.** Evaluating the logarithm: $\log_{16} 8 = \dfrac{\log 8}{\log 16} = \dfrac{\log 2^3}{\log 2^4} = \dfrac{3}{4}$

59. Evaluating the logarithm: $\log_7 15 = \dfrac{\log 15}{\log 7} \approx 1.3917$ **61.** Evaluating the logarithm: $\log_{15} 7 = \dfrac{\log 7}{\log 15} \approx 0.7186$

63. Evaluating the logarithm: $\log_8 240 = \dfrac{\log 240}{\log 8} \approx 2.6356$ **65.** Evaluating the logarithm: $\log_4 321 = \dfrac{\log 321}{\log 4} \approx 4.1632$

67. For the 1906 earthquake:
$$\log T = 8.3$$
$$T = 10^{8.3} = 1.995 \times 10^8$$
For the atomic bomb test:
$$T = \frac{1.995 \times 10^8}{2,000} = 9.976 \times 10^4$$
$$\log T = \log(9.976 \times 10^4) \approx 5.0$$
The earthquake caused by the test was approximately 5.0 on the Richter scale.

69. Completing the table:

Location	Date	Magnitude (M)	Shockwave (T)
Moresby Island	January 23	4.0	1.00×10^4
Vancouver Island	April 30	5.3	1.99×10^5
Quebec City	June 29	3.2	1.58×10^3
Mould Bay	November 13	5.2	1.58×10^5
St. Lawrence	December 14	3.7	5.01×10^3

71. Computing the pH: $\text{pH} = -\log(6.50 \times 10^{-4}) \approx 3.19$

73. Finding the logarithm: $\log 0.001 = \log 10^{-3} = -3$. The correct answer is d.

75. Expanding the logarithm: $\ln 50e^{0.6t} = \ln 50 + \ln e^{0.6t} = \ln 50 + 0.6t$. The correct answer is a.

77. Solving the equation:
$$5(2x+1) = 12$$
$$10x + 5 = 12$$
$$10x = 7$$
$$x = \frac{7}{10}$$

79. Using a calculator: $\dfrac{100,000}{32,000} = 3.1250$

81. Using a calculator: $\dfrac{1}{2}\left(\dfrac{-0.6931}{1.4289} + 3\right) \approx 1.2575$

83. Rewriting the logarithm: $\log 1.05^t = t \log 1.05$

85. Simplifying: $\ln e^{0.05t} = 0.05t$

87. Using a calculator: $10^{-5.6} \approx 2.5 \times 10^{-6}$

89. Using a calculator: $\dfrac{2.00 \times 10^8}{3.96 \times 10^6} \approx 51$

9.6 Exponential and Logarithmic Equations

1. Solving the equation:
$$3^x = 5$$
$$\ln 3^x = \ln 5$$
$$x \ln 3 = \ln 5$$
$$x = \frac{\ln 5}{\ln 3} \approx 1.4650$$

3. Solving the equation:
$$5^x = 3$$
$$\ln 5^x = \ln 3$$
$$x \ln 5 = \ln 3$$
$$x = \frac{\ln 3}{\ln 5} \approx 0.6826$$

5. Solving the equation:
$$5^{-x} = 12$$
$$\ln 5^{-x} = \ln 12$$
$$-x \ln 5 = \ln 12$$
$$x = -\frac{\ln 12}{\ln 5} \approx -1.5440$$

7. Solving the equation:
$$12^{-x} = 5$$
$$\ln 12^{-x} = \ln 5$$
$$-x \ln 12 = \ln 5$$
$$x = -\frac{\ln 5}{\ln 12} \approx -0.6477$$

9. Solving the equation:
$$8^{x+1} = 4$$
$$2^{3x+3} = 2^2$$
$$3x + 3 = 2$$
$$3x = -1$$
$$x = -\frac{1}{3} \approx -0.3333$$

11. Solving the equation:
$$4^{x-1} = 4$$
$$4^{x-1} = 4^1$$
$$x - 1 = 1$$
$$x = 2$$

13. Solving the equation:
$$3^{2x+1} = 2$$
$$\ln 3^{2x+1} = \ln 2$$
$$(2x+1)\ln 3 = \ln 2$$
$$2x + 1 = \frac{\ln 2}{\ln 3}$$
$$2x = \frac{\ln 2}{\ln 3} - 1$$
$$x = \frac{1}{2}\left(\frac{\ln 2}{\ln 3} - 1\right) \approx -0.1845$$

15. Solving the equation:
$$3^{1-2x} = 2$$
$$\ln 3^{1-2x} = \ln 2$$
$$(1-2x)\ln 3 = \ln 2$$
$$1 - 2x = \frac{\ln 2}{\ln 3}$$
$$-2x = \frac{\ln 2}{\ln 3} - 1$$
$$x = \frac{1}{2}\left(1 - \frac{\ln 2}{\ln 3}\right) \approx 0.1845$$

17. Solving the equation:

$$15^{3x-4} = 10$$
$$\ln 15^{3x-4} = \ln 10$$
$$(3x-4)\ln 15 = \ln 10$$
$$3x - 4 = \frac{\ln 10}{\ln 15}$$
$$3x = \frac{\ln 10}{\ln 15} + 4$$
$$x = \frac{1}{3}\left(\frac{\ln 10}{\ln 15} + 4\right) \approx 1.6168$$

19. Solving the equation:

$$6^{5-2x} = 4$$
$$\ln 6^{5-2x} = \ln 4$$
$$(5 - 2x)\ln 6 = \ln 4$$
$$5 - 2x = \frac{\ln 4}{\ln 6}$$
$$-2x = \frac{\ln 4}{\ln 6} - 5$$
$$x = \frac{1}{2}\left(5 - \frac{\ln 4}{\ln 6}\right) \approx 2.1131$$

21. Solving the equation:

$$3^{-4x} = 81$$
$$3^{-4x} = 3^4$$
$$-4x = 4$$
$$x = -1$$

23. Solving the equation:

$$5^{3x-2} = 15$$
$$\ln 5^{3x-2} = \ln 15$$
$$(3x-2)\ln 5 = \ln 15$$
$$3x - 2 = \frac{\ln 15}{\ln 5}$$
$$3x = \frac{\ln 15}{\ln 5} + 2$$
$$x = \frac{1}{3}\left(\frac{\ln 15}{\ln 5} + 2\right) \approx 1.2275$$

25. Solving the equation:

$$100e^{3t} = 250$$
$$e^{3t} = \frac{5}{2}$$
$$3t = \ln\frac{5}{2}$$
$$t = \frac{1}{3}\ln\frac{5}{2} \approx 0.3054$$

27. Solving the equation:

$$1200\left(1 + \frac{0.072}{4}\right)^{4t} = 25000$$
$$\left(1 + \frac{0.072}{4}\right)^{4t} = \frac{125}{6}$$
$$\ln\left(1 + \frac{0.072}{4}\right)^{4t} = \ln\frac{125}{6}$$
$$4t\ln\left(1 + \frac{0.072}{4}\right) = \ln\frac{125}{6}$$
$$t = \frac{\ln\dfrac{125}{6}}{4\ln\left(1 + \dfrac{0.072}{4}\right)} \approx 42.5528$$

29. Solving the equation:

$$50e^{-0.0742t} = 32$$
$$e^{-0.0742t} = \frac{16}{25}$$
$$-0.0742t = \ln\frac{16}{25}$$
$$t = \frac{\ln\dfrac{16}{25}}{-0.0742} \approx 6.0147$$

31. Solving the equation:

$$\log_3 x = 2$$
$$x = 3^2 = 9$$

33. Solving the equation:
$$\log_5 x = -3$$
$$x = 5^{-3} = \frac{1}{125}$$

35. Solving the equation:
$$\log_x 4 = 2$$
$$x^2 = 4$$
$$x = 2$$

37. Solving the equation:
$$\log_x 5 = 3$$
$$x^3 = 5$$
$$x = \sqrt[3]{5}$$

39. Solving the equation:
$$\log_x 36 = 2$$
$$x^2 = 36$$
$$x = 6$$

41. Solving the equation:
$$\log_8 x = -2$$
$$x = 8^{-2} = \frac{1}{64}$$

43. Solving the equation:
$$\log x = 1$$
$$x = 10^1 = 10$$

45. Solving for x:
$$\log x = -2$$
$$x = 10^{-2} = \frac{1}{100}$$

47. Solving for x:
$$\ln x = -1$$
$$x = e^{-1} = \frac{1}{e}$$

49. Solving for x:
$$\log x = 10$$
$$x = 10^{10}$$

51. Solving for x:
$$\log x = -20$$
$$x = 10^{-20}$$

53. Solving for x:
$$\log x = \log_2 8$$
$$\log x = 3$$
$$x = 10^3 = 1,000$$

55. Solving for x:
$$\log x = 2.8802$$
$$x = 10^{2.8802} \approx 759$$

57. Solving for x:
$$\log x = -2.1198$$
$$x = 10^{-2.1198} \approx 0.00759$$

59. Solving for x:
$$\log x = 3.1553$$
$$x = 10^{3.1553} \approx 1,430$$

61. Solving for x:

$$\ln x = -5.3497$$
$$x = e^{-5.3497} \approx 0.00475$$

63. Solving for x:
$$\log_2 x + \log_2 3 = 1$$
$$\log_2 3x = 1$$
$$3x = 2^1$$
$$3x = 2$$
$$x = \frac{2}{3}$$

65. Solving the equation:
$$\log_3 x - \log_3 2 = 2$$
$$\log_3 \frac{x}{2} = 2$$
$$\frac{x}{2} = 3^2$$
$$\frac{x}{2} = 9$$
$$x = 18$$

67. Solving the equation:
$$\log_3 x + \log_3 (x-2) = 1$$
$$\log_3 (x^2 - 2x) = 1$$
$$x^2 - 2x = 3^1$$
$$x^2 - 2x - 3 = 0$$
$$(x-3)(x+1) = 0$$
$$x = 3, -1$$
The solution is 3 (−1 does not check).

69. Solving the equation:

$$\log_3(x+3) - \log_3(x-1) = 1$$
$$\log_3\frac{x+3}{x-1} = 1$$
$$\frac{x+3}{x-1} = 3^1$$
$$x+3 = 3x-3$$
$$-2x = -6$$
$$x = 3$$

71. Solving the equation:

$$\log_2 x + \log_2(x-2) = 3$$
$$\log_2(x^2 - 2x) = 3$$
$$x^2 - 2x = 2^3$$
$$x^2 - 2x - 8 = 0$$
$$(x-4)(x+2) = 0$$
$$x = 4, -2$$

The solution is 4 (–2 does not check).

73. Solving the equation:

$$\log_8 x + \log_8(x-3) = \frac{2}{3}$$
$$\log_8(x^2 - 3x) = \frac{2}{3}$$
$$x^2 - 3x = 8^{2/3}$$
$$x^2 - 3x - 4 = 0$$
$$(x-4)(x+1) = 0$$
$$x = 4, -1$$

The solution is 4 (–1 does not check).

75. Solving the equation:

$$\log_3(x+2) - \log_3 x = 1$$
$$\log_3\frac{x+2}{x} = 1$$
$$\frac{x+2}{x} = 3^1$$
$$x+2 = 3x$$
$$2x = 2$$
$$x = 1$$

77. Solving the equation:

$$\log_2(x+1) + \log_2(x+2) = 1$$
$$\log_2(x^2 + 3x + 2) = 1$$
$$x^2 + 3x + 2 = 2^1$$
$$x^2 + 3x = 0$$
$$x(x+3) = 0$$
$$x = 0, -3$$

The solution is 0 (–3 does not check).

79. Solving the equation:

$$\log_9 \sqrt{x} + \log_9 \sqrt{2x+3} = \frac{1}{2}$$
$$\log_9 \sqrt{2x^2 + 3x} = \frac{1}{2}$$
$$\sqrt{2x^2 + 3x} = 9^{1/2}$$
$$2x^2 + 3x = 9$$
$$2x^2 + 3x - 9 = 0$$
$$(2x-3)(x+3) = 0$$
$$x = \frac{3}{2}, -3$$

The solution is $\frac{3}{2}$ (–3 does not check).

81. Solving the equation:

$$4\log_3 x - \log_3 x^2 = 6$$
$$4\log_3 x - 2\log_3 x = 6$$
$$2\log_3 x = 6$$
$$\log_3 x = 3$$
$$x = 3^3$$
$$x = 27$$

83. Solving the equation:

$$\log_5 \sqrt{x} + \log_5 \sqrt{6x+5} = 1$$
$$\log_5 \sqrt{6x^2 + 5x} = 1$$
$$\frac{1}{2}\log_5(6x^2 + 5x) = 1$$
$$\log_5(6x^2 + 5x) = 2$$
$$6x^2 + 5x = 5^2$$
$$6x^2 + 5x - 25 = 0$$
$$(3x-5)(2x+5) = 0$$
$$x = \frac{5}{3}, -\frac{5}{2}$$

The solution is $\frac{5}{3}$ ($-\frac{5}{2}$ does not check).

85. Solving for x:
$$\log x = 2\log 5$$
$$\log x = \log 5^2$$
$$x = 25$$

87. Solving for x:
$$\ln x = -3\ln 2$$
$$\ln x = \ln 2^{-3}$$
$$x = \frac{1}{8}$$

89. Using the compound interest formula:
$$500\left(1+\frac{0.06}{2}\right)^{2t} = 1000$$
$$\left(1+\frac{0.06}{2}\right)^{2t} = 2$$
$$\ln\left(1+\frac{0.06}{2}\right)^{2t} = \ln 2$$
$$2t\ln\left(1+\frac{0.06}{2}\right) = \ln 2$$
$$t = \frac{\ln 2}{2\ln\left(1+\frac{0.06}{2}\right)} \approx 11.72$$

It will take 11.72 years.

91. Using the compound interest formula:
$$1000\left(1+\frac{0.12}{6}\right)^{6t} = 3000$$
$$\left(1+\frac{0.12}{6}\right)^{6t} = 3$$
$$\ln\left(1+\frac{0.12}{6}\right)^{6t} = \ln 3$$
$$6t\ln\left(1+\frac{0.12}{6}\right) = \ln 3$$
$$t = \frac{\ln 3}{6\ln\left(1+\frac{0.12}{6}\right)} \approx 9.25$$

It will take 9.25 years.

93. Using the compound interest formula:
$$P\left(1+\frac{0.08}{4}\right)^{4t} = 2P$$
$$\left(1+\frac{0.08}{4}\right)^{4t} = 2$$
$$\ln\left(1+\frac{0.08}{4}\right)^{4t} = \ln 2$$
$$4t\ln\left(1+\frac{0.08}{4}\right) = \ln 2$$
$$t = \frac{\ln 2}{4\ln\left(1+\frac{0.08}{4}\right)} \approx 8.75$$

It will take 8.75 years.

95. Using the compound interest formula:
$$25\left(1+\frac{0.06}{2}\right)^{2t} = 75$$
$$\left(1+\frac{0.06}{2}\right)^{2t} = 3$$
$$\ln\left(1+\frac{0.06}{2}\right)^{2t} = \ln 3$$
$$2t\ln\left(1+\frac{0.06}{2}\right) = \ln 3$$
$$t = \frac{\ln 3}{2\ln\left(1+\frac{0.06}{2}\right)} \approx 18.58$$

It was invested 18.58 years ago.

97. Using the continuous interest formula:
$$500e^{0.06t} = 1000$$
$$e^{0.06t} = 2$$
$$0.06t = \ln 2$$
$$t = \frac{\ln 2}{0.06} \approx 11.55$$

It will take 11.55 years.

99. Using the continuous interest formula:
$$500e^{0.06t} = 1500$$
$$e^{0.06t} = 3$$
$$0.06t = \ln 3$$
$$t = \frac{\ln 3}{0.06} \approx 18.31$$

It will take 18.31 years.

101. Using the continuous interest formula:
$$1000e^{0.08t} = 2500$$
$$e^{0.08t} = 2.5$$
$$0.08t = \ln 2.5$$
$$t = \frac{\ln 2.5}{0.08} \approx 11.45$$

It will take 11.45 years.

103. Solving the equation:
$$0.85^t = \frac{1}{2}$$
$$\ln 0.85^t = \ln 0.5$$
$$t \ln 0.85 = \ln 0.5$$
$$t = \frac{\ln 0.5}{\ln 0.85} \approx 4.27$$
The taste quality will be one-half its original value after 4.27 days.

105. Substituting $s = 15$:
$$5 \ln x = 20$$
$$\ln x = 4$$
$$x = e^4 \approx 54.6$$
Approximately 20% of students enrolled are in the age range in the year $1989 + 54 = 2043$.

107. Finding the magnitude:
$$5.5 = \log T$$
$$T = 10^{5.5} \approx 3.16 \times 10^5$$

109. Finding the magnitude:
$$8.3 = \log T$$
$$T = 10^{8.3} \approx 2.00 \times 10^8$$

111. Finding the concentration:
$$4.75 = -\log\left[H^+\right]$$
$$-4.75 = \log\left[H^+\right]$$
$$\left[H^+\right] = 10^{-4.75} \approx 1.78 \times 10^{-5}$$

113. Using the population model:
$$32{,}000 e^{0.05t} = 80{,}000$$
$$e^{0.05t} = 2.5$$
$$0.05t = \ln 2.5$$
$$t = \frac{\ln 2.5}{0.05} \approx 18.3$$
The city will reach 80,000 in the year $2005 + 18 = 2023$.

115. Using the exponential model:
$$466 \cdot 1.035^t = 1{,}900$$
$$1.035^t = \frac{1{,}900}{466}$$
$$\ln 1.035^t = \ln \frac{1{,}900}{466}$$
$$t \ln 1.035 = \ln \frac{1{,}900}{466}$$
$$t = \frac{\ln \dfrac{1{,}900}{466}}{\ln 1.035} \approx 40.9$$
Thus 1.9 billion passengers will travel by airplane in the year $1990 + 40 = 2030$.

117. Using the exponential model:

$$78.16(1.11)^t = 40{,}000$$

$$1.11^t = \frac{40{,}000}{78.16}$$

$$\ln 1.11^t = \ln\frac{40{,}000}{78.16}$$

$$t\ln 1.11 = \ln\frac{40{,}000}{78.16}$$

$$t = \frac{\ln\dfrac{40{,}000}{78.16}}{\ln 1.11} \approx 59.8$$

Thus $40 trillion will be spent on health care in the year $1970 + 59 = 2029$.

119. Using the exponential formula:

$$1000 \cdot 2^{-t/5600} = 600$$

$$2^{-t/5600} = 0.6$$

$$\ln 2^{-t/5600} = \ln 0.6$$

$$-\frac{t}{5600}\ln 2 = \ln 0.6$$

$$-\frac{t}{5600} = \frac{\ln 0.6}{\ln 2}$$

$$t = -\frac{5600\ln 0.6}{\ln 2} \approx 4{,}127$$

The organism died 4,127 years ago.

121. Finding the rate of depreciation:

$$\log(1-r) = \frac{1}{5}\log\frac{4500}{9000}$$

$$\log(1-r) \approx -0.0602$$

$$1-r \approx 10^{-0.0602}$$

$$r = 1 - 10^{-0.0602}$$

$$r \approx 0.129 = 12.9\%$$

123. Finding the rate of depreciation:

$$\log(1-r) = \frac{1}{5}\log\frac{5750}{7550}$$

$$\log(1-r) \approx -0.0237$$

$$1-r \approx 10^{-0.0237}$$

$$r = 1 - 10^{-0.0237}$$

$$r \approx 0.053 = 5.3\%$$

125. Solving the equation:

$$3^{2x-9} = 30$$

$$\ln 3^{2x-9} = \ln 30$$

$$(2x-9)\ln 3 = \ln 30$$

$$2x - 9 = \frac{\ln 30}{\ln 3}$$

$$2x = \frac{\ln 30}{\ln 3} + 9$$

$$x = \frac{1}{2}\left(\frac{\ln 30}{\ln 3} + 9\right) \approx 6.05$$

The correct answer is a.

127. Using the exponential formula:

$$0.10e^{0.0576t} = 1.00$$

$$e^{0.0576t} = 10$$

$$0.0576t = \ln 10$$

$$t = \frac{\ln 10}{0.0576} \approx 40$$

A Coca Cola will cost $1.00 in the year 2000. The correct answer is d.

129. Completing the square: $y = 3x^2 - 9x - 10 = 3\left(x^2 - 3x + \frac{9}{4}\right) - \frac{27}{4} - 10 = 3\left(x - \frac{3}{2}\right)^2 - \frac{67}{4}$

The lowest point is $\left(\frac{3}{2}, -\frac{67}{4}\right)$.

131. Completing the square: $y = 18x - 6x^2 = -6\left(x^2 - 3x + \frac{9}{4}\right) + \frac{27}{2} = -6\left(x - \frac{3}{2}\right)^2 + \frac{27}{2}$. The highest point is $\left(\frac{3}{2}, \frac{27}{2}\right)$.

133. Completing the square: $h = 40 + 64t - 16t^2 = -16\left(t^2 - 4t + 4\right) + 64 + 40 = -16\left(t - 2\right)^2 + 104$

The object reaches a maximum height after 2 seconds, and the maximum height is 104 feet.

Chapter 9 Test

1. Graphing the function:

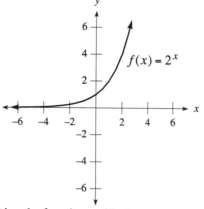

2. Graphing the function:

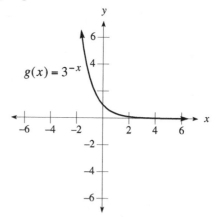

3. Graphing the function and its inverse:

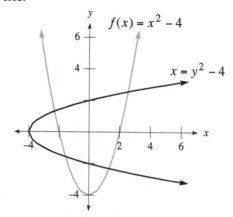

4. Finding the inverse:
$$2y - 3 = x$$
$$2y = x + 3$$
$$y = \frac{x + 3}{2}$$

The inverse is $f^{-1}(x) = \frac{x + 3}{2}$. Sketching the graph:

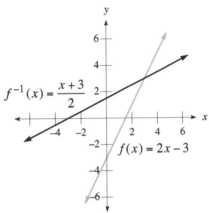

5. Graphing the function:

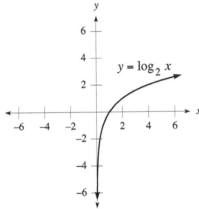

6. Graphing the function:

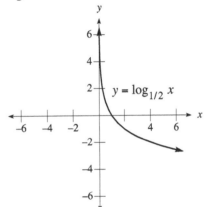

7. Evaluating the logarithm: $\log_7 \frac{1}{49} = \log_7 7^{-2} = -2$

8. Evaluating the logarithm:
$$x = \log_8 4$$
$$8^x = 4$$
$$2^{3x} = 2^2$$
$$3x = 2$$
$$x = \frac{2}{3}$$

9. Evaluating the logarithm: $\log 23,400 \approx 4.3692$

10. Evaluating the logarithm: $\ln 0.0462 \approx -3.0748$

11. Expanding the logarithm: $\log_2 \frac{8x^2}{y} = \log_2 2^3 + \log_2 x^2 - \log_2 y = 3 + 2\log_2 x - \log_2 y$

12. Expanding the logarithm: $\log \frac{\sqrt{x}}{y^4 \sqrt[5]{z}} = \log \frac{x^{1/2}}{y^4 z^{1/5}} = \log x^{1/2} - \log y^4 - \log z^{1/5} = \frac{1}{2}\log x - 4\log y - \frac{1}{5}\log z$

13. Writing as a single logarithm: $2\log_3 x - \dfrac{1}{2}\log_3 y = \log_3 x^2 - \log_3 y^{1/2} = \log_3 \dfrac{x^2}{\sqrt{y}}$

14. Writing as a single logarithm: $\dfrac{1}{3}\log x - \log y - 2\log z = \log x^{1/3} - \log y - \log z^2 = \log \dfrac{\sqrt[3]{x}}{yz^2}$

15. Using the change of base formula: $\log_9 100 = \dfrac{\log 100}{\log 9} \approx 2.0959$

16. Using the change of base formula: $\log_{100} 0.9 = \dfrac{\log 0.9}{\log 100} \approx -0.0229$

17. Solving for x:

$\log x = 4.8476$

$x = 10^{4.8476} \approx 70{,}404$

18. Solving for x:

$\log x = -2.6478$

$x = 10^{-2.6478} \approx 0.00225$

19. Solving for x:

$\log_4 x = 3$

$x = 4^3 = 64$

20. Solving for x:

$\log_x 5 = 2$

$x^2 = 5$

$x = \sqrt{5}$

21. Solving for x:

$3^x = 5$

$\ln 3^x = \ln 5$

$x\ln 3 = \ln 5$

$x = \dfrac{\ln 5}{\ln 3} \approx 1.4650$

22. Solving for x:

$4^{2x-1} = 8$

$2^{4x-2} = 2^3$

$4x - 2 = 3$

$4x = 5$

$x = \dfrac{5}{4}$

23. Solving for x:

$\log_5 x - \log_5 3 = 1$

$\log_5 \dfrac{x}{3} = 1$

$\dfrac{x}{3} = 5^1$

$x = 15$

24. Solving for x:

$\log_2 x + \log_2 (x-7) = 3$

$\log_2 (x^2 - 7x) = 3$

$x^2 - 7x = 2^3$

$x^2 - 7x - 8 = 0$

$(x-8)(x+1) = 0$

$x = 8, -1$

The solution is 8 (–1 does not check).

25. Finding the pH: $\text{pH} = -\log(6.6 \times 10^{-7}) \approx 6.18$

26. Using the compound interest formula: $A = 400\left(1 + \dfrac{0.10}{2}\right)^{2 \cdot 5} = 400(1.05)^{10} \approx 651.56$

There will be $651.56 in the account after 5 years.

27. Using the depreciation formula: $V(4) = 18{,}000(1-0.20)^4 = 18{,}000(0.8)^4 \approx \$7{,}372.80$

The car will be worth approximately $7,373 after 4 years.

28. Using the compound interest formula:

$$600\left(1+\frac{0.08}{4}\right)^{4t}=1800$$

$$\left(1+\frac{0.08}{4}\right)^{4t}=3$$

$$\ln(1.02)^{4t}=\ln 3$$

$$4t\ln 1.02=\ln 3$$

$$t=\frac{\ln 3}{4\ln 1.02}\approx 13.87$$

It will take 13.87 years for the account to reach $1,800.

Chapter 10
Sequences and Series

10.1 Sequences

1. The first five terms are: $4, 7, 10, 13, 16$

3. The first five terms are: $3, 7, 11, 15, 19$

5. The first five terms are: $1, 2, 3, 4, 5$

7. The first five terms are: $4, 7, 12, 19, 28$

9. The first five terms are: $\dfrac{1}{4}, \dfrac{2}{5}, \dfrac{1}{2}, \dfrac{4}{7}, \dfrac{5}{8}$

11. The first five terms are: $1, \dfrac{1}{4}, \dfrac{1}{9}, \dfrac{1}{16}, \dfrac{1}{25}$

13. The first five terms are: $2, 4, 8, 16, 32$

15. The first five terms are: $2, \dfrac{3}{2}, \dfrac{4}{3}, \dfrac{5}{4}, \dfrac{6}{5}$

17. The first five terms are: $-2, 4, -8, 16, -32$

19. The first five terms are: $3, 5, 3, 5, 3$

21. The first five terms are: $1, -\dfrac{2}{3}, \dfrac{3}{5}, -\dfrac{4}{7}, \dfrac{5}{9}$

23. The first five terms are: $\dfrac{1}{2}, 1, \dfrac{9}{8}, 1, \dfrac{25}{32}$

25. Finding the term: $a_8 = (8)^2 + 2(8) = 64 + 16 = 80$

27. Finding the term: $a_{100} = \dfrac{(-1)^{100}}{2(100) + 3} = \dfrac{1}{200 + 3} = \dfrac{1}{203}$

29. The first five terms are: $3, -9, 27, -81, 243$

31. The first five terms are: $1, 5, 13, 29, 61$

33. The first five terms are: $2, 3, 5, 9, 17$

35. The first five terms are: $5, 11, 29, 83, 245$

37. The first five terms are: $4, 4, 4, 4, 4$

39. The general term is: $a_n = 4n$

41. The general term is: $a_n = n^2$

43. The general term is: $a_n = 2^{n+1}$

45. The general term is: $a_n = \dfrac{1}{2^{n+1}}$

47. The general term is: $a_n = 3n + 2$

49. The general term is: $a_n = -4n + 2$

51. The general term is: $a_n = (-2)^{n-1}$

53. The general term is: $a_n = \log_{n+1}(n + 2)$

55. **a.** The sequence of salaries is: $28000, $29120, $30284.80, $31,496.19, $32756.04

    b. The general term is: $a_n = 28{,}000(1.04)^{n-1}$

57. **a.** The sequence of values is: 16 ft, 48 ft, 80 ft, 112 ft, 144 ft

    b. The sum of the values is 400 feet.

    c. No, since the sum is less than 420 feet.

59. **a.** The distances traveled are: $10\text{ ft}, 8\text{ ft}, 6.4\text{ ft}$

b. The general term is: $a_n = 10\left(\dfrac{4}{5}\right)^{n-1}$

c. Substituting $n = 10$: $a_{10} = 10\left(\dfrac{4}{5}\right)^9 \approx 1.34$ feet

61. The first five terms are: $6, 13, 27, 55, 111$. The correct answer is c.

63. Simplifying: $-2 + 6 + 4 + 22 = 30$

65. Simplifying: $-8 + 16 - 32 + 64 = 40$

67. Simplifying: $(1-3)+(4-3)+(9-3)+(16-3) = -2+1+6+13 = 18$

69. Simplifying: $-\dfrac{1}{3}+\dfrac{1}{9}-\dfrac{1}{27}+\dfrac{1}{81} = -\dfrac{27}{81}+\dfrac{9}{81}-\dfrac{3}{81}+\dfrac{1}{81} = -\dfrac{20}{81}$

71. Simplifying: $\dfrac{1}{3}+\dfrac{1}{2}+\dfrac{3}{5}+\dfrac{2}{3} = \dfrac{10}{30}+\dfrac{15}{30}+\dfrac{18}{30}+\dfrac{20}{30} = \dfrac{63}{30} = \dfrac{21}{10}$

10.2 Series

1. Expanding the sum: $\displaystyle\sum_{i=1}^{4}(2i+4) = 6+8+10+12 = 36$

3. Expanding the sum: $\displaystyle\sum_{i=2}^{3}(i^2-1) = 3+8 = 11$

5. Expanding the sum: $\displaystyle\sum_{i=1}^{4}(i^2-3) = -2+1+6+13 = 18$

7. Expanding the sum: $\displaystyle\sum_{i=1}^{4}\dfrac{i}{1+i} = \dfrac{1}{2}+\dfrac{2}{3}+\dfrac{3}{4}+\dfrac{4}{5} = \dfrac{30}{60}+\dfrac{40}{60}+\dfrac{45}{60}+\dfrac{48}{60} = \dfrac{163}{60}$

9. Expanding the sum: $\displaystyle\sum_{i=1}^{4}(-3)^i = -3+9-27+81 = 60$

11. Expanding the sum: $\displaystyle\sum_{i=3}^{6}(-2)^i = -8+16-32+64 = 40$

13. Expanding the sum: $\displaystyle\sum_{i=2}^{6}(-2)^i = 4-8+16-32+64 = 44$

15. Expanding the sum: $\displaystyle\sum_{i=1}^{5}\left(-\dfrac{1}{2}\right)^i = -\dfrac{1}{2}+\dfrac{1}{4}-\dfrac{1}{8}+\dfrac{1}{16}-\dfrac{1}{32} = -\dfrac{16}{32}+\dfrac{8}{32}-\dfrac{4}{32}+\dfrac{2}{32}-\dfrac{1}{32} = -\dfrac{11}{32}$

17. Expanding the sum: $\displaystyle\sum_{i=2}^{5}\dfrac{i-1}{i+1} = \dfrac{1}{3}+\dfrac{1}{2}+\dfrac{3}{5}+\dfrac{2}{3} = 1+\dfrac{5}{10}+\dfrac{6}{10} = \dfrac{21}{10}$

19. Expanding the sum: $\displaystyle\sum_{i=1}^{5}(x+i) = (x+1)+(x+2)+(x+3)+(x+4)+(x+5)$

21. Expanding the sum: $\displaystyle\sum_{i=1}^{4}(x-2)^i = (x-2)+(x-2)^2+(x-2)^3+(x-2)^4$

23. Expanding the sum: $\displaystyle\sum_{i=1}^{5}\dfrac{x+i}{x-1} = \dfrac{x+1}{x-1}+\dfrac{x+2}{x-1}+\dfrac{x+3}{x-1}+\dfrac{x+4}{x-1}+\dfrac{x+5}{x-1}$

25. Expanding the sum: $\sum_{i=3}^{8}(x+i)^i = (x+3)^3 + (x+4)^4 + (x+5)^5 + (x+6)^6 + (x+7)^7 + (x+8)^8$

27. Expanding the sum: $\sum_{i=3}^{6}(x-2i)^{i+3} = (x-6)^6 + (x-8)^7 + (x-10)^8 + (x-12)^9$

29. Writing with summation notation: $2+4+8+16 = \sum_{i=1}^{4} 2^i$

31. Writing with summation notation: $4+8+16+32+64 = \sum_{i=2}^{6} 2^i$

33. Writing with summation notation: $5+9+13+17+21 = \sum_{i=1}^{5}(4i+1)$

35. Writing with summation notation: $-4+8-16+32 = \sum_{i=2}^{5} -(-2)^i$

37. Writing with summation notation: $\dfrac{3}{4}+\dfrac{4}{5}+\dfrac{5}{6}+\dfrac{6}{7}+\dfrac{7}{8} = \sum_{i=3}^{7}\dfrac{i}{i+1}$

39. Writing with summation notation: $\dfrac{1}{3}+\dfrac{2}{5}+\dfrac{3}{7}+\dfrac{4}{9} = \sum_{i=1}^{4}\dfrac{i}{2i+1}$

41. Writing with summation notation: $(x-2)^6 + (x-2)^7 + (x-2)^8 + (x-2)^9 = \sum_{i=6}^{9}(x-2)^i$

43. Writing with summation notation: $\left(1+\dfrac{1}{x}\right)^2 + \left(1+\dfrac{2}{x}\right)^3 + \left(1+\dfrac{3}{x}\right)^4 + \left(1+\dfrac{4}{x}\right)^5 = \sum_{i=1}^{4}\left(1+\dfrac{i}{x}\right)^{i+1}$

45. Writing with summation notation: $\dfrac{x}{x+3}+\dfrac{x}{x+4}+\dfrac{x}{x+5} = \sum_{i=3}^{5}\dfrac{x}{x+i}$

47. Writing with summation notation: $x^2(x+2) + x^3(x+3) + x^4(x+4) = \sum_{i=2}^{4} x^i(x+i)$

49. a. Writing as a series: $\dfrac{1}{3} = 0.3 + 0.03 + 0.003 + 0.0003 + \ldots$

    b. Writing as a series: $\dfrac{2}{9} = 0.2 + 0.02 + 0.002 + 0.0002 + \ldots$

    c. Writing as a series: $\dfrac{3}{11} = 0.27 + 0.0027 + 0.000027 + \ldots$

51. The sequence of values he falls is: $16, 48, 80, 112, 144, 176, 208$
    During the seventh second he falls 208 feet, and the total he falls is 784 feet.

53. a. The series is $16 + 48 + 80 + 112 + 144$.

    b. Writing in summation notation: $\sum_{i=1}^{5}(32i-16)$

55. Expanding the sum: $\sum_{i=3}^{5}(i^2-2i) = (9-6)+(16-8)+(25-10) = 3+8+15 = 26$. The correct answer is b.

57. Simplifying: $2+9(8) = 2+72 = 74$

59. Simplifying: $\dfrac{10}{2}\left(\dfrac{1}{2}+5\right) = 5\left(\dfrac{1}{2}+\dfrac{10}{2}\right) = 5\left(\dfrac{11}{2}\right) = \dfrac{55}{2}$

61. Simplifying: $3 + (n-1)(2) = 3 + 2n - 2 = 2n + 1$

63. Multiplying the first equation by -1:
$$-x - 2y = -7$$
$$x + 7y = 17$$
Adding yields:
$$5y = 10$$
$$y = 2$$
Substituting into the first equation:
$$x + 2(2) = 7$$
$$x + 4 = 7$$
$$x = 3$$
The solution is $(3,2)$.

10.3 Arithmetic Sequences

1. The sequence is arithmetic: $d = 1$

5. The sequence is arithmetic: $d = -5$

9. The sequence is arithmetic: $d = \dfrac{2}{3}$

3. The sequence is not arithmetic.

7. The sequence is not arithmetic.

11. Finding the general term: $a_n = 3 + (n-1) \cdot 4 = 3 + 4n - 4 = 4n - 1$. Therefore: $a_{24} = 4 \cdot 24 - 1 = 96 - 1 = 95$

13. Finding the required term: $a_{10} = 6 + (10-1) \cdot (-2) = 6 - 18 = -12$. Finding the sum: $S_{10} = \dfrac{10}{2}(6 - 12) = 5(-6) = -30$

15. Writing out the equations:
$$a_6 = a_1 + 5d \qquad a_{12} = a_1 + 11d$$
$$17 = a_1 + 5d \qquad 29 = a_1 + 11d$$
The system of equations is:
$$a_1 + 11d = 29$$
$$a_1 + 5d = 17$$
Subtracting yields:
$$6d = 12$$
$$d = 2$$
$$a_1 = 7$$
Finding the required term: $a_{30} = 7 + 29 \cdot 2 = 7 + 58 = 65$

17. Writing out the equations:

$$a_3 = a_1 + 2d \qquad a_8 = a_1 + 7d$$
$$16 = a_1 + 2d \qquad 26 = a_1 + 7d$$

The system of equations is:

$$a_1 + 7d = 26$$
$$a_1 + 2d = 16$$

Subtracting yields:

$$5d = 10$$
$$d = 2$$
$$a_1 = 12$$

Finding the required term: $a_{20} = 12 + 19 \cdot 2 = 12 + 38 = 50$. Finding the sum: $S_{20} = \dfrac{20}{2}(12 + 50) = 10 \cdot 62 = 620$

19. Finding the required term: $a_{20} = 3 + 19 \cdot 4 = 3 + 76 = 79$. Finding the sum: $S_{20} = \dfrac{20}{2}(3 + 79) = 10 \cdot 82 = 820$

21. Writing out the equations:

$$a_4 = a_1 + 3d \qquad a_{10} = a_1 + 9d$$
$$14 = a_1 + 3d \qquad 32 = a_1 + 9d$$

The system of equations is:

$$a_1 + 9d = 32$$
$$a_1 + 3d = 14$$

Subtracting yields:

$$6d = 18$$
$$d = 3$$
$$a_1 = 5$$

Finding the required term: $a_{40} = 5 + 39 \cdot 3 = 5 + 117 = 122$. Finding the sum: $S_{40} = \dfrac{40}{2}(5 + 122) = 20 \cdot 127 = 2{,}540$

23. Using the summation formula:

$$S_6 = \frac{6}{2}(a_1 + a_6)$$
$$-12 = 3(a_1 - 17)$$
$$a_1 - 17 = -4$$
$$a_1 = 13$$

Now find d:

$$a_6 = 13 + 5 \cdot d$$
$$-17 = 13 + 5d$$
$$5d = -30$$
$$d = -6$$

25. Using $a_1 = 14$ and $d = -3$: $a_{85} = 14 + 84 \cdot (-3) = 14 - 252 = -238$

27. Using the summation formula:

$$S_{20} = \frac{20}{2}(a_1 + a_{20})$$

$$80 = 10(-4 + a_{20})$$

$$-4 + a_{20} = 8$$

$$a_{20} = 12$$

Now finding d:

$$a_{20} = a_1 + 19d$$

$$12 = -4 + 19d$$

$$16 = 19d$$

$$d = \frac{16}{19}$$

Finding the required term: $a_{39} = -4 + 38\left(\frac{16}{19}\right) = -4 + 32 = 28$

29. Using $a_1 = 5$ and $d = 4$: $a_{100} = a_1 + 99d = 5 + 99 \cdot 4 = 5 + 396 = 401$

Now finding the required sum: $S_{100} = \frac{100}{2}(5 + 401) = 50 \cdot 406 = 20,300$

31. Using $a_1 = 12$ and $d = -5$: $a_{35} = a_1 + 34d = 12 + 34 \cdot (-5) = 12 - 170 = -158$

33. Using $a_1 = \frac{1}{2}$ and $d = \frac{1}{2}$: $a_{10} = a_1 + 9d = \frac{1}{2} + 9 \cdot \frac{1}{2} = \frac{10}{2} = 5$. Finding the sum: $S_{10} = \frac{10}{2}\left(\frac{1}{2} + 5\right) = \frac{10}{2} \cdot \frac{11}{2} = \frac{55}{2}$

35. **a.** The first five terms are: $18,000, $14,700, $11,400, $8,100, $4,800

b. The common difference is –$3,300.

c. Constructing a line graph:

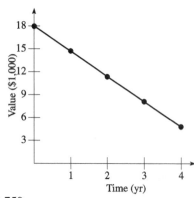

d. The value is approximately $9,750.

e. The recursive formula is: $a_0 = 18000; a_n = a_{n-1} - 3300$ for $n \geq 1$

37. **a.** The sequence of values is: 1500 ft, 1460 ft, 1420 ft, 1380 ft, 1340 ft, 1300 ft

b. It is arithmetic because the same amount is subtracted from each succeeding term.

c. The general term is: $a_n = 1500 + (n-1) \cdot (-40) = 1500 - 40n + 40 = 1540 - 40n$

39. **a.** The first 15 triangular numbers is: 1, 3, 6, 10, 15, 21, 28, 36, 45, 55, 66, 78, 91, 105, 120

b. The recursive formula is: $a_1 = 1; a_n = n + a_{n-1}$ for $n \geq 2$

c. It is not arithmetic because the same amount is not added to each term.

41. **a.** The general term is: $a_n = 16 + (n-1) \cdot 32 = 16 + 32n - 32 = 32n - 16$

b. Substituting $n = 10$: $a_{10} = 32 \cdot 10 - 16 = 304$ feet

c. Finding the sum: $S_{10} = \dfrac{10}{2}(16 + 304) = 5 \cdot 320 = 1600$ feet

43. The first sequence is an arithmetic sequence with $d = -3$. The correct answer is a.

45. Using $a_1 = 15$ and $d = 6$: $a_{10} = a_1 + 9d = 15 + 9 \cdot 6 = 15 + 54 = 69$. The correct answer is d.

47. Simplifying: $\dfrac{1}{8}\left(\dfrac{1}{2}\right) = \dfrac{1}{16}$

49. Simplifying: $\dfrac{3\sqrt{3}}{3} = \sqrt{3}$

51. Simplifying: $2 \cdot 2^{n-1} = 2^{1+n-1} = 2^n$

53. Simplifying: $\dfrac{ar^6}{ar^3} = r^{6-3} = r^3$

55. Simplifying: $\dfrac{\frac{1}{5}}{1 - \frac{1}{2}} = \dfrac{\frac{1}{5}}{1 - \frac{1}{2}} \cdot \dfrac{10}{10} = \dfrac{2}{10 - 5} = \dfrac{2}{5}$

57. Simplifying: $\dfrac{3\left[(-2)^8 - 1\right]}{-2 - 1} = \dfrac{3(256 - 1)}{-2 - 1} = \dfrac{3(255)}{-3} = -255$

10.4 Geometric Sequences

1. The sequence is geometric: $r = 5$

3. The sequence is geometric: $r = \dfrac{1}{3}$

5. The sequence is not geometric.

7. The sequence is geometric: $r = -2$

9. The sequence is not geometric.

11. Finding the general term: $a_n = 4 \cdot 3^{n-1}$

13. Finding the term: $a_6 = -2\left(-\dfrac{1}{2}\right)^{6-1} = -2\left(-\dfrac{1}{2}\right)^5 = -2\left(-\dfrac{1}{32}\right) = \dfrac{1}{16}$

15. Finding the term: $a_{20} = 3(-1)^{20-1} = 3(-1)^{19} = -3$

17. Finding the sum: $S_{10} = \dfrac{10\left(2^{10} - 1\right)}{2 - 1} = 10 \cdot 1023 = 10{,}230$

19. Finding the sum: $S_{20} = \dfrac{1\left((-1)^{20} - 1\right)}{-1 - 1} = \dfrac{1 \cdot 0}{-2} = 0$

21. Using $a_1 = \dfrac{1}{5}$ and $r = \dfrac{1}{2}$, the term is: $a_8 = \dfrac{1}{5} \cdot \left(\dfrac{1}{2}\right)^{8-1} = \dfrac{1}{5} \cdot \left(\dfrac{1}{2}\right)^7 = \dfrac{1}{5} \cdot \dfrac{1}{128} = \dfrac{1}{640}$

23. Using $a_1 = \dfrac{1}{2}$ and $r = \dfrac{1}{2}$, the sum is: $S_5 = \dfrac{-\dfrac{1}{2}\left(\left(\dfrac{1}{2}\right)^5 - 1\right)}{\dfrac{1}{2} - 1} = \dfrac{-\dfrac{1}{2}\left(\dfrac{1}{32} - 1\right)}{-\dfrac{1}{2}} = \dfrac{1}{32} - 1 = -\dfrac{31}{32}$

25. Using $a_1 = \sqrt{2}$ and $r = \sqrt{2}$, the term is: $a_{10} = \sqrt{2}\left(\sqrt{2}\right)^9 = \left(\sqrt{2}\right)^{10} = 2^5 = 32$

The sum is: $S_{10} = \dfrac{\sqrt{2}\left(\left(\sqrt{2}\right)^{10} - 1\right)}{\sqrt{2} - 1} = \dfrac{\sqrt{2}(32 - 1)}{\sqrt{2} - 1} = \dfrac{31\sqrt{2}}{\sqrt{2} - 1} \cdot \dfrac{\sqrt{2} + 1}{\sqrt{2} + 1} = \dfrac{62 + 31\sqrt{2}}{2 - 1} = 62 + 31\sqrt{2}$

27. Using $a_1 = 100$ and $r = 0.1$, the term is: $a_6 = 100(0.1)^5 = 10^2\left(10^{-5}\right) = 10^{-3} = \dfrac{1}{1000}$

The sum is: $S_6 = \dfrac{100\left((0.1)^6 - 1\right)}{0.1 - 1} = \dfrac{100\left(10^{-6} - 1\right)}{-0.9} = \dfrac{-99.9999}{-0.9} = 111.111$

29. Since $a_4 \cdot r \cdot r = a_6$, we have the equation:

$$a_4 r^2 = a_6$$
$$40 r^2 = 160$$
$$r^2 = 4$$
$$r = \pm 2$$

31. Since $a_1 = -3$ and $r = -2$, the values are:

$$a_8 = -3(-2)^7 = -3(-128) = 384$$
$$S_8 = \frac{-3\left((-2)^8 - 1\right)}{-2 - 1} = \frac{-3(256 - 1)}{-3} = 255$$

33. Since $a_7 \cdot r \cdot r \cdot r = a_{10}$, we have the equation:

$$a_7 r^3 = a_{10}$$
$$13 r^3 = 104$$
$$r^3 = 8$$
$$r = 2$$

35. Using $a_1 = \dfrac{1}{2}$ and $r = \dfrac{1}{2}$ in the sum formula: $S = \dfrac{\frac{1}{2}}{1 - \frac{1}{2}} = \dfrac{\frac{1}{2}}{\frac{1}{2}} = 1$

37. Using $a_1 = 4$ and $r = \dfrac{1}{2}$ in the sum formula: $S = \dfrac{4}{1 - \frac{1}{2}} = \dfrac{4}{\frac{1}{2}} = 8$

39. Using $a_1 = 2$ and $r = \dfrac{1}{2}$ in the sum formula: $S = \dfrac{2}{1 - \frac{1}{2}} = \dfrac{2}{\frac{1}{2}} = 4$

41. Using $a_1 = \dfrac{4}{3}$ and $r = -\dfrac{1}{2}$ in the sum formula: $S = \dfrac{\frac{4}{3}}{1 + \frac{1}{2}} = \dfrac{\frac{4}{3}}{\frac{3}{2}} = \dfrac{4}{3} \cdot \dfrac{2}{3} = \dfrac{8}{9}$

43. Using $a_1 = \dfrac{2}{5}$ and $r = \dfrac{2}{5}$ in the sum formula: $S = \dfrac{\frac{2}{5}}{1 - \frac{2}{5}} = \dfrac{\frac{2}{5}}{\frac{3}{5}} = \dfrac{2}{5} \cdot \dfrac{5}{3} = \dfrac{2}{3}$

45. Using $a_1 = \dfrac{3}{4}$ and $r = \dfrac{1}{3}$ in the sum formula: $S = \dfrac{\frac{3}{4}}{1 - \frac{1}{3}} = \dfrac{\frac{3}{4}}{\frac{2}{3}} = \dfrac{3}{4} \cdot \dfrac{3}{2} = \dfrac{9}{8}$

47. Interpreting the decimal as an infinite sum with $a_1 = 0.4$ and $r = 0.1$: $S = \dfrac{0.4}{1 - 0.1} = \dfrac{0.4}{0.9} \cdot \dfrac{10}{10} = \dfrac{4}{9}$

49. Interpreting the decimal as an infinite sum with $a_1 = 0.27$ and $r = 0.01$: $S = \dfrac{0.27}{1 - 0.01} = \dfrac{0.27}{0.99} \cdot \dfrac{100}{100} = \dfrac{27}{99} = \dfrac{3}{11}$

51. **a.** The first five terms are: $450,000, $315,000, $220,500, $154,350, $108,045

b. The common ratio is 0.7.

c. Constructing a line graph:

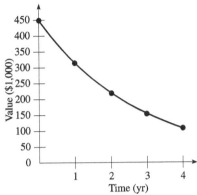

d. The value is approximately $90,000.

e. The recursive formula is: $a_0 = 450000; a_n = 0.7a_{n-1}$ for $n \geq 1$

53. **a.** Using $a_1 = \dfrac{1}{3}$ and $r = \dfrac{1}{3}$ in the sum formula: $S = \dfrac{\frac{1}{3}}{1 - \frac{1}{3}} = \dfrac{\frac{1}{3}}{\frac{2}{3}} = \dfrac{1}{2}$

b. Finding the sum: $S_6 = \dfrac{\frac{1}{3}\left(\left(\frac{1}{3}\right)^6 - 1\right)}{\frac{1}{3} - 1} = \dfrac{\frac{1}{3}\left(\frac{1}{729} - 1\right)}{-\frac{2}{3}} = \dfrac{\frac{1}{3}\left(-\frac{728}{729}\right)}{-\frac{2}{3}} = -\dfrac{1}{2}\left(-\dfrac{728}{729}\right) = \dfrac{364}{729}$

c. Finding the difference of these two answers: $S - S_6 = \dfrac{1}{2} - \dfrac{364}{729} = \dfrac{729}{1,458} - \dfrac{728}{1,458} = \dfrac{1}{1,458}$

55. **a.** The pile is now $2(0.002) = 0.004$ inches.

b. Using $a_1 = 0.002$ and $r = 2$, find the term: $a_5 = 0.002(2)^5 = 0.064$ inches

c. Using $a_1 = 0.002$ and $r = 2$, find the term: $a_{25} = 0.002(2)^{25} = 67,108.864$ inches

57. **a.** The sequence of incomes is: $60,000, $64,200, $68,694, $73,503, $78,648

b. The general term is: $a_n = 60000(1.07)^{n-1}$

c. Finding the sum: $S_{10} = \dfrac{60000\left(1.07^{10} - 1\right)}{1.07 - 1} = \$828,987$

59. The common ration is $\dfrac{1}{10} = 0.1$. The correct answer is a.

61. Using $a_1 = 64$ and $r = -\dfrac{1}{4}$ in the sum formula: $S = \dfrac{64}{1 - \left(-\frac{1}{4}\right)} = \dfrac{64}{\frac{5}{4}} = 64 \cdot \dfrac{4}{5} = \dfrac{256}{5}$. The correct answer is d.

63. Expanding: $(x + y)^1 = x + y$

65. Expanding: $(x+y)^3 = (x+y)(x+y)^2 = (x+y)(x^2+2xy+y^2) = x^3+3x^2y+3xy^2+y^3$

67. Simplifying: $\dfrac{7 \cdot 6 \cdot 5 \cdot 4 \cdot 3 \cdot 2 \cdot 1}{(5 \cdot 4 \cdot 3 \cdot 2 \cdot 1)(2 \cdot 1)} = \dfrac{7 \cdot 6}{2 \cdot 1} = \dfrac{42}{2} = 21$

10.5 The Binomial Expansion

1. Using the binomial formula:

$$(x+2)^4 = \binom{4}{0}x^4 + \binom{4}{1}x^3(2) + \binom{4}{2}x^2(2)^2 + \binom{4}{3}x(2)^3 + \binom{4}{4}(2)^4$$

$$= x^4 + 4 \cdot 2x^3 + 6 \cdot 4x^2 + 4 \cdot 8x + 16$$

$$= x^4 + 8x^3 + 24x^2 + 32x + 16$$

3. Using the binomial formula:

$$(x+y)^6 = \binom{6}{0}x^6 + \binom{6}{1}x^5y + \binom{6}{2}x^4y^2 + \binom{6}{3}x^3y^3 + \binom{6}{4}x^2y^4 + \binom{6}{5}xy^5 + \binom{6}{6}y^6$$

$$= x^6 + 6x^5y + 15x^4y^2 + 20x^3y^3 + 15x^2y^4 + 6xy^5 + y^6$$

5. Using the binomial formula:

$$(2x+1)^5 = \binom{5}{0}(2x)^5 + \binom{5}{1}(2x)^4(1) + \binom{5}{2}(2x)^3(1)^2 + \binom{5}{3}(2x)^2(1)^3 + \binom{5}{4}(2x)(1)^4 + \binom{5}{5}(1)^5$$

$$= 32x^5 + 5 \cdot 16x^4 + 10 \cdot 8x^3 + 10 \cdot 4x^2 + 5 \cdot 2x + 1$$

$$= 32x^5 + 80x^4 + 80x^3 + 40x^2 + 10x + 1$$

7. Using the binomial formula:

$$(x-2y)^5 = \binom{5}{0}x^5 + \binom{5}{1}x^4(-2y) + \binom{5}{2}x^3(-2y)^2 + \binom{5}{3}x^2(-2y)^3 + \binom{5}{4}x(-2y)^4 + \binom{5}{5}(-2y)^5$$

$$= x^5 - 5 \cdot 2x^4y + 10 \cdot 4x^3y^2 - 10 \cdot 8x^2y^3 + 5 \cdot 16xy^4 - 32y^5$$

$$= x^5 - 10x^4y + 40x^3y^2 - 80x^2y^3 + 80xy^4 - 32y^5$$

9. Using the binomial formula:

$$(3x-2)^4 = \binom{4}{0}(3x)^4 + \binom{4}{1}(3x)^3(-2) + \binom{4}{2}(3x)^2(-2)^2 + \binom{4}{3}(3x)(-2)^3 + \binom{4}{4}(-2)^4$$

$$= 81x^4 - 4 \cdot 54x^3 + 6 \cdot 36x^2 - 4 \cdot 24x + 16$$

$$= 81x^4 - 216x^3 + 216x^2 - 96x + 16$$

11. Using the binomial formula:

$$(4x-3y)^3 = \binom{3}{0}(4x)^3 + \binom{3}{1}(4x)^2(-3y) + \binom{3}{2}(4x)(-3y)^2 + \binom{3}{3}(-3y)^3$$

$$= 64x^3 - 3 \cdot 48x^2y + 3 \cdot 36xy^2 - 27y^3$$

$$= 64x^3 - 144x^2y + 108xy^2 - 27y^3$$

13. Using the binomial formula:

$$(x^2+2)^4 = \binom{4}{0}(x^2)^4 + \binom{4}{1}(x^2)^3(2) + \binom{4}{2}(x^2)^2(2)^2 + \binom{4}{3}(x^2)(2)^3 + \binom{4}{4}(2)^4$$

$$= x^8 + 4 \cdot 2x^6 + 6 \cdot 4x^4 + 4 \cdot 8x^2 + 16$$

$$= x^8 + 8x^6 + 24x^4 + 32x^2 + 16$$

15. Using the binomial formula:

$$\left(x^2+y^2\right)^3=\binom{3}{0}\left(x^2\right)^3+\binom{3}{1}\left(x^2\right)^2\left(y^2\right)+\binom{3}{2}\left(x^2\right)\left(y^2\right)^2+\binom{3}{3}\left(y^2\right)^3=x^6+3x^4y^2+3x^2y^4+y^6$$

17. Using the binomial formula:

$$(2x+3y)^4=\binom{4}{0}(2x)^4+\binom{4}{1}(2x)^3(3y)+\binom{4}{2}(2x)^2(3y)^2+\binom{4}{3}(2x)(3y)^3+\binom{4}{4}(3y)^4$$
$$=16x^4+4\cdot24x^3y+6\cdot36x^2y^2+4\cdot54xy^3+81y^4$$
$$=16x^4+96x^3y+216x^2y^2+216xy^3+81y^4$$

19. Using the binomial formula:

$$\left(\frac{x}{2}+\frac{y}{3}\right)^3=\binom{3}{0}\left(\frac{x}{2}\right)^3+\binom{3}{1}\left(\frac{x}{2}\right)^2\left(\frac{y}{3}\right)+\binom{3}{2}\left(\frac{x}{2}\right)\left(\frac{y}{3}\right)^2+\binom{3}{3}\left(\frac{y}{3}\right)^3$$
$$=\frac{x^3}{8}+3\cdot\frac{x^2y}{12}+3\cdot\frac{xy^2}{18}+\frac{y^3}{27}$$
$$=\frac{x^3}{8}+\frac{x^2y}{4}+\frac{xy^2}{6}+\frac{y^3}{27}$$

21. Using the binomial formula:

$$\left(\frac{x}{2}-4\right)^3=\binom{3}{0}\left(\frac{x}{2}\right)^3+\binom{3}{1}\left(\frac{x}{2}\right)^2(-4)+\binom{3}{2}\left(\frac{x}{2}\right)(-4)^2+\binom{3}{3}(-4)^3$$
$$=\frac{x^3}{8}-3\cdot x^2+3\cdot8x-64$$
$$=\frac{x^3}{8}-3x^2+24x-64$$

23. Using the binomial formula:

$$\left(\frac{x}{3}+\frac{y}{2}\right)^4=\binom{4}{0}\left(\frac{x}{3}\right)^4+\binom{4}{1}\left(\frac{x}{3}\right)^3\left(\frac{y}{2}\right)+\binom{4}{2}\left(\frac{x}{3}\right)^2\left(\frac{y}{2}\right)^2+\binom{4}{3}\left(\frac{x}{3}\right)\left(\frac{y}{2}\right)^3+\binom{4}{4}\left(\frac{y}{2}\right)^4$$
$$=\frac{x^4}{81}+4\cdot\frac{x^3y}{54}+6\cdot\frac{x^2y^2}{36}+4\cdot\frac{xy^3}{24}+\frac{y^4}{16}$$
$$=\frac{x^4}{81}+\frac{2x^3y}{27}+\frac{x^2y^2}{6}+\frac{xy^3}{6}+\frac{y^4}{16}$$

25. Evaluating the factorial: $6!=6\cdot5\cdot4\cdot3\cdot2\cdot1=720$

27. Evaluating the factorial: $10!=10\cdot9\cdot8\cdot7\cdot6\cdot5\cdot4\cdot3\cdot2\cdot1=3,628,800$

29. Evaluating the binomial coefficient: $\binom{10}{0}=\frac{10!}{0!(10-0)!}=\frac{10!}{0!10!}=1$

31. Evaluating the binomial coefficient: $_8C_1=\frac{8!}{1!(8-1)!}=\frac{8!}{1!7!}=8$

33. Evaluating the binomial coefficient: $\binom{15}{11}=\frac{15!}{11!(15-11)!}=\frac{15!}{11!4!}=\frac{15\cdot14\cdot13\cdot12}{4\cdot3\cdot2\cdot1}=1,365$

35. Evaluating the binomial coefficient: $_{20}C_7=\frac{20!}{7!(20-7)!}=\frac{20!}{7!13!}=\frac{20\cdot19\cdot18\cdot17\cdot16\cdot15\cdot14}{7\cdot6\cdot5\cdot4\cdot3\cdot2\cdot1}=77,520$

37. Writing the first four terms:

$$\binom{9}{0}x^9 + \binom{9}{1}x^8(2) + \binom{9}{2}x^7(2)^2 + \binom{9}{3}x^6(2)^3 = x^9 + 9 \cdot 2x^8 + 36 \cdot 4x^7 + 84 \cdot 8x^6$$

$$= x^9 + 18x^8 + 144x^7 + 672x^6$$

39. Writing the first four terms:

$$\binom{10}{0}x^{10} + \binom{10}{1}x^9(-y) + \binom{10}{2}x^8(-y)^2 + \binom{10}{3}x^7(-y)^3 = x^{10} - 10x^9 y + 45x^8 y^2 - 120x^7 y^3$$

41. Writing the first four terms:

$$\binom{25}{0}x^{25} + \binom{25}{1}x^{24}(3) + \binom{25}{2}x^{23}(3)^2 + \binom{25}{3}x^{22}(3)^3 = x^{25} + 25 \cdot 3x^{24} + 300 \cdot 9x^{23} + 2{,}300 \cdot 27x^{22}$$

$$= x^{25} + 75x^{24} + 2{,}700x^{23} + 62{,}100x^{22}$$

43. Writing the first four terms:

$$\binom{60}{0}x^{60} + \binom{60}{1}x^{59}(-2) + \binom{60}{2}x^{58}(-2)^2 + \binom{60}{3}x^{57}(-2)^3 = x^{60} - 60 \cdot 2x^{59} + 1{,}770 \cdot 4x^{58} - 34{,}220 \cdot 8x^{57}$$

$$= x^{60} - 120x^{59} + 7{,}080x^{58} - 273{,}760x^{57}$$

45. Writing the first four terms:

$$\binom{18}{0}x^{18} + \binom{18}{1}x^{17}(-y) + \binom{18}{2}x^{16}(-y)^2 + \binom{18}{3}x^{15}(-y)^3 = x^{18} - 18x^{17} y + 153x^{16} y^2 - 816x^{15} y^3$$

47. Writing the first three terms: $\binom{15}{0}x^{15} + \binom{15}{1}x^{14}(1) + \binom{15}{2}x^{13}(1)^2 = x^{15} + 15x^{14} + 105x^{13}$

49. Writing the first three terms: $\binom{12}{0}x^{12} + \binom{12}{1}x^{11}(-y) + \binom{12}{2}x^{10}(-y)^2 = x^{12} - 12x^{11} y + 66x^{10} y^2$

51. Writing the first three terms:

$$\binom{20}{0}x^{20} + \binom{20}{1}x^{19}(2) + \binom{20}{2}x^{18}(2)^2 = x^{20} + 20 \cdot 2x^{19} + 190 \cdot 4x^{18} = x^{20} + 40x^{19} + 760x^{18}$$

53. Writing the first two terms: $\binom{100}{0}x^{100} + \binom{100}{1}x^{99}(2) = x^{100} + 100 \cdot 2x^{99} = x^{100} + 200x^{99}$

55. Writing the first two terms: $\binom{50}{0}x^{50} + \binom{50}{1}x^{49} y = x^{50} + 50x^{49} y$

57. Finding the required term: $\binom{12}{8}(2x)^4(3y)^8 = 495 \cdot 2^4 \cdot 3^8 x^4 y^8 = 51{,}963{,}120x^4 y^8$

59. Finding the required term: $\binom{10}{4}x^6(-2)^4 = 210 \cdot 16x^6 = 3{,}360x^6$

61. Finding the required term: $\binom{12}{5}x^7(-2)^5 = -792 \cdot 32x^7 = -25{,}344x^7$

63. Finding the required term: $\binom{25}{2}x^{23}(-3y)^2 = 300 \cdot 9x^{23} y^2 = 2{,}700x^{23} y^2$

65. Finding the required term: $\dbinom{20}{11}(2x)^9(5y)^{11} = \dfrac{20!}{11!9!}(2x)^9(5y)^{11}$

67. Writing the first three terms:

$$\dbinom{10}{0}(x^2y)^{10} + \dbinom{10}{1}(x^2y)^9(-3) + \dbinom{10}{2}(x^2y)^8(-3)^2 = x^{20}y^{10} - 10\cdot 3x^{18}y^9 + 45\cdot 9x^{16}y^8$$

$$= x^{20}y^{10} - 30x^{18}y^9 + 405x^{16}y^8$$

69. Finding the third term: $\dbinom{7}{2}\left(\dfrac{1}{2}\right)^5\left(\dfrac{1}{2}\right)^2 = 21\cdot\dfrac{1}{128} = \dfrac{21}{128}$

71. Expanding the binomial:

$$(x-2y)^4 = \dbinom{4}{0}x^4 + \dbinom{4}{1}x^3(-2y) + \dbinom{4}{2}x^2(-2y)^2 + \dbinom{4}{3}x(-2y)^3 + \dbinom{4}{4}(-2y)^4$$

$$= x^4 - 4\cdot 2x^3y + 6\cdot 4x^2y^2 - 4\cdot 8xy^3 + 1\cdot 16y^4$$

$$= x^4 - 8x^3y + 24x^2y^2 - 32xy^3 + 16y^4$$

The correct answer is b.

73. Finding the fourth term: $\dbinom{7}{3}(3x)^4(-2y)^3 = 35\cdot 81x^4\cdot(-8y^3) = -22{,}680x^4y^3$. The correct answer is a.

75. Solving the equation:

$$10^x = 15$$
$$\log 10^x = \log 15$$
$$x\log 10 = \log 15$$
$$x = \frac{\log 15}{\log 10} \approx 1.18$$

77. Solving the equation:

$$9^{3x-1} = 27$$
$$3^{6x-2} = 3^3$$
$$6x-2 = 3$$
$$6x = 5$$
$$x = \frac{5}{6}$$

79. Using the compound interest formula:

$$200\left(1+\frac{0.08}{4}\right)^{4t} = 800$$
$$(1.02)^{4t} = 4$$
$$\ln(1.02)^{4t} = \ln 4$$
$$4t\ln 1.02 = \ln 4$$
$$t = \frac{\ln 4}{4\ln 1.02} \approx 17.5$$

It will take approximately 17.5 years.

81. Evaluating the logarithm: $\log_7 21 = \dfrac{\log 21}{\log 7} \approx 1.56$

83. Evaluating the logarithm: $\ln 5{,}760 \approx 8.66$

85. Solving for t:

$$A = Pe^{-5t}$$

$$\frac{A}{P} = e^{-5t}$$

$$-5t = \ln\left(\frac{A}{P}\right)$$

$$t = -\frac{1}{5}\ln\left(\frac{A}{P}\right)$$

Chapter 10 Test

1. The first five terms are: $-2, 1, 4, 7, 10$

2. The first five terms are: $3, 7, 11, 15, 19$

3. The first five terms are: $2, 5, 10, 17, 26$

4. The first five terms are: $2, 16, 54, 128, 250$

5. The first five terms are: $2, \dfrac{3}{4}, \dfrac{4}{9}, \dfrac{5}{16}, \dfrac{6}{25}$

6. The first five terms are: $4, -8, 16, -32, 64$

7. Writing the general term: $a_n = 4n + 2$. It can also be written in recursive form: $a_n = a_{n-1} + 4; a_1 = 6$.

8. Writing the general term: $a_n = 2^{n-1}$. It can also be written in recursive form: $a_n = 2a_{n-1}; a_1 = 1$.

9. Writing the general term: $a_n = \left(\dfrac{1}{2}\right)^n = \dfrac{1}{2^n}$. It can also be written in recursive form: $a_n = \dfrac{1}{2}a_{n-1}; a_1 = \dfrac{1}{2}$.

10. Writing the general term: $a_n = (-3)^n$. It can also be written in recursive form: $a_n = -3a_{n-1}; a_1 = -3$.

11. **a.** Expanding the sum: $\displaystyle\sum_{i=1}^{5}(5i+3) = 8 + 13 + 18 + 23 + 28 = 90$

   b. Expanding the sum: $\displaystyle\sum_{i=3}^{5}(2^i - 1) = 7 + 15 + 31 = 53$

   c. Expanding the sum: $\displaystyle\sum_{i=2}^{6}(i^2 + 2i) = 8 + 15 + 24 + 35 + 48 = 130$

12. First write the equations:

$$a_5 = a_1 + 4d \qquad a_9 = a_1 + 8d$$

$$11 = a_1 + 4d \qquad 19 = a_1 + 8d$$

We have the system of equations:

$$a_1 + 8d = 19$$

$$a_1 + 4d = 11$$

Subtracting yields:

$$4d = 8$$

$$d = 2$$

$$a_1 = 19 - 8 \cdot 2 = 3$$

13. Since $a_3 \cdot r \cdot r = a_5$, we have:

$$18 \cdot r^2 = 162$$

$$r^2 = 9$$

$$r = \pm 3$$

Since $a_2 \cdot r = a_3$, $a_2 = \pm 6$.

14. Using $a_1 = 5$ and $d = 6$: $a_{10} = 5 + 9 \cdot 6 = 59$. Now finding the sum: $S_{10} = \dfrac{10}{2}(5 + 59) = 5 \cdot 64 = 320$

15. Using $a_1 = 25$ and $d = -5$: $a_{10} = 25 + 9 \cdot (-5) = -20$. Now finding the sum: $S_{10} = \dfrac{10}{2}(25 - 20) = 5 \cdot 5 = 25$

16. Using $a_1 = 3$ and $r = 2$: $S_{50} = \dfrac{3\left(2^{50} - 1\right)}{2 - 1} = 3\left(2^{50} - 1\right)$

17. Using $a_1 = \dfrac{1}{2}$ and $r = \dfrac{1}{3}$: $S = \dfrac{\dfrac{1}{2}}{1 - \dfrac{1}{3}} = \dfrac{\dfrac{1}{2}}{\dfrac{2}{3}} = \dfrac{1}{2} \cdot \dfrac{3}{2} = \dfrac{3}{4}$

18. Using the binomial formula:

$$(x - 3)^4 = \binom{4}{0}x^4 + \binom{4}{1}x^3(-3) + \binom{4}{2}x^2(-3)^2 + \binom{4}{3}x(-3)^3 + \binom{4}{4}(-3)^4$$

$$= x^4 - 4 \cdot 3x^3 + 6 \cdot 9x^2 - 4 \cdot 27x + 81$$

$$= x^4 - 12x^3 + 54x^2 - 108x + 81$$

19. Using the binomial formula:

$$(2x - 1)^5 = \binom{5}{0}(2x)^5 + \binom{5}{1}(2x)^4(-1) + \binom{5}{2}(2x)^3(-1)^2 + \binom{5}{3}(2x)^2(-1)^3 + \binom{5}{4}(2x)(-1)^4 + \binom{5}{5}(-1)^5$$

$$= 32x^5 - 5 \cdot 16x^4 + 10 \cdot 8x^3 - 10 \cdot 4x^2 + 5 \cdot 2x - 1$$

$$= 32x^5 - 80x^4 + 80x^3 - 40x^2 + 10x - 1$$

20. Evaluating the binomial coefficient: $\binom{12}{9} = \dfrac{12!}{9!(12 - 9)!} = \dfrac{12!}{9!3!} = \dfrac{12 \cdot 11 \cdot 10}{3 \cdot 2 \cdot 1} = 220$

21. Evaluating the binomial coefficient: $_{15}C_5 = \dfrac{15!}{5!(15 - 5)!} = \dfrac{15!}{5!10!} = \dfrac{15 \cdot 14 \cdot 13 \cdot 12 \cdot 11}{5 \cdot 4 \cdot 3 \cdot 2 \cdot 1} = 3{,}003$

22. Finding the first three terms: $\binom{20}{0}x^{20} + \binom{20}{1}x^{19}(-1) + \binom{20}{2}x^{18}(-1)^2 = x^{20} - 20x^{19} + 190x^{18}$

23. Finding the sixth term: $\binom{8}{5}(2x)^3(-3y)^5 = -56 \cdot 1944x^3y^5 = -108{,}864x^3y^5$

Chapter 11
Conic Sections

11.1 The Distance Formula and Circles

1. Using the distance formula: $d = \sqrt{(6-3)^2 + (3-7)^2} = \sqrt{9+16} = \sqrt{25} = 5$

3. Using the distance formula: $d = \sqrt{(5-0)^2 + (0-9)^2} = \sqrt{25+81} = \sqrt{106}$

5. Using the distance formula: $d = \sqrt{(-2-3)^2 + (1+5)^2} = \sqrt{25+36} = \sqrt{61}$

7. Using the distance formula: $d = \sqrt{(-10+1)^2 + (5+2)^2} = \sqrt{81+49} = \sqrt{130}$

9. Solving the equation:
$$\sqrt{(x-1)^2 + (2-5)^2} = \sqrt{13}$$
$$(x-1)^2 + 9 = 13$$
$$(x-1)^2 = 4$$
$$x - 1 = \pm 2$$
$$x - 1 = -2, 2$$
$$x = -1, 3$$

11. Solving the equation:
$$\sqrt{(x-3)^2 + (5-9)^2} = 5$$
$$(x-3)^2 + 16 = 25$$
$$(x-3)^2 = 9$$
$$x - 3 = \pm 3$$
$$x - 3 = -3, 3$$
$$x = 0, 6$$

13. Solving the equation:
$$\sqrt{(2x+1-x)^2 + (6-4)^2} = 6$$
$$(x+1)^2 + 4 = 36$$
$$(x+1)^2 = 32$$
$$x + 1 = \pm\sqrt{32}$$
$$x + 1 = \pm 4\sqrt{2}$$
$$x = -1 \pm 4\sqrt{2}$$

15. The equation is $(x-3)^2 + (y+2)^2 = 9$.

17. The equation is $(x+5)^2 + (y+1)^2 = 5$.

19. The equation is $x^2 + (y+5)^2 = 1$.

21. The equation is $x^2 + y^2 = 4$.

23. The center is (0,0) and the radius is 2.

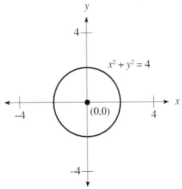

25. The center is (1,3) and the radius is 5.

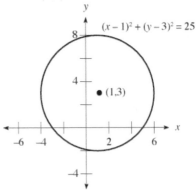

27. The center is (–2,4) and the radius is $2\sqrt{2} \approx 2.8$.

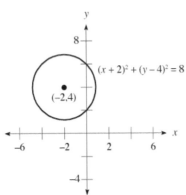

29. The center is (–2,4) and the radius is $\sqrt{17} \approx 4.1$.

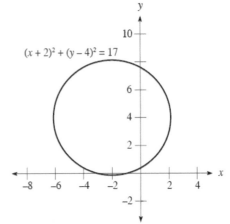

31. Completing the square:
$$x^2 + y^2 + 2x - 4y = 4$$
$$\left(x^2 + 2x + 1\right) + \left(y^2 - 4y + 4\right) = 4 + 1 + 4$$
$$\left(x + 1\right)^2 + \left(y - 2\right)^2 = 9$$

The center is (–1,2) and the radius is 3.

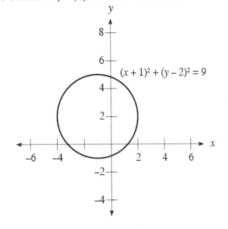

33. Completing the square:
$$x^2 + y^2 - 6y = 7$$
$$x^2 + \left(y^2 - 6y + 9\right) = 7 + 9$$
$$x^2 + \left(y - 3\right)^2 = 16$$

The center is (0,3) and the radius is 4.

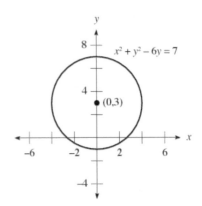

35. Completing the square:

$$x^2 + y^2 + 2x = 1$$
$$\left(x^2 + 2x + 1\right) + y^2 = 1 + 1$$
$$(x+1)^2 + y^2 = 2$$

The center is $(-1,0)$ and the radius is $\sqrt{2} \approx 1.4$.

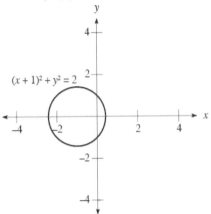

37. Completing the square:

$$x^2 + y^2 - 4x - 6y = -4$$
$$\left(x^2 - 4x + 4\right) + \left(y^2 - 6y + 9\right) = -4 + 4 + 9$$
$$(x-2)^2 + (y-3)^2 = 9$$

The center is $(2,3)$ and the radius is 3.

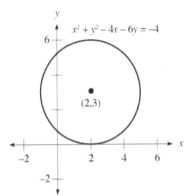

39. Completing the square:

$$x^2 + y^2 + 2x + y = \frac{11}{4}$$
$$\left(x^2 + 2x + 1\right) + \left(y^2 + y + \frac{1}{4}\right) = \frac{11}{4} + 1 + \frac{1}{4}$$
$$(x+1)^2 + \left(y + \frac{1}{2}\right)^2 = 4$$

The center is $\left(-1, -\frac{1}{2}\right)$ and the radius is 2.

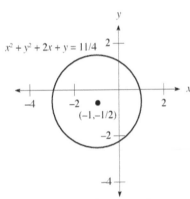

41. Completing the square:

$$4x^2 + 4y^2 - 4x + 8y = 11$$
$$x^2 + y^2 - x + 2y = \frac{11}{4}$$
$$\left(x^2 - x + \frac{1}{4}\right) + \left(y^2 + 2y + 1\right) = \frac{11}{4} + \frac{1}{4} + 1$$
$$\left(x - \frac{1}{2}\right)^2 + (y+1)^2 = 4$$

The center is $\left(\frac{1}{2}, -1\right)$ and the radius is 2.

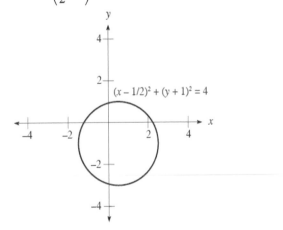

43. The equation is $(x-3)^2 + (y-4)^2 = 25$.

45. The equations are:

A: $\left(x-\dfrac{1}{2}\right)^2+(y-1)^2=\dfrac{1}{4}$

B: $(x-1)^2+(y-1)^2=1$

C: $(x-2)^2+(y-1)^2=4$

47. The radius is given by: $r=\sqrt{(3-0)^2+(4-0)^2}=\sqrt{9+16}=\sqrt{25}=5$

So the equation of the circle is $x^2+y^2=25$.

49. The radius is 3, so the equation of the circle is $x^2+y^2=9$.

51. The radius is given by: $r=\sqrt{(-1-4)^2+(3-3)^2}=\sqrt{25+0}=\sqrt{25}=5$

So the equation of the circle is $(x+1)^2+(y-3)^2=25$.

53. The radius is given by: $r=\sqrt{(1+2)^2+(-3-5)^2}=\sqrt{9+64}=\sqrt{73}$

So the equation of the circle is $(x+2)^2+(y-5)^2=73$.

55. The center will be on the y-axis at the midpoint of the two y-intercepts, which is the point $(-3,0)$. So the radius of the circle is 4, and its equation is $x^2+(y-2)^2=16$.

57. The radius of the circle is $\sqrt{18}=3\sqrt{2}$, so the circumference and area are given by:

$$C=2\pi\left(3\sqrt{2}\right)=6\pi\sqrt{2} \qquad\qquad A=\pi\left(3\sqrt{2}\right)^2=18\pi$$

59. First complete the square:

$$x^2+y^2+4x+2y=20$$
$$\left(x^2+4x+4\right)+\left(y^2+2y+1\right)=20+4+1$$
$$(x+2)^2+(y+1)^2=25$$

The radius of the circle is 5, so the circumference and area are given by:

$$C=2\pi(5)=10\pi \qquad\qquad A=\pi(5)^2=25\pi$$

61. Finding the distance from the starting point $(0,0)$: $d=\sqrt{(5-0)^2+(3-0)^2}=\sqrt{25+9}=\sqrt{34}\approx 5.8$ blocks

Yes, the child is within the 6 block search area.

63. The x-coordinate of the center is $x=500$, the y-coordinate of the center is $12+120=132$, and the radius is 120. Thus the equation of the circle is $(x-500)^2+(y-132)^2=120^2$.

65. Using the distance formula: $d=\sqrt{(2-5)^2+(4+1)^2}=\sqrt{9+25}=\sqrt{34}$

The correct answer is d.

67. Completing the square:

$$x^2+y^2+4y=5$$
$$x^2+\left(y^2+4y+4\right)=5+4$$
$$x^2+(y+2)^2=9$$

The center is $(0,-2)$ and the radius is 3. The correct answer is a.

69. Solving for p:

$$4p=12$$
$$p=3$$

71. Solving for p:

$$4p=-1$$
$$p=-\dfrac{1}{4}$$

73. The vertex is $(4,1)$.

75. Sketching the graph:

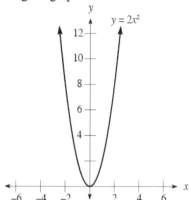

$y = 2x^2$

77. Sketching the graph:

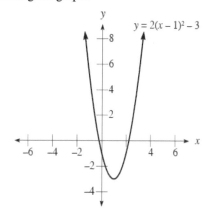

$y = 2(x - 1)^2 - 3$

11.2 Parabolas

1. Finding p:

$$4p = 4$$
$$p = 1$$

The focus is $(0,1)$. Graphing the parabola:

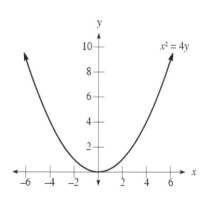

$x^2 = 4y$

3. Finding p:

$$4p = 1$$
$$p = \frac{1}{4}$$

The focus is $\left(0, \frac{1}{4}\right)$. Graphing the parabola:

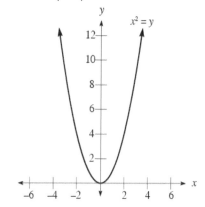

$x^2 = y$

5. Finding p:

$$4p = -\frac{1}{2}$$

$$p = -\frac{1}{8}$$

The focus is $\left(0, -\frac{1}{8}\right)$. Graphing the parabola:

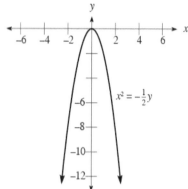

7. Finding p:

$$4p = -2$$

$$p = -\frac{1}{2}$$

The focus is $\left(-\frac{1}{2}, 0\right)$. Graphing the parabola:

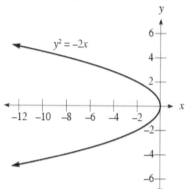

9. Finding p:

$$4p = -1$$

$$p = -\frac{1}{4}$$

The focus is $\left(-\frac{1}{4}, 0\right)$. Graphing the parabola:

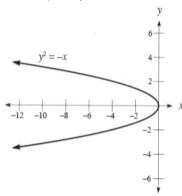

11. Finding p:

$$4p = \frac{1}{3}$$

$$p = \frac{1}{12}$$

The focus is $\left(\frac{1}{12}, 0\right)$. Graphing the parabola:

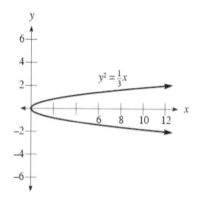

13. Finding p:

$$4p = 2$$

$$p = \frac{1}{2}$$

The vertex is $(-1,-3)$ and the focus is $\left(-1,-\frac{5}{2}\right)$. Graphing the parabola:

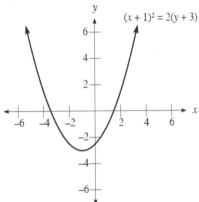

$(x+1)^2 = 2(y+3)$

15. Finding p:

$$4p = -1$$

$$p = -\frac{1}{4}$$

The vertex is $(4,2)$ and the focus is $\left(4,\frac{7}{4}\right)$. Graphing the parabola:

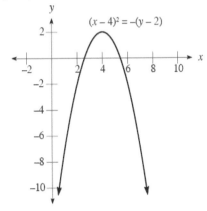

$(x-4)^2 = -(y-2)$

17. Finding p:

$$4p = -\frac{1}{3}$$

$$p = -\frac{1}{12}$$

The vertex is $(-2,1)$ and the focus is $\left(-2, \frac{11}{12}\right)$. Graphing the parabola:

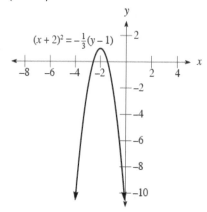

19. Finding p:

$$4p = 3$$

$$p = \frac{3}{4}$$

The vertex is $(2,1)$ and the focus is $\left(\frac{11}{4}, 1\right)$. Graphing the parabola:

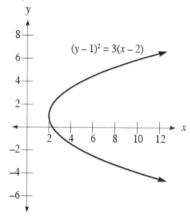

21. Finding p:

$$4p = 1$$
$$p = \frac{1}{4}$$

The vertex is $(3,-3)$ and the focus is $\left(\frac{13}{4},-3\right)$. Graphing the parabola:

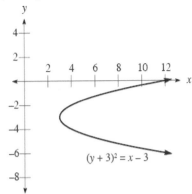

$(y+3)^2 = x - 3$

23. Finding p:

$$4p = -\frac{1}{3}$$
$$p = -\frac{1}{12}$$

The vertex is $(5,2)$ and the focus is $\left(\frac{59}{12},2\right)$. Graphing the parabola:

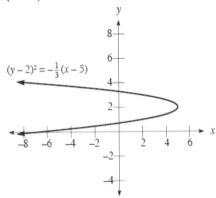

$(y-2)^2 = -\frac{1}{3}(x-5)$

25. First complete the square:
$$x^2 - 4x - y + 1 = 0$$
$$x^2 - 4x = y - 1$$
$$x^2 - 4x + 4 = y - 1 + 4$$
$$(x-2)^2 = y + 3$$

Finding p:
$$4p = 1$$
$$p = \frac{1}{4}$$

The vertex is $(2,-3)$ and the focus is $\left(2, -\frac{11}{4}\right)$. Graphing the parabola:

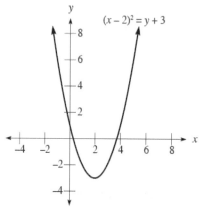

27. First complete the square:
$$x^2 + 2x + 8y - 23 = 0$$
$$x^2 + 2x = -8y + 23$$
$$x^2 + 2x + 1 = -8y + 23 + 1$$
$$(x+1)^2 = -8y + 24$$
$$(x+1)^2 = -8(y-3)$$

Finding p:
$$4p = -8$$
$$p = -2$$

The vertex is $(-1,3)$ and the focus is $(-1,1)$. Graphing the parabola:

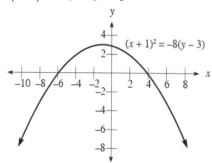

29. First complete the square:
$$y^2 - x + 4y + 7 = 0$$
$$y^2 + 4y = x - 7$$
$$y^2 + 4y + 4 = x - 7 + 4$$
$$(y+2)^2 = x - 3$$

Finding p:
$$4p = 1$$
$$p = \frac{1}{4}$$

The vertex is $(3,-2)$ and the focus is $\left(\frac{13}{4}, -2\right)$. Graphing the parabola:

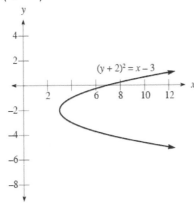

$(y + 2)^2 = x - 3$

31. First complete the square:
$$y^2 + 6x - 2y + 7 = 0$$
$$y^2 - 2y = -6x - 7$$
$$y^2 - 2y + 1 = -6x - 7 + 1$$
$$(y-1)^2 = -6x - 6$$
$$(y-1)^2 = -6(x+1)$$

Finding p:
$$4p = -6$$
$$p = -\frac{3}{2}$$

The vertex is $(-1,1)$ and the focus is $\left(-\frac{5}{2}, 1\right)$. Graphing the parabola:

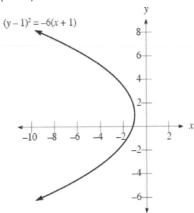

$(y - 1)^2 = -6(x + 1)$

33. Using the points (0,1) and (10,1) as points on the parabola, with the vertex at (5,0), the parabola has the form $y = a(x-5)^2$. Substituting the point (0,1):

$$1 = a(0-5)^2$$
$$25a = 1$$
$$a = \frac{1}{25}$$

So the equation is $y = \frac{1}{25}(x-5)^2$, or $(x-5)^2 = 25y$. Finding p:

$$4p = 25$$
$$p = \frac{25}{4} = 6.25$$

The lens should be placed 6.25 inches from the base of the mirror.

35. Using the points (0,12) and (24,12) as points on the parabola, with the vertex at (12,12), the parabola has the form $y = a(x-12)^2$. Substituting the point (0,12):

$$12 = a(0-12)^2$$
$$144a = 12$$
$$a = \frac{1}{12}$$

So the equation is $y = \frac{1}{12}(x-12)^2$, or $(x-12)^2 = 12y$. Finding p:

$$4p = 12$$
$$p = 3$$

The receiver should be placed 3 inches from the base of the dish.

37. The vertex is (0,0) and the parabola is pointed to the left, so the correct answer is d.

39. Finding p:

$$4p = -5$$
$$p = -\frac{5}{4}$$

Since the parabola is pointed down and the vertex is (0,0), the focus is $\left(0, -\frac{5}{4}\right)$. The correct answer is d.

41. Solving the equation:

$$x^2 = 25$$
$$x = \pm\sqrt{25} = \pm 5$$

43. Solving the equation:

$$-x^2 = 16$$
$$x^2 = -16$$
$$x = \pm\sqrt{-16} = \pm 4i$$

45. Solving the equation:

$$y^2 = 100$$
$$y = \pm\sqrt{100} = \pm 10$$

47. Dividing: $\dfrac{25x^2 + 4y^2}{100} = \dfrac{25x^2}{100} + \dfrac{4y^2}{100} = \dfrac{x^2}{4} + \dfrac{y^2}{25}$

49. To find the x-intercepts, let $y = 0$:

$$3x^2 + 5x - 2 = 0$$
$$(3x-1)(x+2) = 0$$
$$x = -2, \frac{1}{3}$$

To find the y-intercept, let $x = 0$:

$$y = 3(0)^2 + 5(0) - 2 = -2$$

The x-intercepts are -2 and $\frac{1}{3}$, and the y-intercept is -2.

51. Substituting $x = -4$:

$$\frac{(-4)^2}{25} + \frac{y^2}{9} = 1$$

$$\frac{16}{25} + \frac{y^2}{9} = 1$$

$$\frac{y^2}{9} = \frac{9}{25}$$

$$y^2 = \frac{81}{25}$$

$$y = \pm\sqrt{\frac{81}{25}} = \pm\frac{9}{5}$$

11.3 Ellipses and Hyperbolas

1. Graphing the ellipse:

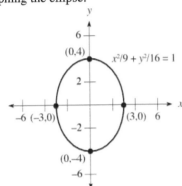

3. Graphing the ellipse:

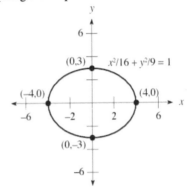

5. Graphing the ellipse:

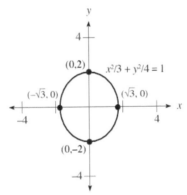

7. The standard form is $\frac{x^2}{25} + \frac{y^2}{4} = 1$. Graphing the ellipse:

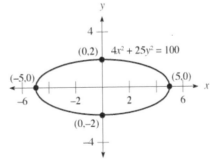

9. The standard form is $\dfrac{x^2}{16} + \dfrac{y^2}{2} = 1$. Graphing the ellipse:

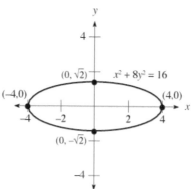

11. Graphing the hyperbola:

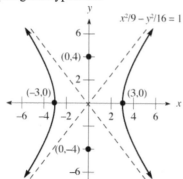

13. Graphing the hyperbola:

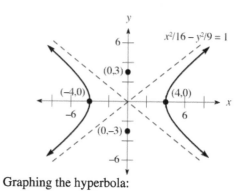

15. Graphing the hyperbola:

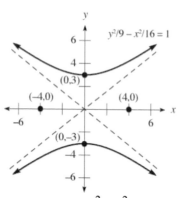

17. Graphing the hyperbola:

19. The standard form is $\dfrac{x^2}{4} - \dfrac{y^2}{1} = 1$. Graphing the hyperbola:

21. The standard form is $\dfrac{y^2}{9} - \dfrac{x^2}{16} = 1$. Graphing the hyperbola:

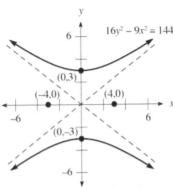

23. For the x-intercepts, set $y = 0$:

$$0.4x^2 = 3.6$$
$$x^2 = 9$$
$$x = \pm 3$$

For the y-intercepts, set $x = 0$:

$$0.9y^2 = 3.6$$
$$y^2 = 4$$
$$y = \pm 2$$

25. For the x-intercepts, set $y = 0$:

$$\dfrac{x^2}{0.04} = 1$$
$$x^2 = 0.04$$
$$x = \pm 0.2$$

For the y-intercepts, set $x = 0$:

$$-\dfrac{y^2}{0.09} = 1$$
$$y^2 = -0.09$$
$$y = \pm 0.3i$$

There are no y-intercepts.

27. For the x-intercepts, set $y = 0$:

$$\dfrac{25x^2}{9} = 1$$
$$x^2 = \dfrac{9}{25}$$
$$x = \pm\dfrac{3}{5}$$

For the y-intercepts, set $x = 0$:

$$\dfrac{25y^2}{4} = 1$$
$$y^2 = \dfrac{4}{25}$$
$$y = \pm\dfrac{2}{5}$$

29. Graphing the ellipse:

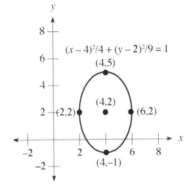

31. Completing the square:
$$4x^2 + y^2 - 4y - 12 = 0$$
$$4x^2 + (y^2 - 4y + 4) = 12 + 4$$
$$4x^2 + (y-2)^2 = 16$$
$$\frac{x^2}{4} + \frac{(y-2)^2}{16} = 1$$
Graphing the ellipse:

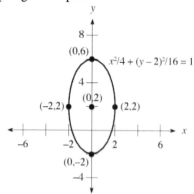

33. Completing the square:
$$x^2 + 9y^2 + 4x - 54y + 76 = 0$$
$$(x^2 + 4x + 4) + 9(y^2 - 6y + 9) = -76 + 4 + 81$$
$$(x+2)^2 + 9(y-3)^2 = 9$$
$$\frac{(x+2)^2}{9} + \frac{(y-3)^2}{1} = 1$$
Graphing the ellipse:

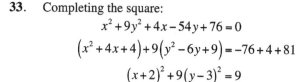

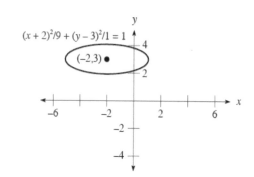

35. Graphing the hyperbola:

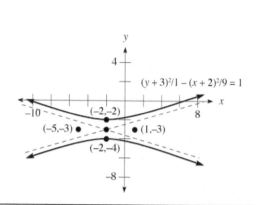

37. Completing the square:
$$9y^2 - x^2 - 4x + 54y + 68 = 0$$
$$9(y^2 + 6y + 9) - (x^2 + 4x + 4) = -68 + 81 - 4$$
$$9(y+3)^2 - (x+2)^2 = 9$$
$$\frac{(y+3)^2}{1} - \frac{(x+2)^2}{9} = 1$$
Graphing the hyperbola:

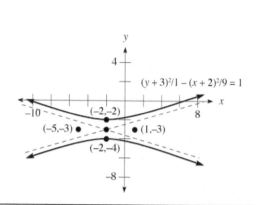

39. Completing the square:
$$4y^2 - 9x^2 - 16y + 72x - 164 = 0$$
$$4(y^2 - 4y + 4) - 9(x^2 - 8x + 16) = 164 + 16 - 144$$
$$4(y-2)^2 - 9(x-4)^2 = 36$$
$$\frac{(y-2)^2}{9} - \frac{(x-4)^2}{4} = 1$$
Graphing the hyperbola:

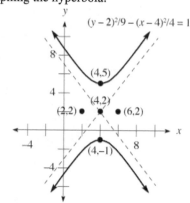

41. Substituting $y = 4$:

$$\frac{x^2}{25} + \frac{4^2}{16} = 1$$

$$\frac{x^2}{25} + 1 = 1$$

$$\frac{x^2}{25} = 0$$

$$x = 0$$

43. Substituting $x = -3$:

$$\frac{(-3)^2}{9} + \frac{y^2}{16} = 1$$

$$1 + \frac{y^2}{16} = 1$$

$$\frac{y^2}{16} = 0$$

$$y = 0$$

45. The major axis length is 8.

47. The curve is an ellipse with $a = \dfrac{615}{2} = 307.5$ and $b = \dfrac{510}{2} = 255$, so the equation is $\dfrac{x^2}{307.5^2} + \dfrac{y^2}{255^2} = 1$.

49. The curve is an ellipse with $a = \dfrac{458}{2} = 229$ and $b = \dfrac{390}{2} = 195$, so the equation is $\dfrac{x^2}{229^2} + \dfrac{y^2}{195^2} = 1$.

51. Substituting $a = 4$ and $c = 3$:

$$4^2 = b^2 + 3^2$$

$$16 = b^2 + 9$$

$$b^2 = 7$$

$$b = \sqrt{7} \approx 2.65$$

The width should be approximately $2(2.65) = 5.3$ feet wide.

53. We have $a = \sqrt{6} \approx 2.4$ and $b = 2$, with the ellipse oriented vertically. The correct answer is a.

55. Completing the square:

$$x^2 + 4y^2 + 2x - 24y + 33 = 0$$

$$\left(x^2 + 2x + 1\right) + 4\left(y^2 - 6y + 9\right) = -33 + 1 + 36$$

$$(x+1)^2 + 4(y-3)^2 = 4$$

$$\frac{(x+1)^2}{4} + \frac{(y-3)^2}{1} = 1$$

The center of the ellipse is $(-1,3)$. The correct answer is b.

57. Since $4^2 + 0^2 = 16$ and $0^2 + 5^2 = 25$, while $0^2 + 0^2 = 0$, only $(0,0)$ is a solution.

59. Multiplying: $(2y+4)^2 = (2y)^2 + 2(2y)(4) + 4^2 = 4y^2 + 16y + 16$

61. Solving for x:

$$x - 2y = 4$$

$$x = 2y + 4$$

63. Simplifying: $x^2 - 2\left(x^2 - 3\right) = x^2 - 2x^2 + 6 = -x^2 + 6$

65. Factoring: $5y^2 + 16y + 12 = (5y+6)(y+2)$

67. Solving the equation:

$$y^2 = 4$$

$$y = \pm\sqrt{4} = \pm 2$$

69. Solving the equation:

$$-x^2 + 6 = 2$$

$$-x^2 = -4$$

$$x^2 = 4$$

$$x = \pm\sqrt{4} = \pm 2$$

11.4 Second-Degree Inequalities and Nonlinear Systems

1. Graphing the inequality:

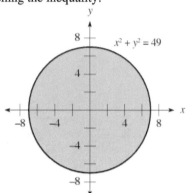

3. Graphing the inequality:

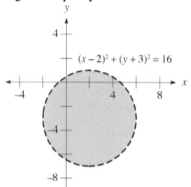

5. Graphing the inequality:

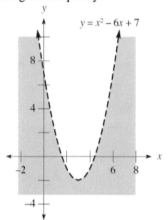

7. Graphing the inequality:

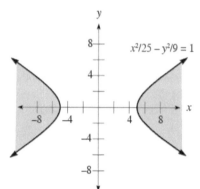

9. Graphing the inequality:

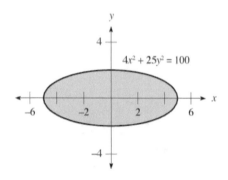

11. Graphing the inequality:

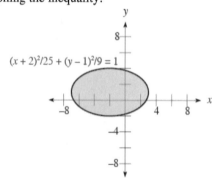

13. Graphing the inequality $\dfrac{x^2}{9} - \dfrac{y^2}{16} \geq 1$:

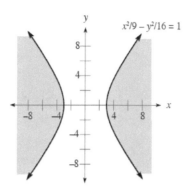

15. Completing the square:
$$9x^2 + 4y^2 + 36x - 8y + 4 < 0$$
$$9\left(x^2 + 4x + 4\right) + 4\left(y^2 - 2y + 1\right) < -4 + 36 + 4$$
$$9\left(x + 2\right)^2 + 4\left(y - 1\right)^2 < 36$$
$$\frac{\left(x + 2\right)^2}{4} + \frac{\left(y - 1\right)^2}{9} < 1$$

Graphing the inequality:

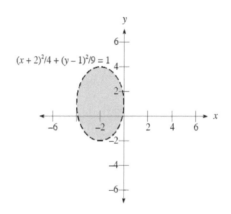

17. Completing the square:
$$9y^2 - x^2 + 18y + 2x > 1$$
$$9\left(y^2 + 2y + 1\right) - \left(x^2 - 2x + 1\right) > 1 + 9 - 1$$
$$9\left(y + 1\right)^2 - \left(x - 1\right)^2 > 9$$
$$\frac{\left(y + 1\right)^2}{1} - \frac{\left(x - 1\right)^2}{9} > 1$$

Graphing the inequality:

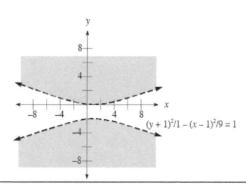

19. Solving the second equation for y yields $y = 3 - 2x$. Substituting into the first equation:

$$x^2 + (3 - 2x)^2 = 9$$
$$x^2 + 9 - 12x + 4x^2 = 9$$
$$5x^2 - 12x = 0$$
$$x(5x - 12) = 0$$
$$x = 0, \frac{12}{5}$$
$$y = 3, -\frac{9}{5}$$

The solutions are $(0,3), \left(\frac{12}{5}, -\frac{9}{5}\right)$.

21. Solving the second equation for x yields $x = 8 - 2y$. Substituting into the first equation:

$$(8 - 2y)^2 + y^2 = 16$$
$$64 - 32y + 4y^2 + y^2 = 16$$
$$5y^2 - 32y + 48 = 0$$
$$(y - 4)(5y - 12) = 0$$
$$y = 4, \frac{12}{5}$$
$$x = 0, \frac{16}{5}$$

The solutions are $(0,4), \left(\frac{16}{5}, \frac{12}{5}\right)$.

23. Adding the two equations yields:

$$2x^2 = 50$$
$$x^2 = 25$$
$$x = -5, 5$$
$$y = 0$$

The solutions are $(-5, 0), (5, 0)$.

25. Substituting into the first equation:

$$x^2 + \left(x^2 - 3\right)^2 = 9$$
$$x^2 + x^4 - 6x^2 + 9 = 9$$
$$x^4 - 5x^2 = 0$$
$$x^2\left(x^2 - 5\right) = 0$$
$$x = 0, -\sqrt{5}, \sqrt{5}$$
$$y = -3, 2, 2$$

The solutions are $(0, -3), \left(-\sqrt{5}, 2\right), \left(\sqrt{5}, 2\right)$.

27. Substituting into the first equation:

$$\left(y^2 - 4\right)^2 + y^2 = 16$$
$$y^4 - 8y^2 + 16 + y^2 = 16$$
$$y^4 - 7y^2 = 0$$
$$y^2\left(y^2 - 7\right) = 0$$
$$y = 0, -\sqrt{7}, \sqrt{7}$$
$$x = -4, 3, 3$$

The solutions are $(-4, 0), \left(3, -\sqrt{7}\right), \left(3, \sqrt{7}\right)$.

29. Substituting into the first equation:

$$3x + 2\left(x^2 - 5\right) = 10$$
$$3x + 2x^2 - 10 = 10$$
$$2x^2 + 3x - 20 = 0$$
$$(x + 4)(2x - 5) = 0$$
$$x = -4, \frac{5}{2}$$
$$y = 11, \frac{5}{4}$$

The solutions are $(-4, 11), \left(\frac{5}{2}, \frac{5}{4}\right)$.

31. Substituting into the first equation:
$$-x+1 = x^2 + 2x - 3$$
$$x^2 + 3x - 4 = 0$$
$$(x+4)(x-1) = 0$$
$$x = -4, 1$$
$$y = 5, 0$$
The solutions are $(-4,5)$, $(1,0)$.

33. Substituting into the first equation:
$$y - 5 = y^2 - 6y + 5$$
$$y^2 - 7y + 10 = 0$$
$$(y-2)(y-5) = 0$$
$$y = 2, 5$$
$$x = -3, 0$$
The solutions are $(-3,2)$, $(0,5)$.

35. Adding the two equations yields:
$$8x^2 = 72$$
$$x^2 = 9$$
$$x = \pm 3$$
$$y = 0$$
The solutions are $(-3,0)$, $(3,0)$.

37. Solving the first equation for x yields $x = y + 4$. Substituting into the second equation:
$$(y+4)^2 + y^2 = 16$$
$$y^2 + 8y + 16 + y^2 = 16$$
$$2y^2 + 8y = 0$$
$$2y(y+4) = 0$$
$$y = 0, -4$$
$$x = 4, 0$$
The solutions are $(0,-4)$, $(4,0)$.

39. Adding the two equations:
$$3x^2 = 8$$
$$x^2 = \frac{8}{3}$$
$$x = \pm\sqrt{\frac{8}{3} \cdot \frac{3}{3}} = \pm\frac{2\sqrt{6}}{3}$$

Substituting to find y: $y = 7 - x^2 = 7 - \left(\pm\frac{2\sqrt{6}}{3}\right)^2 = 7 - \frac{8}{3} = \frac{13}{3}$

The solutions are $\left(\frac{2\sqrt{6}}{3}, \frac{13}{3}\right)$ and $\left(-\frac{2\sqrt{6}}{3}, \frac{13}{3}\right)$.

41. Setting the two equations equal:
$$x^2 - 3 = x^2 - 2x - 1$$
$$-3 = -2x - 1$$
$$2x = 2$$
$$x = 1$$
$$y = 1^2 - 3 = -2$$
The solution is $(1,-2)$.

43. Adding the two equations:
$$8x^2 = 80$$
$$x^2 = 10$$
$$x = \pm\sqrt{10}$$

Substituting to find y:
$$4\left(\pm\sqrt{10}\right)^2 + 5y^2 = 40$$
$$40 + 5y^2 = 40$$
$$5y^2 = 0$$
$$y = 0$$

The solutions are $\left(-\sqrt{10}, 0\right)$ and $\left(\sqrt{10}, 0\right)$.

45. Graphing the inequalities:

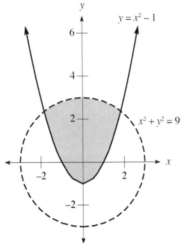

47. Graphing the inequalities:

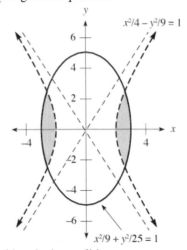

49. There is no intersection.

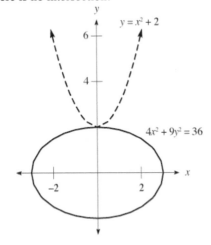

51. Graphing the inequalities:

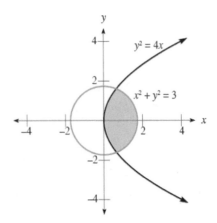

53. Graphing the inequalities:

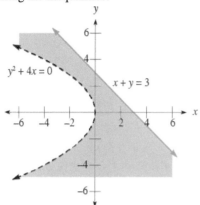

55. Graphing the inequalities:

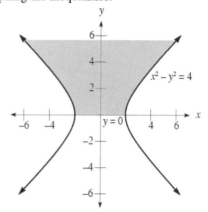

57. Graphing the inequalities:

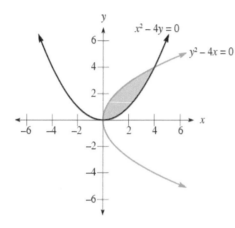

59. Graphing the inequalities:

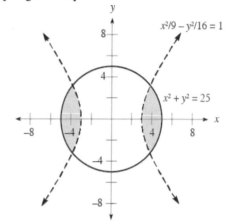

61. Graphing the inequalities:

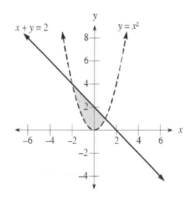

63. The system of equations is:

$$x^2 + y^2 = 89$$
$$x^2 - y^2 = 39$$

Adding the two equations yields:

$$2x^2 = 128$$
$$x^2 = 64$$
$$x = \pm 8$$
$$y = \pm 5$$

The numbers are either 8 and 5, 8 and –5, –8 and 5, or –8 and –5.

65. **a.** Subtracting the two equations yields:

$$(x+8)^2 - x^2 = 0$$
$$x^2 + 16x + 64 - x^2 = 0$$
$$16x = -64$$
$$x = -4$$

Substituting to find y:

$$(-4)^2 + y^2 = 64$$
$$y^2 + 16 = 64$$
$$y^2 = 48$$
$$y = \pm\sqrt{48} = \pm 4\sqrt{3}$$

The intersection points are $\left(-4, -4\sqrt{3}\right)$ and $\left(-4, 4\sqrt{3}\right)$.

b. Subtracting the two equations yields:

$$x^2 - (x-8)^2 = 0$$
$$x^2 - x^2 + 16x - 64 = 0$$
$$16x = 64$$
$$x = 4$$

Substituting to find y:

$$4^2 + y^2 = 64$$
$$y^2 + 16 = 64$$
$$y^2 = 48$$
$$y = \pm\sqrt{48} = \pm 4\sqrt{3}$$

The intersection points are $\left(4, -4\sqrt{3}\right)$ and $\left(4, 4\sqrt{3}\right)$.

67. This is shaded outside (not including) the circle $x^2 + y^2 = 16$. The correct answer is b.

69. Adding the two equations yields:

$$5x^2 = 20$$
$$x^2 = 4$$
$$x = \pm 2$$
$$y = 0$$

The solutions are $(-2,0)$ and $(2,0)$. The correct answer is d.

71. Expanding using the binomial theorem:

$$(x+2)^4 = \binom{4}{0}x^4 + \binom{4}{1}x^3(2) + \binom{4}{2}x^2(2)^2 + \binom{4}{3}x(2)^3 + \binom{4}{4}(2)^4 = x^4 + 8x^3 + 24x^2 + 32x + 16$$

73. Expanding using the binomial theorem:

$$(2x+y)^3 = \binom{3}{0}(2x)^3 + \binom{3}{1}(2x)^2 y + \binom{3}{2}(2x)y^2 + \binom{3}{3}y^3 = 8x^3 + 12x^2 y + 6xy^2 + y^3$$

75. The first two terms are: $\binom{50}{0}x^{50} + \binom{50}{1}x^{49}(3) = x^{50} + 150x^{49}$

Chapter 11 Test

1. Solving the equation:
$$\sqrt{(x+1)^2 + (2-4)^2} = 2\sqrt{5}$$
$$(x+1)^2 + (-2)^2 = \left(2\sqrt{5}\right)^2$$
$$(x+1)^2 + 4 = 20$$
$$(x+1)^2 = 16$$
$$x+1 = \pm 4$$
$$x+1 = -4, 4$$
$$x = -5, 3$$

2. The equation is $(x+2)^2 + (y-4)^2 = 9$.

3. Finding the radius: $r = \sqrt{(-3-0)^2 + (-4-0)^2} = \sqrt{9+16} = \sqrt{25} = 5$. The equation is $x^2 + y^2 = 25$.

4. Completing the square:
$$x^2 + y^2 - 10x + 6y = 5$$
$$\left(x^2 - 10x + 25\right) + \left(y^2 + 6y + 9\right) = 5 + 25 + 9$$
$$(x-5)^2 + (y+3)^2 = 39$$

   The center is (5,–3) and the radius is $\sqrt{39}$.

5. The standard form is $\dfrac{x^2}{4} - \dfrac{y^2}{16} = 1$. Graphing the hyperbola:

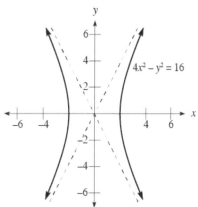

6. Graphing the ellipse:

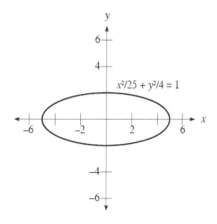

7. This is a circle with center (0,0) and radius = 4. Graphing the circle:

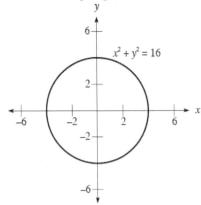

8. Graphing the parabola:

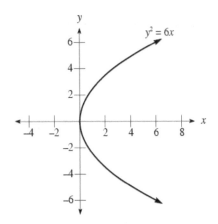

9. Completing the square:

$$9x^2 + 4y^2 - 72x - 16y + 124 = 0$$
$$9\left(x^2 - 8x\right) + 4\left(y^2 - 4y\right) = -124$$
$$9\left(x^2 - 8x + 16\right) + 4\left(y^2 - 4y + 4\right) = -124 + 144 + 16$$
$$9\left(x - 4\right)^2 + 4\left(y - 2\right)^2 = 36$$
$$\frac{\left(x - 4\right)^2}{4} + \frac{\left(y - 2\right)^2}{9} = 1$$

Graphing the ellipse:

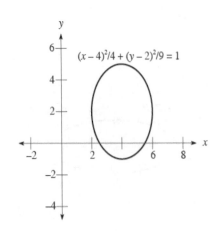

10. This is a circle with center $(1,-3)$ and radius $= 2$. Graphing the circle:

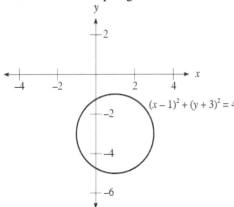

$$(x-1)^2 + (y+3)^2 = 4$$

11. Graphing the hyperbola:

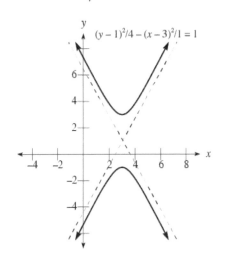

$(y-1)^2/4 - (x-3)^2/1 = 1$

12. Completing the square:
$$x^2 + 4x + 4y + 8 = 0$$
$$x^2 + 4x = -4y - 8$$
$$x^2 + 4x + 4 = -4y - 8 + 4$$
$$(x+2)^2 = -4y - 4$$
$$(x+2)^2 = -4(y+1)$$

This is a parabola with vertex $(-2,-1)$. Graphing the parabola:

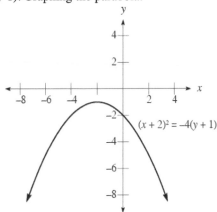

$(x+2)^2 = -4(y+1)$

13. Graphing the inequality:

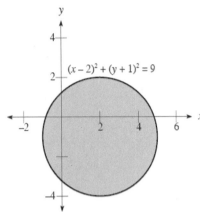

$(x-2)^2 + (y+1)^2 = 9$

14. Graphing the inequality $\dfrac{x^2}{4} - \dfrac{y^2}{9} < 1$:

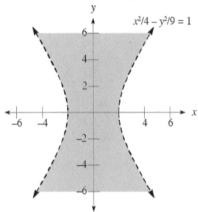

$x^2/4 - y^2/9 = 1$

15. Solving the second equation for y yields $y = 5 - 2x$. Substituting into the first equation:

$$x^2 + (5-2x)^2 = 25$$
$$x^2 + 25 - 20x + 4x^2 = 25$$
$$5x^2 - 20x = 0$$
$$5x(x-4) = 0$$
$$x = 0, 4$$
$$y = 5, -3$$

The solutions are $(0,5), (4,-3)$.

16. Substituting into the first equation:

$$x^2 + (x^2 - 4)^2 = 16$$
$$x^2 + x^4 - 8x^2 + 16 = 16$$
$$x^4 - 7x^2 = 0$$
$$x^2(x^2 - 7) = 0$$
$$x = 0, -\sqrt{7}, \sqrt{7}$$
$$y = -4, 3, 3$$

The solutions are $(0,-4), (-\sqrt{7},3), (\sqrt{7},3)$.

17. Graphing the solution set:

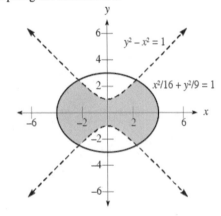

$y^2 - x^2 = 1$

$x^2/16 + y^2/9 = 1$

18. Graphing the solution set:

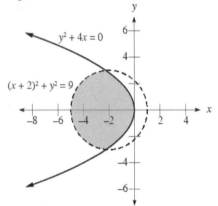

$y^2 + 4x = 0$

$(x+2)^2 + y^2 = 9$